The Essex Scrubber

Keeping it Clean

By Christine Beedle

1

Although this book is mainly based on a true story, any character with bad qualities is purely fictional. Any reference to historical events, to real people, living or dead, or to real locales are intended only to give the story a sense of reality and authenticity. If anyone thinks they do recognise themselves within these pages the author hopes it will simply bring back warm memories of former times.

Printed in the United Kingdom

First Printing, 2014

ISBN 978-0-9929831-0-9

Mrs Christine Beedle
Colchester Essesx

www.theessexscrubber.co.uk/

About the author

Christine Beedle came to Colchester in 1968. When her husband developed cancer a few years later she became a cleaner to help pay the bills. After his death she found herself with a large mortgage, debts and two small children to support. Rising to the challenge she built up a highly successful commercial cleaning business, received the East of England Businesswoman of the Year Award in 1992, the National Woman into Business Award from the Chancellor of the Exchequer three years later and finally the M.B.E. She sold the business in 1999 but is proud that it continues to flourish.

www.theessexscrubber.co.uk

This book is dedicated to

all the wonderful people I have met along the way
and who are such an important part of this story.

Also to my long suffering family

– who continue to suffer.

Acknowledgements

I would like to especially thank
Ros, Lawrence and Rohan for their support and
assistance throughout the writing of this book as
well as many others who have enabled me to make
it a reality.

CHAPTER 1 – A CLEAN START   June 1978

All six of them stared blankly at her, their white faces shining in the harsh lights. Their toothless mouths gaped open like a row of ghastly faces from Munch's The Scream, noiselessly challenging her to take them on.

Christine shivered. Despite this, perspiration prickled her armpits. Her clothes felt as though they were sticking to her body and she wasn't at all sure that her legs, let alone her stomach, could cope with this test. She had to overcome her mounting panic and master this alien ordeal.

Suddenly the acrid stench caught the back of her throat, making her gag and she struggled to overcome the feeling of nausea as her insides threatened to rebel.

To turn and run would be the easy choice.

There was, however, one problem, one over-riding problem - her family were depending on her, even though they were not aware of where she was at this very moment, or just how important it was that she succeeded.

In essence, not just their continuing lifestyle but the very roof over their heads, depended on her facing up to this challenge and she had to face it alone.

Her desire to turn and run was heightened when suddenly, in guttural unison the open orifices in front of her belched and each spewed forth a fierce jet of water, swirling it around their cavernous mouths. A fine spray of liquid wet the tiles at her feet. She jumped back in horror.

No, this was pathetic. She had to tackle them, she couldn't fall at this the first hurdle. She had more guts than that. With the grim determination of a mother with a family to protect, Christine resolved to attack.

Taking a deep breath, she extracted the white plastic lavatory brush from its holder. Holding the repugnant implement at arm's length she advanced and poked tentatively at the nearest basin. She stared.

The bristles were entwined with shreds of toilet paper and, her stomach gave another heave. It couldn't be, surely …bits of pooh …

MAN-pooh at that. Animal pooh, and baby pooh, of course, would have been fine – she could have handled them … no problem. But this was…. what would her daughter say? ….. "Gross". And now the wretched brush was shedding black bristles. It was disgusting. She stood back appalled.

This was her first close encounter with one of these performing urinal things. Indeed, this was the first time she'd been in a GENTS loo.

Then, as though to repulse her further, the contraption let out a deep, warning gurgle, and sucked noisily.

Fascinated and at the same time slightly repelled, Christine watched the yellowish liquid drain away. She watched in horror as the bristles swirled around the basin and then collected themselves in the central trap.

Dear God. Would she have to pick them out with her fingers?

Things were getting worse by the minute.

She had no idea she would be expected to tackle this sort of thing - these unmentionable repositories. She wasn't even sure how you pronounced them: UR-in-al or was it ur-I-nal?

On the farm where she had grown up, in the wilds of Cornwall, mucking out was the accepted order of the day but this… this was repugnant.

She glanced over her shoulder. She was hot and she was exhausted. She had already been cleaning for over an hour and no one, apart from the cleaning team, would know if she flunked it and fled. Even if they did find out, no one who knew her would blame her for taking the sensible, the rational way out. In fact, they would probably be appalled that she had put herself in this position in the first place.

Pulling herself together, she imagined a row of suited executives (yes, her husband, Peter, included), standing legs apart, each focused on the white tiled wall ahead.

"What must it sound like when they all went off in chorus? … the tinkling of pee, the hiss of urgent piss, the cascade as the powerful flush exploded and then the final dying babble as the golden ripples drained away."

She mused ….

"Hardly Handel's Water Music, ….. a John Williams' prelude to a powerful Western maybe……? Probably better suited to a 'FLY ON THE WALL' documentary!" she thought and almost smiled.

She could see how all this might appear amusing to some, however, at this moment she was far from amused. Nothing had prepared her for this, for this horrible situation.

But back to harsh reality. What on earth was she doing here alone in the gents? Her mother, her friends, her work colleagues would stare in disbelief if they could see her. So once again … Why WAS she here?

Cleaning seemed the answer to the immediate, financial side of her family's problems. With this extra part-time work she could begin to pay off their mounting pile of debts. Her day-time secretarial post brought in enough to cover the main household bills so if she could just manage an additional two hours in the evening, it would be perfect.

She would get the children ready for bed and then leave them in front of the television, giving Peter strict instructions: the children must be tucked in by seven o'clock, latest. They would think this a huge treat. Anya would certainly understand, perhaps even feel responsible. At the age of nearly seven, she was certainly that - sensible well beyond her years and bossy enough to sort out her little brother, James who was only three and a bit.

Since Peter had left his job as Export Manager at VE Ventilation, the major manufacturer of industrial fans, to set up his own consultancy business, things had been hard for them. When, ten months later, he was diagnosed with a particularly malignant melanoma, the timing couldn't have been worse. No income and, worse still, no company insurance. They realised all their energies and all their savings needed to be channelled into beating this killer cancer and so Peter's dream export consultancy went into liquidation before it had really started. Christine was now the principal breadwinner, and this extra job had to be the right thing to do.

But Christine's mother, a product of Cheltenham Ladies College, would be, quite simply, appalled. Christine dare not think about the reaction she knew there would be. She could hear her, sounding just like Lady Bracknell in The Importance of Being Earnest. However, instead of the famous "A Handbag?" line, she would be booming out...   "A Cleaner? A CLEANER?"

Of course, it wouldn't end there. "Cleaning, cleaning … surely with your education you could have found something better than that."

Christine had attended Horwell Grammar School for Girls in Launceston, on the Cornwall/Devon border. The school, like all grammar schools, was renowned for its discipline and sound grounding in mathematics, English and Latin. Not that a good education was going to be much use to her at this precise moment.

'Was Latrine the word for WC in Latin? It sounded like it could be a Latin stem," she mused to herself. But if you wanted to go to the loo in Italy, it was "andare in bagno", that she did remember!

No matter, the thing was she needed work NOW, work that would fit in with the family without stress or responsibility, and which brought an instant boost to their finances.

When Christine had telephoned in reply to the advertisement in the Colchester Gazette for evening cleaners, the woman who answered her tentative call sounded incredibly relaxed about it all, almost off-hand - "Interview? No, we don't do interviews. Anyway you SOUND fine."

Just … "Turn up about quarter to six, and I'll get Mrs Dunbarton, the supervisor to meet you in reception."

They did not want any references either, much to Christine's relief. Who on earth would she have dared confide in, before asking them to vouch for her? Who amongst her friends would actually confirm that she was any good as a cleaner? They'd probably just laugh, knowing full well that Rebecca, her home help, did all her cleaning.

It had all seemed too easy and at that stage men's urinals had not even crossed her mind – now they would probably be etched there for ever!

So, she had arrived hot and bothered that Monday evening at the five storey BComm building, anxious not to be late. The pretty young girl on the reception desk looked up and smiled with an automatic "Can I help you?"

Christine gave her a big smile, "I was told to report here - I'm starting tonight as a cleaner."

The girl's face changed immediately. She looked Christine up and down, frowned and said, this time rather petulantly, her tone condescending, "Well, you can't stay in reception. You'll have to wait outside, I'm afraid. They're due to start work at six" adding, almost under her breath, "but they usually turn up about 5 past."

With that she turned away, full of her own importance as a receptionist, so much more elevated than a mere cleaner, and picked up the telephone, cooing in a silky voice to the incoming caller, "BComm, good afternoon. Can I help you?"

Slightly taken aback, and feeling properly put in her place, Christine retreated to the car park. Sure enough, at five minutes to six the first two cleaning ladies, and she recognised immediately that they were the cleaners, waddled slowly round the corner of the building. Each had a cigarette loosely attached to her mouth and with this precariously attached, they talked non-stop, punctuated occasionally with outbursts of raucous laughter. Their arms were weighed down with Asda carrier bags so heavy that their puffy, purple wrists seemed to be pulled out of their coat sleeves. Only a bout of coughing made them stop and rest their shopping on the pavement.

The older woman having the coughing fit, removed her cigarette from the thick red lipstick adhesive which had kept it in place. Leaning against the brick wall of the building she casually finished off her "fag" before discarding the burning stub on the pavement. Christine raised a disapproving eyebrow – perhaps she had more in common with the toffee-nosed little receptionist than she realised!

Picking up their bags the two drifted amiably into reception, at which point the receptionist, with a snooty toss of her streaked hair, flounced past them to the ladies toilet. Her high heels clicked on the marble floor and her neat bottom in its tight pencil skirt gave a dismissive wiggle as the door closed behind her.

Christine followed the women to the desk. "Excuse me. I wonder if you can help. I'm the new cleaning lady."

"Oh, are you, pet? Well, come with us. We sit in the canteen until Doris arrives."

Doris presumably was Mrs Dunbarton, the supervisor. The two ladies sat chatting at a table catching up with all the weekend gossip, totally ignoring Christine, as other cleaners drifted in. She opened her mouth to say "Good evening" but they too acted as if she were not there.

At five past six 'precisely' Doris duly arrived. In her early fifties, she looked worn and harassed. She pulled out her dog-eared, plastic file and turned to the motley crew in front of her, who by then were shedding their coats to reveal an assorted collection of flowery overalls.

Doris scowled. "Who've we got tonight? Aaw Gawd, that new lady hasn't come back and on top of that Mary's sick and Phyllis ain't in again."

Somebody piped up "Darryl weren't on the bus."

Quick arithmetic – she was four short. Then she spotted Christine.

"Aw yeah. The office phoned about you. What's yer name? Done cleaning work before 'ave yuh?"

When Christine tried to reply that she had no experience, only at home, Doris just shrugged and said "You'll pick it up, easy – I'll put you on Mary's floor. What did you say yer name was? Christine. Oh yeah How do you spell that? C R I S T E E N …. That'll do. The office can fill in the rest."

Doris had mentally clocked this latest recruit's posh accent and scornfully dismissed her as another one- night stand. Not much point in wasting time on training or trying to integrate her into the team. Resignedly she nodded to Christine to follow her.

Heading off through a maze of corridors and up a flight of concrete stairs she finally stopped in front of a cupboard door. As she pulled it open the distinctive stench of stale mops wafted out. The offensive odour hit Christine's supposedly refined nostrils. The smell was reminiscent of day-old vomit after the children had been sick in the car – so at least this was vaguely familiar.

Doris pulled out a handful of black plastic rubbish sacks, a bucket containing a dirty yellow duster and a can of polish, and pointed out the vacuum cleaner.

"Start with the bins," she pointed Christine towards the office, "I'll be back in a mo but I've got three to cover, you know." Shoving eight or more sacks into her waistband, she turned and disappeared up the stairs with not a word of encouragement or explanation.

Christine took stock and walked to the far corner of the deserted office, with the rubbish bags tucked into her waist just as she had seen Doris do. She began to empty the waste bins, retrieving the errant ones from corners deep under the desks. Not as easy as it looked. It almost felt as though the occupants of some desks derived perverse pleasure in making their bin retrieval as tricky as possible.

After several clumsy attempts at transferring rubbish to bag during which the contents spilled out over the floor, she devised a method of covering the bin with the sack and then tipping the rubbish in. Several of the bins contained vending cups with coffee dregs and papers saturated with coffee.

Annoyed, she went all the way back to the cupboard, retrieved the bucket, filled it with hot water and hunted for a cloth, finally finding another dirty duster under a dustpan full of grey fluff and rubber bands. Properly equipped, she trudged back once more. She could now wipe out the sticky, coffee-encrusted bins.

There seemed to be dozens of desks, every one with a rubbish bin. The office stretched out before her. Eventually she reached the far side and collected up her four bulging black rubbish bags, noticing to her horror that one was dripping coffee and had left a long tell-tale line across the carpet.

"Deal with that later," she thought as she changed the smelly rubbish bag in the kitchen swing bin checking that this too did not leak. She looked with dismay at the washing up piled high in the bowl and along the work surfaces. Before she could clean, she would have to wash up.

She had almost finished doing this when she jumped out of her skin. Doris was standing behind her, "Where the bleedin' 'ell have you got to? The rubbish should've gone out ages ago! Oh no! YOU don't do the washing up, you stupid ….." Doris swallowed the word, but Christine knew she was going to say "cow". "THEY do."

Christine assumed by 'THEY', she meant the office staff should do their own washing up. If only Doris had spent a little time explaining things to her. This was awful.

"You've still got your toilets and the vacuuming to do. You'll have to bleedin' move it," and with these warm words of encouragement Doris dashed off again.

Christine grabbed her bucket and dashed to the toilets. The GENTS - what if someone was inside? She knocked and called out tentatively "Cleaners," before pushing the door open very slowly and peering gingerly inside.

"Phew. Coast clear."

This was the moment Christine faced those gaping mouths for the first time. Now, getting over her initial panic and firmly resolving to make a go of things, she dabbed at them with her damp duster, put the brush back in its holder and moved quickly on.

With the same yellow duster she had been using all night, which by now was a jolly sight cleaner than when she started, she gingerly wiped the toilet seats. Vague thoughts of germs and syphilis and the need for rubber gloves crossed her mind but somehow Doris breathing down her neck was the more imminent concern.

She swiftly moved on to tackle the washbasins and taps. Something inside her told her she had got this the wrong way round and that there should perhaps be a different cloth for the toilets.

Should she have filled up the toilet rolls? Must ask Doris.

Casting a venomous glance behind her at the beastly urinals, she quickly wiped round surfaces in the ladies. She then hurried back to the cupboard and had just pulled out the vacuum cleaner when she again heard Doris's strident voice behind her.

"You haven't got time fer that. You'll just have to pick up the bits. It's nearly 8 o'clock and I've got a bus to catch."

Looking with dismay at her floor, Christine did as she was told, wondering where on earth the time had gone. Tomorrow she would have to pace herself better.

CHAPTER 2 - A LEARNING CURVE

The following evening, determined to make a go of this, she arrived on time, with a smile for everyone. She sat determinedly at the cleaners' table in the canteen and, as each woman came in, she made a point of introducing herself. Joan and Freda, the two ladies who had been first to arrive the night before were chatty and said they would get Doris to show her how to clean the toilets.

"Don't yer husband work at VE?" asked Joan and Christine nodded. "Thought so. So does my Jim, on the shop floor."

Christine was grateful. It was comforting to find common ground. VE Ventilation was the biggest employer in the town, manufacturing fans and exporting them worldwide. Christine's husband Peter had been their export manager, working overseas before melanoma, the cancer caused by the sun had caught up with him and ultimately had led to her need to be here.

Conversation was cut short by the arrival of Doris, obviously not at peace with the world and muttering that there were complaints to be sorted. Waving the cleaners' log book meaningfully in Christine's direction she snapped, "No toilet paper in the gents. Bins missed. Floor weren't 'oovered."

Christine's colour rose and she looked down at her feet. She felt like a naughty schoolgirl being told off in front of the class. Joan's elbow nudged her side and she whispered, "Don't let her get to you. It were yer first night. She's a moody cow. No one likes 'er."

Determined not to let the side down again, Christine rushed to her floor, emptied the bins and then got the vacuum cleaner out – a Henry, just like the one she had at home.

She plugged it in and switched it on, feeling confident that tonight she was winning.

The wretched thing belched dust as she tried to coax it to pick up the little rounds of punch machine confetti. Sigh! It looked as if there had been a wedding in the aisle between desks. On top of that the hoover was creating more dust than it was sucking up. Two steps forward, three steps back!

Carefully she released the top off the tub vacuum cleaner, noting the mocking smile on the face of the " 'Enry 'Oover" as she had heard the other cleaners calling them. She removed the filter, which was so laden with dirt that long strands of dust hung like stalactites from the bottom. She shook this over the bin, immediately realising her mistake as clouds of dust floated upwards and, unfortunately, outwards as well.

Obviously not satisfied with causing one mess, the vacuum cleaner protesting at months of neglect, had decided the dust bag was so full, it would choose this moment to split. With a sigh of dismay, Christine charged up the stairs two at a time, intent on not wasting a second and determined to finish ahead of the game tonight. She didn't want the cleaners' log shaken at her again tomorrow night.

Eventually locating Doris she panted out, "Doris, please could I have a new bag for the hoover." This evoked a sharp retort from her supervisor - "Lazy cow," referring, no doubt, to poor sick Mary, "I don't reckon she has emptied her 'oover since she's bin 'ere. Anyhow, I ain't got no bags. We aren't due any supplies until the end of the month. You will have to empty the one that's in there. Just give it a shake and put it back on again."

Dismayed and out of breath, Christine rushed back to her floor. All that time and energy to achieve absolutely nothing!

She attempted to empty the bag into a black plastic sack, remembering the lesson from the filter earlier, and avoiding too much of a dust storm. By now she was hot and bothered. She wiped her hand across her forehead, unwittingly smearing her face with grey dust.

She straddled the vacuum cleaner holding it firmly between her knees. As she attempted to get the dust bag over the nozzle, she giggled. Pete would love this – here she was straddling her 'enry and struggling to attach the wretched bag.

Then, focussing fiercely on the task in hand, she told herself there must be no more thoughts of funny double entendres to share with Pete. Get the blinking bag back on!

Just as she thought she had managed it, a male voice shattered her concentration. She jumped. A rather grim faced man towered over her, briefcase in hand: "We've just finished a meeting in the conference room. Clean it tonight, would you? We have to resume again in there at 8.00 tomorrow morning."

With that, he walked away without a backward glance, leaving Christine sitting back on her haunches. She stared after him open mouthed. The wicked humour she had seen in her situation just seconds ago vanished. She looked after the rapidly retreating figure in horror.

That was Guy Lattimer. He had looked straight through her. He hadn't even seen her and yet Guy was one of Peter's close friends. They had attended a GEC conference together at the University in Bahrain two years ago and occasionally they all met up at mutual friends' for dinner.

Despite the indignity of not being visible, Christine suddenly felt a surge of relief: "At least if he didn't recognise me, he won't tell Alison that I am working as a cleaner in his office". But it niggled, it really hurt. Whenever they met socially there was always a peck on the cheek and an enquiry about the children.

Shaking herself, she abandoned the vacuum cleaner and set off to find the conference room. Cups, plates, half eaten sandwiches and screwed up paper napkins littered the board room table. Slowly she began to pile the plates and clear the debris, still thinking about Guy. Absentmindedly she picked up a sandwich curled at the edges and bit into it.

Her thoughts were cut short by the sharp voice of Doris, who had the uncanny knack of always turning up at the worst possible moment. "You're not supposed to help yourself to office food. You can be sacked for that!"

Guiltily engulfing the rest of the sandwich into a dirty napkin, Christine turned to face the rest of the tirade: "Didn't I make it clear that you don't touch the cups. They have a flippin' catering department for that."

Going red in the face, Christine protested: "But Guy Lattimer has just told me to clear it up ready for a meeting at 8.00 tomorrow morning."

"Mr Lattimer to you. Anyhow what are you doing talking to HIM? He's the boss on this floor. How do you know 'im then?" Doris's voice was now thick with suspicion and dislike.

With a shrug and drooping shoulders Christine turned away, not wanting to get into complicated explanations. What should she do about the conference room? She didn't want another complaint tomorrow, especially from Guy. Perhaps if Doris disappeared again she could whip through the vacuuming and still clear the conference room. But Doris was not going to let it drop that easily.

Following Christine across the floor, she proceeded to fire questions.

"Yeah, just who are you? Are you here to spy on us? You talk all posh. How do you know the boss 'ere after just one night, eh?"

Hoping desperately to shake her off, Christine smiled sweetly and said, "He used to work with my husband. But what should I do about the conference room?"

"You get your job done. I don't want no more complaints from this floor. I'll look after the conference room. I'm in charge round here."

"Yes," thought Christine, "and you don't like me one bit."

No wonder they didn't work as a team. No wonder cleaners left after just one night. That woman should never be in charge. She didn't even look the part with her stained black trousers, her bobbly jumper and rounded shoulders. Everything about her looked down-at-heel and grubby, plus she had no idea how to organise her staff. Christine was seething.

Glancing at her watch, she hurriedly put her 'enry back together and vacuumed the visible bits, all the time conscious that her apology of a vacuum cleaner was grinning at her. Periodically, and as if to emphasize the point, it maliciously belched out puffs of dust.

Why did these vacuum cleaners have that stupid smiling face on them anyway and why were they called Henry? Why not a feminine name? She could have kicked hateful Henry in the teeth. No, that was unfair, her Henry at home was perfect and she loved it. What was wrong was that this poor thing had been neglected, abused even, so now it was just getting its own back.

Having done the best she could with the 'oover, and with can of polish in hand, she now furiously sprayed any desks that were clear of paper. At least tonight it would smell as if she had cleaned her area and that had to be some kind of progress.

As she dragged the malfunctioning Henry back to the cupboard, there was Doris, struggling with sacks of rubbish. Gritting her teeth, Christine said with a smile, "Thank you for doing the conference room for me. Can I take one of those rubbish bags for you?" For two pins she would have hit the woman with it but instead she meekly carried the heavy bag downstairs, following two steps behind the, thankfully, now silent Doris.

Something was very wrong with the whole cleaning environment. It shouldn't be like this.

Still, she couldn't wait to get home and tell Peter about Guy. She hoped they would have a laugh together about her "struggle with 'enery" and Guy not recognising her.

Peter, however, was far from happy about her working in the evenings like this, even though it meant she could be there after school for Anya and do early supper for them all. As it happened, she didn't dare mention the incident with Guy, let alone her reason for sticking it out - namely her worries about money.

Night Three – Christine arrived on the dot of six. Doris was there waiting for her. "Tonight I'm putting you with Joan. You can work together. We don't do that normally but I ain't got time fer trainin' and Joan's got it down to a fine art." Joan gave her a big wink. "That's right pet. I've had a word. You're to come with me. We'll start on your floor. Mine won't take a tick. It's a doddle when you get used to it."

Working with Joan was an eye opener. This 60 year-old woman, with her faded overall and permed-grey hair, was transformed from the round-shouldered, work-worn granny figure into a purposeful, sharp-eyed worker. She came alive. Her efficient routine meant nothing was overlooked and her non-stop commentary while they worked was better than any training manual.

As they emptied the bins, "Look at this lazy bugger – supposed to put his plastic vending cup in the coffee recycling bin. Too much trouble to lift his arse off the chair. Just leave the ruddy cup on his desk. When 'e 'as a line of them growin' mould, he might do something about it."

A constant flow of sound advice – "Wipe out any coffee in the bin otherwise papers get stuck to the bottom and then you'll have to soak 'em. Why don't they drink the flippin' lot? Charge 'em 20p a cup and they would! Free coffee, daft. Spend half the day peeing if you ask me. I could teach 'em a thing or two about man management."

On to Christine's toilets. "Here's yer Marigolds, pet. Bring in some talc – keeps them nice inside." From her ample overall pockets Joan had produced pink rubber gloves followed by clean cotton cloths, two blue and two white.

"Blue for loos, pet. Always remember that. Take home yer cloths every night. I put them in the wash regular – can't clean with dirty cloths. White for basins, mirrors and taps."

She handed Christine cloths and a spray cleaner.

"Spray loos and them gents jobbies first, then the stuff has time to work."

"Oh yes, Joan. Can you tell me about urinals, please?"

Head on one side Joan said with a grin, "What do you want to know about them old chappies, pet?"

"I can never get my timing right – they seem to flush just when I'm trying to clean."

"They flush automatic. They aren't too bad 'ere. It's when they only flush once an hour you have trouble – saving money, they call it."

"Oh, I see. But they smell disgusting."

"The reason this lot stink is they ain't been cleaned proper in ages. You take a gander under 'ere." With her pink rubber gloved finger she pointed under the lip of the urinal. "See them brown crystals, them's the culprit." Bending even lower, she pointed at the dark yellow rivulet of urine caked on the outside of the pan. "Crystallised pee - That's yer problem. We ain't got no descaler but a bit of pine and some scourers'll help. Hang on … I'll be back in a mo."

Leaving Christine with clear instructions "Do the basins, polish up them mirrors. Buff taps last - white cloth mind. Door 'andles and push plates – we don't want no germs on them."

Joan returned out of breath but triumphant, "Just raided the store cupboard. Doris weren't nowhere. 'ere we are, Demon Descaler, just the ticket."

"And this," she said with flourish, "is me secret weapon." From her ample overall pocket she produced a well-chewed, old toothbrush. "Gets in all them places that others can't reach!" Perhaps Christine's earlier vision of the urinals as mouths was more appropriate than she had thought.

Joan proceeded to scour every nook and cranny of the offending urinal, all the time keeping up a steady flow of instructions: "Watch it don't splash. That stuff's a bugger on yer skin – neat hydrochloric acid. Yer don't want to get it in yer eyes neither and always make sure yer got yer rubber gloves on."

Christine warily sniffed the thick purple viscous liquid. Her eyes watered – this was no ordinary domestic cleaning fluid and when it came into contact with the offending crystals, a foam of frothing yellow bubbles grew before her watering eyes. The fumes were overpowering.

"Don't breathe in too deep, pet. Mind, ammonia, it doesn't 'arf clear yer sinuses good and proper! And never, ever use it with bleach. Them fumes can knock you out. We had one cleaner, Samantha … she were out cold, and Doris wouldn't call an ambulance. She were OK but that were a bit of luck. Could have had a corpse on our hands."

One by one the urinals responded. Christine scouring with gusto and giggling every time the wretched thing flushed. Joan started laughing too. She was in her element.

"Look at the pee on the floor. Think themselves so bloomin'
macho but can they aim straight, can they hell? Couldn't hit
a barn at twenty paces…"

The urinals flushed again. A fine spray of water covered
Joan's shoes. She glanced down. "Typically male – no
bloody control. But I reckon these ole chaps (referring to the
ur I nals) aren't 'arf 'appy to see us. Bingo! Look at that,
don't they look better, not to mention the smell. I LOVE doing
loos!!!"

Eventually, Joan disappeared back to the store with the
astounding acid cleaner hidden in a black bag. "Better if
Doris don't know." She winked confidingly at Christine.

Christine couldn't believe it. Loos done and back to the
offices. Armed with a bucket of water and a white cloth, plus
duster and polish, she waited for her next instructions.
"Damp wipe any nasties but otherwise spray your duster with
polish and dust desks. Never spray the furniture – you don't
want smears and a build-up. Telephones – once a week with
damp white cloth, disinfectant in yer water, mind. I do about
ten desks and then vacuum the area so I don't have to go
back." Sure enough together they whisked through,
Christine struggling to keep pace with Joan.

When they both reached the end of the floor, red in the face,
Joan beamed at her – "Don't that look better." She surveyed
the office behind them with pride. There would be no
complaints tomorrow! She turned to Christine, "You're going
to be a natural, you know. Let's have a breather. Now, tell
me about your ole man."

Christine could feel the tears welling up.

Immediately Joan's arm went round her. "Sorry pet. Shouldn't have asked. Let's have a cuppa – just don't let Doris see! I'll get them. Tea OK?"

By the time she came back with two plastic cups, Christine had composed herself. "Thank you – I never thought I could manage this but working with you, it seems so much easier – even though I'm shattered!"

"You're just a spring chicken – reckon I'm old enough to be your gran! Come on drink up and we'll whip through my floor before we have Dodgey Doris on our backs. I'll tell you about 'er one of these days."

Christine smiled sipping the hot sweet tea. How different working here would be if Joan were the boss. She certainly should be the person in charge of training every new lady.

She couldn't resist asking Joan where she had learnt to clean. "Never thought about that, pet. From me mam, I reckon. Up home in Gateshead. She were a cleaner all her life. You learn most things from yer mam, don't you, pet?"

Christine nodded, thinking yes, how true – the difference being that Christine's mother had taught her how to ride a horse, arrange flowers and write elegant thank-you letters – not how to clean or cook!

The next twenty minutes flew by. Christine couldn't believe how much she had enjoyed it. She thanked Joan, genuinely grateful.

As they stacked their equipment back into the cupboard, Joan said, "I'll help you sort out yer cupboard tomorrah. Don't you fret about Doris, pet. She's got a real chip on her shoulder but we aren't a bad bunch! I'll have a word with

Doris about us working together again. We'll have yer floor up and sorted, and you'll be laughing."

Christine had to smile at the thought of getting Guy Lattimer's office sorted, but her heart went out to Joan for her kindness and encouragement and with tears in her eyes she called, "Good night and thank you so much!"

She dashed to the car and as she backed out she caught sight of Joan and Freda heading, heads down against the biting wind, for the bus stop. "What a dear Joan is – how I misjudged her," thought Christine.

CHAPTER 3 – HOME

Feeling much happier, Christine put her key in the door. No sound, no television.

"Pete" she called anxiously, "Is everything all right?"

"Fine, just exhausted," came from the sitting room. "The children are in bed but I haven't done the washing up or anything."

Christine flicked on the light - he looked drawn and tired. The chemotherapy was really kicking in. "Come and tell me all about this evening."

"I'll just get a gin. Can I get you a cranberry juice or anything?"

No alcohol for Pete, no this, no that … depending on the latest research, the latest conversation with a fellow victim or any cranky healer, their diet changed. You grasped at anything - the alternative was despair.

With gin and tonic in hand, she said "I must tell you about the cleaning. I really think I could enjoy it. But you know, someone needs to give that contract a real shake-up. There are some lovely cleaning ladies there but no one gives a damn and they are treated like dirt. And the supervisor, she's a disaster."

"Yes, thinking about it, it's probably the same at every place I have ever worked," said Peter "The cleaners are paid a pittance and ignored but without them the place would fall apart."

"Tonight I worked with a lovely lady called Joan and we made such an impact. Her husband works at VE and knows you!

But you never guess who is boss of my floor …. Guy Latimer."

"What! Oh, that's great. Yes, he does work at BComm. He's a super chap! What did he have to say?"

"Oh no, it doesn't work like that – the cleaners don't have anything to do with the office staff. I don't think he even noticed me."

"Well, you must give him a ring and tell him you are working in his offices."

Christine looked hard at Peter – "You just don't get it. As a cleaner you are not visible, you are not a person, you're just a .. a function that happens each night. And if you don't get it right they immediately complain in the log book. I can't ring Guy. He'd be horrified. He just looked through me"

She could see Peter's jaw lifting. He had that look in his eye. The same old Pete, however ill, he'd defend her to the hilt, even now that he was a shadow of the man she had married.

She sighed …

You didn't suffer from cancer. Suffer wasn't a strong enough word. You were a victim and it devoured you, body and mind.

Cancer of the liver – melanoma – the very words struck fear in everyone. At the Royal Marsden, the cancer hospital in Surrey, Peter was a guinea pig. The trials were without any measurable scientific successes but Pete wanted to go with it. Once again they grasped at anything.

There were times though when his courage failed and he put his head on Christine's shoulder and said, "I'm not sure how much more I can take. The treatment is worse than the cancer."

Hope came from friends, from trying different things, from prayer. Christine knew she had to keep him fighting, to make him laugh and to make him positive about the future.

Pete had studied for the priest-hood long before he met Christine. If ever he needed his faith, it was now. She always poked fun at him for being anything but a saint and had honestly wondered about his suitability for the priesthood. His Irish catholic mother had been the driving force behind it - of that, she was sure.

Christine was always quick to point out that Peter didn't abandon the church for her. He just wasn't the celibate sort. Indeed, there had been numerous colourful fiancées before she came on the scene. She'd heard about them from Anne, Peter's sister.

There had been Elisabet from Germany – rejected immediately by mother as a Nazi. Mercedes from Spain who hung her knickers on the balcony at the family home in Cheam (you simply don't admit to even doing washing in Cheam, let alone hanging it out to dry where it could possibly be seen. As for knickers on full view at the front of the house!) Well, she didn't last long.

Mind you, that was to be expected. "With a name like Mercedes", muttered mother. "Named after a car, a German car at that." Peter wanted to say it a Spanish name for the Virgin Mary but, loathe to provoke his mother, he didn't!

Then came Aishia from Pakistan. She was a domestic science teacher. Peter loved her curries but she was coffee coloured and smelt spicy. Not a hope.

Finally, there was Della, glamorous Della. She was a promising contender until she was photographed at the local amateur dramatic society, modelling in a risqué bikini. In Mama's book this classified as pornographic. Not that it mattered: Della had dropped Peter when he caught glandular fever, in favour of a glamorous Canadian airman.

It wasn't that Peter was a hen-pecked son. He was just her first-born and Mrs Chapman was a formidable lady with very strong Catholic principles. She was also an accountant so everything was black or white with little room for compromise. In her book, first-born sons were meant for God. When, much to her chagrin this hadn't worked out, she determined that he would at least have the right wife, and she the right grandchildren.

Then Peter and Christine had met and the odds looked slightly better. Christine's father, a Catholic, had been a Polish pilot in Bomber Command and therefore on the same side in the war, and it had to be acknowledged that Polish pilots did play a significant part in defending Britain. Her mother was educated at Cheltenham Ladies College so that too was a plus, even if she was C of E.

In his Mother's eyes Christine certainly was an improvement on the previous ladies. Besides Peter was 32. If not in the church, it was high time he was settled. The odds could be said to be favourable.

Training to be a priest had left its mark on Peter in oh so many ways – some good and some not so good. He had a knack with people. He oozed charm – an obvious statement perhaps, given the above assortment of girlfriends. He always watched for the underdog and seemed to be able to bring out the best in everyone.

33

Christine often felt that he had done that for her – a country bumpkin from Cornwall with no finesse, little love of culture and certainly not of music. She had been given a place in the school choir on condition that she didn't sing, just acted as prompt when they forgot the words.

Fortunately she had been able to read extensively as a child and her grammar school education had been excellent. Her father had been adamant that she should study Latin, not cookery, when a choice had to be made in the Fourth Form, and he encouraged her to learn languages.

Peter always claimed that as a couple they could travel anywhere in the world and be understood – he spoke Spanish, German and Arabic while Christine could get by in French, Polish and, at a push, in Italian. They had English and Latin in common.

They were happy and they both worked hard. With Christine, hard work was perhaps an inherent characteristic of Polish people, an inherited trait. With Peter, discipline and mental agility was part of his make-up, instilled by the Jesuit monks.

They had survived many struggles, Peter's long absences abroad, Christine's meningitis when James was one, Peter's earlier redundancy and then setting up his own business, not forgetting to mention Peter's mother. But now they faced their most serious test – his being diagnosed with terminal cancer. Any relationship had to be strong to survive that. It was also the ultimate test of Peter's faith.

Here they were now chatting on about Dodgy Doris and dear Joan, before Christine said, yawning deeply, "Come on. Let's get you organised for bed. I have to sort out the children's things for the morning." The usual nightly routine of helping Pete to undress and change the dressing on the horrendous radiotherapy burns. Then, the endless pills and more painkillers.

Exhausted, Christine followed him upstairs, popping her head round the children's doors. She was relieved to hear their even breathing. Anya had laid their clothes out for the next day. Christine blew her a heartfelt kiss and then quietly clambered into bed trying not to disturb Pete.

"I want to talk, Chris. I think you have hit on something. You know it may be some time before I can work. Who knows I probably won't even be here in …"

"Don't you dare say THAT! I don't believe it. You are so fit and you are a fighter. Anyway, miracles do happen and YOU of all people should believe in the power of prayer! We must just keep praying. Remember too advances in cancer research are happening all the time. Look at Lucy."

Their friend Lucy had had a mastectomy three years ago and was fine now. She just had to take a pill every day for the next five years.

"We can manage as long as you don't get worse."

Peter squeezed her hand, "I know, I know but we have to be realistic. I want to look at this cleaning with you. It is something we could do together until I can get back on my feet."

Christine sighed but perhaps this would give him an interest. He needed to feel he was contributing. When they married he was very much in control. Their world revolved around his work and his interests and the constant flow of his contacts visiting from all over the world. Perhaps he was right. This was a phase in their lives and they just needed to adapt.

The next morning, the children bounced around bright and bubbly as usual. Anya helping Pete put on his socks to a whole lot of teasing about smelly feet, James giggling that his were the smelliest because he hadn't had a bath for a week. Christine rounded on him, "That can't be true. Dad's in charge of bath-time."

"Yeah" said James with a grin!

"OK, OK. You're in the bath before I go to work tonight. It'll be scrub-a-dub-dub from top to toe."

How blessed she was. Anya always helpful, always sensitive, and James completely unaware of the problems, full of fun and naughtiness. He hadn't earned the nickname Double Trouble for nothing.

She bundled them into the car and dropped Anya off at the Convent and James to his babyminder, before popping back home to check on Pete and to make sure Rebecca had arrived. Rebecca, her trusted cleaning lady.

"How would SHE react if she knew what I was doing last night?" thought Christine. They really couldn't afford to keep Rebecca on every day for three hours but how else could she cope? At least her income from the Colchester English Study Centre, where she worked as School Secretary, was good.

After the birth of James, her second child, her hours at the Study Centre had been reduced to five hours per day, from 10.00 to 3.00 p.m., which was perfect and allowed her to fit everything in with the children. School holidays were tricky but somehow she managed. It would be easier after half term because James would be at the Convent in the reception class. He was so ready for it. She grinned to herself. Her concern should be for the nuns – those wonderful Sisters of Mercy. James had all his father's charm with the ladies.

This morning, she mentally checked the programme for her day at the English Study Centre. Board Meeting – starting at 11.00. Sandwiches would be served for lunch. She was thrilled. Uncle Harold would be there. Harold Abrahams, the Olympic 100m Gold Medalist and uncle to the Chief Executive, Anthony Abrahams. Harold Abrahams of Chariots of Fire fame – the film of his winning a gold medal for England in the Paris Olympics in 1924. If anyone knew about guts and success, it was Uncle Harold.

Christine sat in the office sorting the papers for the board. The figures were good, student numbers were up. The school had just had another contract confirmed – 60 Swedish teachers coming for the summer.

She wondered if she could have a student to stay. All students were housed with local families. The income would help pay for Rebecca. Perhaps it would even be good for Pete, as long as he felt strong enough to have someone else in the house. He became very sick and quite depressed after each bout of chemotherapy so perhaps it wasn't such a good idea after all. She sighed.

Don't day-dream. Get on with the job. She pulled herself together. Must check the china coffee cups are out and take a look at the director's loo before the board arrive.

Sure enough, no hand towel and a tin of polish left on the vanity unit. That would not go down well. Hastily, she tidied up, put out a new towel and dashed off to the kitchen to pop the coffee machine on. Mentally she made a note to check the cleaning contract. The cleaning company must be told when there was going to be a board meeting. Communication was vital.

Emerging from the kitchen, she met Harold. "How's Peter?" He asked concern written all over his face. "Not good," said Christine, knowing she could confide in this lovely gentleman. "He's had to give up work altogether. I don't know quite how we are going to cope. I'm sure it'll work out but sometimes I despair..." she sighed. "I'll bring the papers through as soon as you've all finished coffee."

The board meeting dragged on, with Christine anxiously watching the clock wondering if she was going to have to excuse herself. She had arranged for her friend Simone to pick up the children but she still needed to get away. The Chairman could be prickly.

Harold suddenly yawned, said, "Sorry folks, but I think we've covered everything. There's no point in going over it all when things are running so well. I'd like to get the 3.30 train and Christine has kindly offered to run me to the station. I think we've done, don't you, Tony?" - this to his nephew, Antony Abrahams, Chairman of the consortium running the school.

What a wonderful man! Flashing a grateful look at Harold, Christine picked up her shorthand pad. "I'll have the minutes ready tomorrow!"

Twenty minutes later as they pulled up at the station Harold said, "I want to give you something. It helped me and I still read it when things seem tough. Look at it later and then keep it in your handbag!" Dropping an envelope on the car seat, he squeezed her arm and dashed for the train on the far platform, still a sprinter, even in his late seventies.

Waiting for Anya to emerge from school, she opened it and read the A5 sheet:

If you think you are beaten, you are
If you think you dare not, you don't
If you'd like to win, but think you can't
It's almost certain you won't

If you think you'll lose, you've lost.
For out of the world we find
Success begins with a fellow's will
It's all in the state of mind.

If you think you're outclassed, you are
You've got to think high to rise
You've got to be sure of yourself before
You can ever win a prize.

Life's battles don't always go
To the stronger or faster man
But sooner or later the man who wins
Is the one who thinks he can.

Thinking of the film, Chariots of Fire, and Uncle Harold's courage and achievements, Christine read the poem again and resolved that this too would be her mantra. From now on she would make it work, she would be positive. She could do it.

Home in a hurry. Rebecca had left. Everything was clean and tidy. Quick hug for Pete – he was sitting in the high backed Parker Knoll chair, the one which gave him most support. He reached out his white hand to her to stop her moving away. Christine knew he wanted to talk. She could read the strain in his face. Taking his hand, she automatically thought, "Must cut your finger nails" - they looked yellow and grotesquely long. "No, … Stop it."

Why did she always focus on what needed doing, instead of the caring side? She felt so driven – her must-do syndrome. She took a deep breath. Just slow down. "How have you been today, darling?"

"It's been a long day. I feel so useless."

"I know just what you mean but I've got something I think we should share. You know how you always maintain prayer is the answer. Today, I was given my answer to prayer."

She handed him the poem and told him about Harold's concern and kindness. Peter who had seen the film knew all about the Olympic Gold Medallist and had been thrilled to learn of his connection with the Colchester English Study Centre. "Did you know he was a Jew but he converted to Catholicism?" Peter asked. Christine shook her head, wondering what was coming. Peter had long wanted her to become a Catholic but she steadfastly warded it off.

She had no objection to the children being brought up as Catholics and indeed she was happy to go with them all to Mass. But if she was honest, she felt suffocated by the orthodox demands of Peter's Catholicism. She had her own simple faith and she was comfortable with that.

Back to her defence mechanism again – stick with the practical.

Pause, then "Why don't I bring the carrots in so you can peel them while I do the sauce? And we can carry on chatting."

Cauliflower cheese and carrots. The latest cancer diet was vegetarian. Pete was drinking carrot juice. She had read somewhere that you could buy it ready juiced. Must look in Sainsbury's, she hated the mess of liquidising.

Still, it was so much better than raw liver which one friend had recommended, and at least the children would eat cauliflower cheese. The Convent did excellent school dinners and Ros, her child-minder, ensured James was well fed, too well fed perhaps.

CHAPTER 4 - LIFE'S KOMPLIKATED

She had been forced to tell the Mother Superior, Sister Francis, about Peter's cancer. When they visited the Royal Marsden Hospital for radiotherapy or chemotherapy, she was unable to guarantee picking up Anya on time and on one occasion she had been nearly two hours late. Ever since, the school had been wonderfully accommodating, never minding if she was late on those treatment days which reduced them both to physical wrecks. It was going to be such a relief to have James there too so that she had just one delivery and pick up point, and the Convent had quoted significantly reduced fees for a second child.

Shaking herself, it was just before six, time to go cleaning again. What was she doing? She should be spending time caring for Peter and reading bed-time stories. Sigh. No time for guilt.

At least she had scrubbed James and washed Anya's hair with much splashing and tickling. Sopping wet, she had retreated, saying "Dad's waiting to read you a story."

To Pete she called, "Darling, we'll talk some more when I get back." Kisses all round and then off. At least, with the cleaning she was getting some physical exercise and that meant sleeping better.

Positive thinking; was it kicking in? …. Well, possibly.

Into cleaning mode - would Doris let Joan work with her again tonight? She desperately hoped so. She had brought along a notebook to jot down the routine, and make notes so that she got her timing right. She pulled out her clean cloths and waved them at Joan. A few more nights like this and she would have her section sparkling.

As she walked up the stairs, she noticed Joan ahead of her leaning heavily on the rail. "It's me 'ip. It's really playing up. 'oovering gives it hell. I wish we had uprights. Them tub cleaners don't 'alf bugger me back."

Christine quickly responded, "Why don't you do the desks and I'll hoover both our floors – horses for courses."

Joan beamed, "I like that. Horses fer courses. Looking after the old nag … You are a love." Christine looked at Joan, feeling a surge of affection. Dear Joan with her neatly permed hair and thick stockings. Christine noted too that she had changed into flat black slippers.

Ideas were forming. The Numatic 'enery vacuum cleaners were brilliant for getting into corners and easy to manoeuvre but tub vacuums could play havoc with your back. She could understand why Joan would prefer a light-weight upright. She would ask Doris nicely if she could work with Joan, perhaps citing Joan's hip as the reason but in reality knowing she could learn a very great deal from working alongside someone so experienced. 30 years a cleaner and she still loved it.

There were staffing shortages again. Someone hadn't showed up so Doris was muttering "Trouble is we've never got enough staff. Her, the boss, Mrs Gunther, she expects too much. She don't understand. She just picks up on complaints. She's coming in later to do an inspection. She don't realise that we have two off sick and all the new people she sends is useless." "No they ain't" protested Joan under her breath, "Christine's doing luvly."

Doris just glared, "I don't want no trouble tonight so Joan, you and Freda can cover my area while I do the fourth floor what

SHE should be covering." referring to Phyllis who was off again with her sick grandchild.

Sigh, no chance of working with Joan tonight. Christine shot up to her floor, anxious not to be seen by Mrs Gunther. Several years previously Christine had employed her company, Sunshine Cleaners, to do the cleaning at the Colchester English Study Centre.

Christine had been working as School Secretary there for many years, from within months of its opening. When she was first appointed the school was cleaned by a volatile Irish lady, Mrs O'Riley, whose attendance was spasmodic and directly related to her husband's bouts of boozing. However, to be fair to her husband, the excuses for her regular absences also depended on the painfulness of her own bunions and the weather.

Christine remembered full well going into school early each morning to check the cleaning in case Mrs O'Riley hadn't made it for whatever reason. Regularly Christine had to buckle to and tackle the cleaning before students began to arrive.

Eventually, they had all agreed it was time for the old girl to retire – she had let it slip that she would be 80 at the end of the month. Christine, with a sigh of relief, organised a retirement presentation and a suitable gushing, golden handshake.

She then had called in Mrs Gunther. Mrs Gertrude Gunther was German, an ex nurse with a powerful personality. She was over six foot tall, built to match and with blazing red hair. Her cleaners were in awe but she understood what her customers needed and she delivered.

Christine had spent several hours with Mrs Gunther working out the cleaning specification for the school and ensuring it was in grammatically correct English. She had then relaxed in the knowledge that there would be no further worries regarding the cleaning. Mrs G was a paragon but a tough one.

When Anya was born Mrs G had tried to recruit Christine - she needed someone with good business English as her own written English left a lot to be desired. Christine smiled, remembering trying to decipher a letter written to the Study Centre along the lines:

Dear Madam,

Thank you for aksepting my invitation to arrange a meeting with you and your staffs in order that your public areas kleen will be.

All though komplikated, from the specification provided that there are ways in which we reseptiv will be to taking on this kontrakt saving you unesesary trouble und diffikultis. Your akseptanse will mean that all satisfied will be.

Thank you for this time. Yours fatifully

There was certainly room for improvement!

Then when Christine was pregnant with James, Mrs Gunther had again asked her to come into business, this time as a partner. Christine considered it briefly but the Study Centre was happy to reduce her hours – a perfect situation.

But the seed had been sewn and now here she was again, three years later, working on one of Mrs G's contracts. This could be difficult. She prayed she could keep her head down and go unnoticed. The thought of Mrs G inspecting her work made her shudder. She would surely interpret it that Christine was now interested in her offer. Or perhaps, like Doris, she would think Christine was simply there to spy on them and sack her on the spot.

Anyway there was no future in continuing night after night like this under Doris's regime. She had all sorts of ideas about changing attitudes and running things very differently. She planned to start her own business in her own way – and not in Colchester. She had far too high a regard for Mrs Gunther to set up in opposition but she did wonder how Doris had managed to get the elevated position of supervisor – it didn't add up.

Christine smiled at herself – she had spent the evening constantly glancing over her shoulder or hidden away in the toilets, fearful of being caught out.

The time passed without drama and when she finally congregated with the girls downstairs, everyone seemed relaxed.

Doris, however, looked fed up, "She didn't have time to do an inspection. It's all right for you lot – she's given me these forms to do reports on each area. More bloody paperwork. She's coming back next week to check the contract out." Adding sulkily, "I've told her we need more hours or I'll give in me notice."

Confrontation with Mrs G had been avoided but Christine knew she had to leave – she was beginning to feel uncomfortable, a spy in the camp, as Doris had intimated, and that would be so unfair, especially to Joan.

She made up her mind that for the rest of the week, with or without Doris' blessing she would work with Joan and help her with her vacuuming.

Something told Christine that this contract and Doris were about to come under Mrs Gunther's closer scrutiny and she didn't want to be around for that.

On arriving home, Pete was up and waiting for her – gin and tonic in hand.

"The children left this for you. It's a stiff one!" Frightening", she thought, "when your own children pour you a drink – and a stiff one at that".

"Pete, I've decided. I am setting up my own cleaning business. I'm giving in my notice at the Study Centre as soon as I can. I may have to give a month's notice." She paused for breath, watching his face.

"I'm not going back to BComm after Friday. I just know we could do this so much better. I hate the way everyone treats cleaners. Could you try contacting some of your colleagues in Ipswich? It would be wonderful if you can get me an intro or better still find someone who needs a cleaning quote. I don't want to work in Colchester because of Mrs Gunther and in case I screw up. Too many people know us!"

Peter nodded his approval. "Wow. You really have made your mind up."

Christine was not looking forward to telling Joan she was not staying. She would leave it until Friday but she made sure that every night until then she whisked through her floor and then went to take over Joan's vacuuming.

At the end of Friday evening, she said quietly to Joan, "I shan't be back next week, Joan. I want you to know how grateful I am to you for all your support. I've loved working with you. I have told the office I'm leaving and Doris seems quite relieved."

"Didn't expect you to stay, pet. I just hope your old man goes along OK. You make a good cleaner, you know. They'll have you back anytime. Give us a hug."

Christine felt really mean. Ladies like Joan were the salt of the earth – the genuine women who took pride in their service, the successors of those generations who had always been in service. It was just a pity that today they weren't valued for the vital part they played. Having said that... had they ever been?

Well, it was going to be her mission to change that.

The idea was going round and round in her head. Somehow she had to make this happen and make money too. She could never match the income they had been used to when Peter was working but she kept coming back to the idea of cleaning. It was something she could do without capital and without qualifications, and more importantly around the family.

There was a need for a good organised service, she just knew it.

Someone needed to bridge the gap between customer and cleaners. Managers of companies didn't want to talk to cleaners about bins not getting emptied and lack of loo rolls in the gents. Cleaners did not have the skills to cost, put together and deliver a full cleaning package. This would be Christine's role, and more.

From her limited experience she could see that cleaning companies and communication skills were polls apart. Could she pull this together and provide a service which would bring a pride and professionalism to the industry? A service which could be trusted, was proactive, and where the cleaners were managed and motivated so that they could be accepted as part of the company's team.

Could she? She had helped to set up the Colchester English Study Centre. She had trained in London with an economist and had done a full secretarial course at evening classes. Now, she had worked as a cleaner, albeit for just two weeks but at least this gave her an insight into how things should NOT be done.

She decided to put this to Peter. His help would be invaluable in setting up contracts, pricing, and all the sophisticated legal and commercial knowledge needed to set up and run a company. He also had vast experience writing specifications and running training courses. Admittedly his experience was with high-powered engineering projects, but surely the same principles applied.

Would he really want her to run a business long-term? This had to be better than continuing working for the Study Centre, despite it bringing in a regular wage. How long could she be reliable and be effective there? It was only a matter of time before they had to replace her with a full-time School Secretary.

She knew she couldn't continue to run the show and if Peter got worse she would have to let them down. If she set up her own business she could tailor it to the requirements of the family.

Peter's reaction was upbeat. "We'll get it rolling. It's perfect. You can run things until I am on my feet and can get my business up and running. It's ideal. We can work from the kitchen table – we've got a decent electric typewriter. It'll be tough on you having to work every evening but at least I can do the accounts and letters and things from home."

The very next morning he had picked up the telephone, methodically number crunching through all his contacts, business associates and Thomson's Directory.

CHAPTER 5 – WE'RE OFF

Two weeks later Christine was bombing up the A12 to start her first cleaning contract. The A12 was the main trunk road between Colchester and Ipswich, often prone to long hold-ups due to the sheer volume of container traffic heading to or from the fast growing industrial estates and the ports of Harwich and Felixstowe on the coast.

Today though she was lucky and the speed suited her upbeat, positive mood – they were moving forward. This was the start of something important for all of them and she had the feeling that the future was hers to make.

Those painstaking hours Peter had spent phoning round to friends and acquaintances asking for leads had eventually paid off, and this, their very first contract, had been a hot one.

Christine was thrilled at the new lease of life, literally, that this had given him. They discussed the marketing strategy together at night and agreed that it would be better if she made the call to the prospective client. Peter had gleaned that cleaning companies were generally male-led and that their salesmen had the gift of the gab but very little else. After all, in the league of selling, cleaning had to be very low down the pecking order. "Pretty much at the bottom," said Peter.

He was sure Christine's cultured, public-school voice would be an attractive contrast to the usual telephone sales spiel and once she had an appointment, he knew her charm and charisma would be irresistible. But, as Christine said with a snort, he was biased.

As Export Manager for VE Ventilation, Peter too had been a salesman. He had such a smooth approach, was always well prepared and seemed to know what the customer wanted to hear. Perhaps it was just confidence? After all, selling million pound ventilation projects to Middle Eastern sheikhs and South American business tycoons had made him very professional.

Now he was methodically gleaning information about the cleaning industry:

"You have to know your market, know your customer and then use your intelligence to adapt your service to their needs."

Peter had been a great Dale Carnegie disciple, second only to being a good disciple of Christ. Well, the general message was the same – love thy neighbour and be an honest guy, even if the end gains didn't quite add up. After all the aim of one was to give things away and the aim of the other was to help you make money. Peter liked the good things in life too, so maybe Dale had taken the lead.

Christine had also read the Dale Carnegie bible, "How to win friends and influence people", although she baulked at the over-the-top American gush. Somehow when Peter picked up the telephone and laid it on to prospective clients, it sounded fine, in fact, it was charming. She was going to have to practise.

Peter would give Christine background to the potential client and, where possible, details about their current cleaners, the size of the contract etc. to enable her to create openings. Her very first exploratory call, which she had carefully rehearsed with Peter, was to the firm of builders' merchants – the ones she was driving to now.

Getting through to the MD had been surprisingly easy, "Mr Barton, how kind of you to take my call. I have set up a cleaning company with a completely different approach. If you have a few minutes, I would love to tell you a bit about us." She drew a quick breath. "We tailor our service to your needs, our cleaners are trained to be part of your organisation but we manage everything to do with cleaning and ...." She was cut short.

He had listened briefly and then interrupted to tell her that their cleaning supervisor had recently left and they wanted someone to come in and run the operation. At the moment they had two Italians, should be three, but the lady who had left had been the 'interpreter'.

"They are good cleaners but they don't speak English - don't worry about a contract for now. Can you speak Italian?"

"Yes. Quite well, actually." Christine had done Latin to "O" Level, knew the Ave Maria and had picked up enough to add another "O" Level in Italian later, just for fun. Peter had emphasised the need to sell up, not down - so yes, she DID speak Italian.

"Great. We don't want to lose these guys. They are honest and they know the ropes. We just need someone to come in and organise them. We'll sort the money out later as long as you don't charge the earth. How soon can you start?" Christine couldn't believe her luck. Two evenings later she was there.

The Italian couple, Francesco and Maria were charming and welcomed her with open arms. The first evening was such fun – they sang arias from Verdi's operas. It was so comical to see Francesco's ' rhythmic' bottom coming down the stairs backwards in time to the Grand March from Aida as he systematically treated each wooded step with Bourne Seal.

At the end of the evening they embraced her warmly, with Christine promising to sort out shelving in the cleaners' cupboard and get them another vacuum cleaner. She drove home singing an off-key rendering of Feniculi Fenicula – pathetic compared with Aida's The Grand March but perfect for her upbeat frame of mind.

She was chuckling as she described them to Peter. "Maria's your typical Italian Mama, all smiles and rolls of fat. She perspires and her shiny face looks just as though she has just been cooking pasta over a hot stove – she smells like it too. I bet she's a fantastic cook.

Francesco's the opposite - he smokes like a chimney and is as skinny as a rake. He works in his dazzling white vest and tight, tight trousers. When he polished the stairs on his hands and knees, it was oh so sexy. And you should see him broom in hand, he glides as though he's moving to music. It's magic. What is it about Italian men?" She sighed deeply and gave Peter a deliberately provocative wink.

"Oh yeah … no wonder you are so keen!" retorted Peter with a twinkle in his eye. "Just you watch these Italian gigolos!

The following morning Christine telephoned Rob Barton, the MD of the building company, "Mr Barton, I just thought I had better check about the cleaning."

"Brilliant, brilliant. I told you they were great. Let's see how it goes this week and then fix a meeting for you to come in and sort out the details."

Christine immediately dived in with her ideas on how things could be improved – for the client and the cleaners – her new mission. "But I wanted to ask if it would be possible to put shelves in the cleaners' cupboard and if we could give the stock room a special clean at the weekend. I caught a glimpse of it and it really does need sorting out. Unfortunately we wouldn't have time to do that in the evenings."

"Sounds just the ticket. This is the sort of feedback we need. I'll get the lads from the yard to organise some shelves for you and make sure they tidy up a bit in the stores. Let me know what else you spot. Yep, reckon that's overdue. Smarten us up, girl."

En route to the contract that evening Christine stopped at the corner shop on the Ipswich Road and bought a box of Italian Ferrerro Rocher chocolates for Maria and a bottle of cheap Chianti for Francesco.

They were already taking off their coats when she arrived.

"Derum derum derum," she sang – "Here's to say Grazie mille. You are stupendi. I spoke to Mr Barton today and he is delighted!"

Maria went into full Italian Mamma mode. "'E molto 'appy. We all 'appy. 'Eee giv you these?"

"No, that's not from the company. It is from me. I think you are just wonderful and I want to say thank you."

Francesco grinned, "We good team, like Italian football players, no? English Man U no good team! You OK capitana. We work for you – molto buono, si?"

Then he enthusiastically burst into the first verse of "Nessun Dorma" before opening his arms wide and grinning. "You work with us six weeks and you sing like Callas! Prima Donna Christina!" He roared with laughter.

"Me with my voice – you have to be joking. By the way, we've been asked to clean the stock room at the weekend – ….Pagi .. Pay time and a half, OKay!" she sang.

"Molto bene!" Francesco answered, giving an even bigger smile. "Zat good money. You want you come too?"

That night Christine came back to Pete full of enthusiasm, knowing this had to be the key. She could support the family in this way. Cleaning was fine – in fact she was truly enjoying it. She took Pete into her arms, and really felt they were going to win this battle.

"Yes. Tonight was such fun. If we can find staff like Francesco and Maria, it'll be a joy and I might even learn how to sing in tune!" Peter groaned as Christine started "Doh Ray Me Faaaaaa," totally out of key.

Could this be the answer too for Ros? After all they were in much the same position. Were things really falling into place at last?

CHAPTER 6 - ROS

Just after 9.00 am the following morning, having dropped
Anya at the Convent, Christine took James, her fat little
three-year old son to his baby minder. There was Ros
beaming. She always beamed. Here was someone who
made Christine's problems look like a minor splinter or a sore
thumb. She had carried the weight of the world on her
shoulders and still was calm and smiling.

Christine had known that Ros would be a match for her
boisterous son who could be eminently uncooperative unless
bribed with chocolate. Anya, James's doting sister had waited
on him hand and foot and, as a result, he had long ago
decided there was no need to walk, just to sit on his bottom
and smile sweetly. He did this successfully until he was two
when he became so heavy Christine had to think carefully
about her back before picking him up.

Even though he was now walking, she had spoken to Ros
about his weight and the fact that his chubby little legs could
barely support his Michelin style body. Food, however, kept
him happy and even at the age of three years three months,
sitting on the floor with a good book, Thomas the Tank
Engine for choice, was vastly preferable to moving.

Ros tried to impose a sugar-free diet with pieces of carrot in
lieu of chocolate Penguin biscuits but James was inclined to
throw a paddy when hunger got the better of him. In
desperation Ros would offer him half a Penguin – humph!
The tantrum would continue until the whole Penguin was
produced. Then, with tears brushed away, a broad smile
appeared and James's usual sunny self was restored. Ros's
children quickly adopted him as their little brother, after all
what he got, they got and they weren't adverse to chocolate
biscuits either. Ros's husband had left her to go and live with

her…ex… friend. To add insult to injury the friend's house backed onto Ros's garden and to quote the despicable man's words "So that way I can still see my children."   Yes, what he meant was, he could see them but never lift a finger to help. "What a shit", thought Christine.

Twin boys and a lovely little girl - three under five! Yes, it was tough. For any family it would mean little time or money to go out, even if you could find babysitters prepared to cope but this was what bringing up a family meant. Christine's blood boiled every time she thought about the deal he had dealt his patient, long-suffering wife who refused to run him down or complain.

Before her marriage, Ros had worked at the hospital as an administrator. She could do everything, payroll, wages, personnel and secretarial work using an electric typewriter – the cutting edge of technology in the modern office. Now here she was looking after James so that she could be there for her own children. She was managing on child benefit and little else. Christine felt so angry and just hoped that her child-care payment helped a little. She also felt guilty because Ros always fed James and he had some appetite. He lapped up her home-cooked lunches. When Christine had said she wanted to pay extra for this, Ros had replied "Please don't worry, I'm cooking for my lot and James doesn't make any difference."

To cap it all, when Christine collected James, Ros invariably had an amusing story about her son.

As they had sat down to lunch that particular day it was…..."Auntie Ros, I am allergic to stew." Pause … "but I can eat chocolate." James had never been allergic to anything in his three years on this planet. He had, however, cottoned on to the fact that his friend Simon was allergic to all

58

dairy products and his sister, Anya, was allergic to Penicillin – smart try, James, but shrewd Auntie Ros was having none of that – stew it was for lunch!

Ros could bring so many other skills, payroll and personnel as well as sound doses of common sense which Christine had seen her employ in abundance when dealing with her son, James – always kind but a wonderful no nonsense approach.

What Christine had to do now was to sell her idea for the future to Ros.

Christine asked her if she could come for a chat at home so that Peter could be there too. They arranged it for 9.30 the following day.

Ros duly arrived to find a contented James plonked in front of Bill and Ben on TV with, a chocolate biscuit, and Christine and Peter sitting at the kitchen table with a cup of coffee ready for her.

Christine gave her a wry smile and a "Sorreee" in the direction of the tellie and the Penguin, "but we want to talk."

"Ros, we NEED to talk at length. As you know James is due to go to the Convent with Anya after half term." Ros looked a little anxious.

Christine continued, "We are still going to need a babyminder in the holidays but we have a bigger proposal to put to you."

Ros waited.

Peter outlined their ideas and emphasised how they wanted to build a commercial cleaning service around the children. He explained each function in the company, how they as key players complimented each other and how they saw her role as part baby minder, part administrator with a basic salary and eventually a company car. Ros's eyes opened wide, "But you can't afford that."

"Yes, well perhaps not the car, but while Christine is still working for the Study Centre we will be OK. She has to give that up and to do that we need another couple of cleaning contracts. In the meantime you are an investment. Every new company has to invest and in the service industry, investment has to be in your staff."

These were brave words from a man who had put his business into liquidation. "We know there is a market out there and we know we can bring a pride and professionalism to cleaning".

Christine realised this phrase was becoming a regular refrain.

Ros held out her hands, biting back her tears. "This is an answer to my prayers. What can I say, except thank you? I will give you every support – you know that. And I love your children."

Little did Christine know just what that support would mean in the years to come.

CHAPTER 7 – CONTRACT NO 1

That evening Francesco and Maria greeted her with concerned faces. Francesco said, "We 'ave book. No understand." Sure enough there was a small notebook with CLEANERS' BOOK written in capitals on the front. She picked it up and quickly scanned the attached memo.

"Please put in any comments each day. We will do the same if we require any specific extras or there are any problems. Have taken up your suggestion about Stock room spring clean at weekend. Key No 54 will be left in envelope on reception. Please return to same place when you have finished."

She could fully comprehend their panic at the complicated English, but this was just what they needed. A Log Book. Smiling at the worried Italians, she explained "E un diario. It is a giornale dei giorni. Every day we will read this and I can explain what they want."

In unison they shook their heads. "No. Noi non leggiamo e non scriviamo inglese." No, they couldn't write English but "OK", would usually suffice. After all, Francesco and Maria weren't stupid. If she wasn't around, they could always phone up to ask Peter what the entry meant. He was at the end of the telephone each evening and he had an instinctive ability to understand Italian no doubt due to years of hearing mass in Latin at the seminary. Together they would certainly be able to understand the gist of things. This wasn't going to be a major issue, even if Francesco & Maria had gone into minor panic.

"They want us to spring clean the stock room this weekend." Spring clean ….Primavera pulito?? Obviously spring cleaning was not something you did in Italy. She talked every word through pedantically with the Italians until both were nodding enthusiastically. Once they had grasped the concept, their reaction was typically upbeat: "E facile." Francesco winked. "Capisce. Spring Clean. Pulire di Pasqua. We 'ow you say, Easter clean in Italia. You say us what we do, an' 'ow many hours! Eez OK."

But she really didn't want to have to drive over to Ipswich to work at the weekend. Could they manage without her? "Si sicuro! Non e problema."

Now she just had to gauge how long it ought to take. She found the key and unlocked the stock room to face row upon row of enormous racked shelves and a vast floor which had not seen a broom for months, with piles of rubbish accumulated in the corners. Wow, it did need attention. She looked with dismay at the pallets of cement bags, some which had split and leaked cement dust onto the floor, the stacked boxes of screws, and the valuable tools. How would she calculate the time needed? She would just have to guess.

Two hours per aisle and there were 15 rows. Ok, she would tell Francesco they had 30 hours to do the job. If they each worked 6 hours on Saturday with 5 of them doing the job. She knew spring cleaning always took longer than estimated so she would quote Mr Barton 40 hours and see how he reacted.

Risking his wrath, as she had been told he didn't like to be disturbed when he was working late in the office, she popped her head around the door. "We're all set to clean the stock room on Saturday and perhaps Sunday. I estimate we will need to charge you around £300 …."

She had plucked a figure out of the air. "That's fine! You go ahead." with a wave of his hand. "Slightly tied up just now. Ring me on Monday."

Back to Francesco. "Come and look at the room with me. We need to remove rubbish, sweep, vacuum everything and then wipe down the counters, telephones etc. before finally mopping over the floor. Split cement bags need to be taped up." Her verbal instructions were accompanied by plenty of actions which she hoped made up for her lack of Italian cleaning vocabulary.

"Use one tablespoon of Cleanfresh to a bucket of water." Francesco looked completely blank. Christine picked up the 5 litre container of general purpose cleaner and made a pouring gesture. She did a quick mental calculation, "that's about cinquanta millitres – 50 mls -to a bucket of the water." Francesco was nodding.

"That will leave it smelling nice. Massimo 2 hours' work per row," again she gestured, pointing at each aisle. "I think that will be enough hours to do good job. I pay you weekend rate time and half." Francesco was shaking his head.

"No. You tell me how much money – totale and we do job!"

"£200 OK, Francesco?" That would give her a bit of leeway if she had desperately miscalculated the time needed.

"OK. Molto OK. I bring Julio and Alberto – they good boys. No problema. £200 OK. "

Francesco's English might not be too good but he was quick to work out the money. Her Italian wasn't exactly fluent either. She realised both she and Francesco were now speaking a sort of pigeon Eye-tie/ English - present tense and no definite articles. But it seemed to be getting the message across – at least she was fairly confident it was.

Francesco and Maria were nodding happily. Their mutual understanding seemed to be improving but proof would be in the pudding this weekend and that certainly wouldn't translate!

"Who are Julio and Alberto? " Christine asked a little anxiously. She had a moment of doubt and a fleeting vision of the Italian mafia moving in. There were thousands of pounds worth of stock and although she felt Francesco and Maria were absolutely trustworthy, she couldn't afford anything going missing, especially if she wasn't going to be there.

"Le due sono molti buoni. They children of Maria sister, Teresa. Good boys. Molti forti." Francesco flexed his muscles and pointed at the cement bags. "No problema." He seemed very confident and with those bulging biceps Christine felt she couldn't argue.

Knowing this would be a vital test, for her and for them, Christine took a deep breath and said, "Fine Francesco, I know you do first class job. This is molto importante. If you do this good, we get more work. I telephone you on Saturday evening to see all OK. You have problems, I come in and we work together on Sunday. I want it perfetto, assolutamente perfetto."

Francesco nodded. "Si, assolutamente perfetto."

The manager's office was in darkness. Mr Barton had gone. Another step forward. If this worked out, the profit from this extra clean would help pay Ros' wages for a month. "Never count your chickens," was ringing in her head. Could she

64

depend on Francesco and Maria? Should she go in tomorrow and work with them?" She would ask Peter what he thought. It was so good to have him there as a sounding board.

Getting into the car, Christine put on her tape of hymns. She needed soothing and just prayed her trust would be vindicated. "Lead, kindly light, amid th' encircling gloom, lead thou me on." She didn't join in although the words seemed so apt. She could do with being led very firmly by the hand just now.

At home she poured out her concerns to Peter in jerky sentences as she ate the dried up vegetable lasagne she had served the family before she left. Peter looked at her hard. "You must trust people. Give them a chance to shine. As long as they properly understand what is required of them, they will do a good job. After all it is in their interest to. Leave them to it and have faith!" She just hoped Peter's devout Catholic faith, so much stronger than her own, would hold up and be there for them both.

Saturday dragged – she kept wondering how the clean was going. Watching the clock, she decided to telephone at 6.00 p.m. No answer. Really worried, she tried about twenty minutes later and to her relief Francesco picked up the phone. "Eeza gooda. Mr Barton 'appy. He come to see wiz zee Store Man. He open door for second store room. Puliamo domani. Dirty, dirty. Big job. We do same hours domani."

"You say Mr Barton was there and he is happy."

"Si, si, molto contento. You telephone Monday. He say you, he molto contento."

Christine beamed. "Well done, Francesco." This was fantastic. "More work." She couldn't wait now to talk to Mr Barton and get his allegedly happy reaction.

Sure enough when she phoned on Monday he was delighted.

"Christine, may I call you that? Christine, this is just the sort of proactive cleaning service we need. It would be good if you could come next week and we look at a contract. Meantime, think about what we need, how you can smarten things up for us. We need to compete with the big DIY places and this is all part of it. Oh and by the way, I have a lead I think might be of interest. A colleague of mine, the MD of Duyfken Line Shipping may need a cleaning service. I've left his name and telephone number with Maria. Give him a call sometime."

Excited, she rushed into Peter. "We need to draw up a schedule of extra cleaning. I think we can really build Halls up beautifully and Mr Barton, he's given me a lead."

She couldn't wait to go in that evening to see Maria and Francesco and give them a huge pat on the back. Peter had already started to draw up a schedule of extra work. This was certainly an area they could expand. They were on their way.

CHAPTER 8 – TRADES UNION!

Later that morning, Peter took a call from Ipswich branch office of the AUEW asking if he would be interested in quoting for their cleaning. They didn't want much, just three evenings a week. "What's AUEW?" Christine asked. "The Amalgamated Union of Engineering Workers!" said Pete. "Somehow I can't see you getting that contract. Just as well I took the call. With your plummy voice they'd have put the phone down right away.

Anyway I've made an appointment for you to go and meet a Doug Oliver next Thursday at 11.00. I'm intrigued to know where they got our number from."

Thursday arrived and putting on a grey business suit with a white shirt, high heels, and carefully applying her make-up, Christine felt a little less apprehensive. She had seen too many TV interviews with Trade Union officials during the miners' strike to feel totally comfortable, however, suitably attired, she felt like a business woman.

Christine climbed into the car. As she drove up the A12, not able to bomb up it at this time of the morning, she pondered over the meeting ahead. Maybe she should have dressed down, in her old cleaning clothes. This Mr Oliver, would he be some sort of militant shop steward? How would she handle an aggressive inquisition? She had no idea.

She parked the car, walked into the rather dingy red brick building and stood at the reception counter. An elderly lady looked up and nodded.

"It's Mrs Chapman I presume. I'll tell Mr Oliver you're here. Take a seat."

Christine sat down and looked around. Leaflets were displayed in cracked, yellowing plastic stands. "Take Charge - Workers' rights". She picked one up and started to read. Workers' councils. This made sense. Far from promoting left wing militant propaganda, this actually made sense. Involving staff had to be vital in a service industry. The success of the cleaning company was totally dependent on staff. She coughed and the lady behind the counter looked up.

"Would it be possible for me to take a couple of these leaflets?"

"I don't see why not," she said, with a smile. Christine was just reaching for another leaflet entitled "NEGOTIATE – THE KEY" when the receptionist announced, "He'll see you now. Follow me."

Mr Oliver, clad in a brown suit with a grey and orange tie, was sitting behind a shabby wooden desk with two chairs in front of him. He waved her to a seat. Christine, trying hastily to transfer the leaflets to her briefcase, held out her hand and introduced herself.

"It is good of you to see me, Mr Oliver."

"I see you've picked up a couple of our leaflets. Doing your homework?" Caught by surprise, Christine stammered, "Yes. Well. No. I thought they might be useful for me in my business. "

Mr Oliver put his head on one side quizzically. She had obviously struck a cord.

"You'd better tell me what you want."

"I'm trying to get cleaning work in Ipswich. I have set up a cleaning business. I'm just starting and I am loving it. I thought I would come and talk to you because I want to treat my cleaners properly and I am certain I can grow if I can find and keep good staff. "

"Well, you've got the wrong Union. We're Electrical Workers. I don't see how I can help."

"Surely what applies to your workers can be applied to every worker," she smiled, "but first and foremost I want to do your cleaning."

Tapping his nicotine stained fingers on the desk he said, "We only need a few hours a week and we can't afford anything grand. It's just got to be reliable. How many cleaners have you got?"

"Three including me."

"YOU clean?" He almost choked.

"Yep." ….. "And very well too," she couldn't help adding with a grin.

He looked her up and down, "I don't get it. You could get any high powered job. You don't want to be cleaning. Forget it"

Feeling her blood rising, "Look, I know I can make a success of this. I love cleaning and I want to do something about conditions for cleaners. They never get the credit they deserve. And, if you must know, I've got to do this. I clean at night on top of my secretarial day job. My husband's got terminal cancer and I'm doing this to pay the mortgage. "

There was a sudden silence.

Christine realised she shouldn't have said that. She couldn't retract it so she ploughed on.

"You see, I really believe I can make this work. I want to build a company that gives a good service but more importantly treats cleaners as they should be treated. On my best contract" (gulp, not quite a lie - just her one and only contract) "for Hall Building contractors, I really have made a difference. You can speak to Mr Barton the MD. But what is most important is that I have really sorted things out for the cleaners.

Before everything was in a mess – they had no schedule, no terms and conditions. They didn't know what they were doing. You see, I work with them and then I talk to the boss. They don't need me every night now but we are building up the specification so they don't just do the same things over and over again – we've really smartened the place up and all without pushing costs up - it's fantastic."

She dried up suddenly. In her fervour, Christine's chair had moved forward, she had forgotten to tone down her voice and her hands were half way across the desk in impassioned appeal. She had got totally carried away.

Collecting herself she pulled back and said more quietly, "I do hope you will give me a chance to quote. I promise you won't regret it."

Still no response.

Mr Oliver was looking at her hard, still with his head slightly on one side and a frown on his face. Christine was now feeling embarrassed - she had fluffed it. She picked up her notebook and stuffed it into her briefcase with the leaflets. She stood up and held out her hand.

"Sit down," came the gruff command. "I'm not promising anything but I'll get Marjorie to show you round. Just don't come in with any fancy prices. I don't know why I'm doing this but I think you might have something."

"Marj," he called. "Can you show Mrs Chapman round and tell her what the cleaners do at the moment. She's going to give us a quote."

Christine hastily retrieved her notebook and once again extended her hand across the desk. This time Mr Oliver stood up, shook her hand firmly and said, "I'll wait to hear from you."

Closing the office door as she left, she looked anxiously at Marj. "Oh dear, I thought I'd blown that."

"Don't worry. I heard every word. His bark's worse than his bite. He can be a big softie. Just don't get on the wrong side of him."

They walked round. The offices were tiny, three toilets (two gents and a ladies), a kitchen, a large meeting room and six small offices. Marj looked at Christine, "We had to change the ladies sign on that door to Gents. It's all men at the meetings and the place stinks of smoke afterwards. Generally, it is ladies that queue. Not here." She said with a laugh.

They ended the short tour in the kitchen.

"Just why does he want to change cleaners? It doesn't look too bad to me," Christine asked.

Marj sighed, "We have to charge the TUC for their use of the offices and Doug thinks the cleaners are overcharging us. Quite often they pretend they've put in the hours but we know they haven't. He can't bear to be cheated. Do you want to see the specification they are supposed to work to?" Christine nodded eagerly and Marj handed her a typed piece of paper on which all sorts of hand written notes were scribbled.

"That's their price increase starting next month and Doug reckons we're only getting about half the hours they're charging us for."

"How many should they be doing?" Christine asked innocently.

"Ten" said Marj "but what they don't realise is that since we put in CCTV, after the break-in we had a few months back, we can check when they come and when they go."

"Where did Mr Oliver hear about us?"

"Oh, he phoned a friend at the Chamber of Commerce and they said you were just starting up but couldn't afford to be a member yet. They gave him your number anyway. To be honest, he reckoned you'd be cheap."

Christine hurried back to the car anxious to get the figures written down while she remembered them. She couldn't believe her luck - the competition's figures had been handed to her on a plate.

That afternoon she and Peter chuckled. Mr Oliver had been very different from the "Arthur Scargills" seen at Trade Union conferences on television. Mind you, Marj had implied there would be other companies quoting.

"Do we really want to do a Trade Union, Pete? It might put other companies off, and he wears a BROWN suit."

"God, Chris, you are such a snob. Anyway you don't have to broadcast we are cleaning for a Trade Union. We need clients and this is so small that Francesco and Maria could probably do it as well – if not, one of their extended family would! Let's try and get it. With all this information we can undercut and make the price attractive."

Together they revised the specification and based the quotation on three mornings per week, three hours a time, saving an hour immediately. If there were union meetings on days when they weren't scheduled to come in, the cleaning hours would be adjusted to suit, at no extra cost.

A diary would be kept to notify the cleaners of evening meetings and a weekly attendance sheet would be kept in reception so that the cleaners logged in and out. They could undercut the existing contractors by 15% and still make a handsome profit.

CHAPTER 9 – WHAT'S IN A NAME?

"I'm a bit worried, Pete. If we are really going to do this we need a company, a name at least."

"It's alright, I have already started to work on that. The cheapest way to do that is to buy a company off the shelf. We can get one that has gone bust. It saves all the problems of registering a name and getting it approved. The cheapest going is a company called Monthind for £66."

"It's called WHAT?" retorted Christine, screwing up her face.

"MONT HIND, that's M O N T new word H I N D" spelt Peter.

"It sounds like an insignificant French mountain, Mont Derrier instead of Blanc. It's awful. I don't like the HIND bit. It really is a stupid name. Who on earth would call their company that?"

"The original Essex-boy owners, of course - the directors were a Mr Mont and a Mr Hind, both from Basildon! OK, I know it's not ideal, but it could take several months and many hundreds of pounds to get the name we want approved."

"But we can't use that." Christine was adamant. "It has nothing to do with cleaning. I wanted to use my initials CC and merge them with contract cleaning, it could be quite classy. With big illuminated capital Cs like they do in holy manuscripts."

Peter's eyes grew wide. "You are not serious, are you?" Christine pouted.

"Honestly Chris." He sounded incredulous, "For a start It would a) take months b) somebody has probably already registered it and c) it will cost. No, we will just have to go with Monthind,"

Looking at her unhappy expression, he added, using all his powers of persuasion:

"I think we may have to, just for the time being. After all once this chemotherapy is over, I hope to get my business rolling again and then we can ditch the cleaning and get back to normal."

Hmm. An interesting view of her chances, Christine thought to herself, but at least it showed a positive state of mind from Peter about his future, and anyway he was probably right.

So reluctantly accepting his argument and agreeing cost was a factor, Christine insisted that they played around with the name.

Eventually they decided they would call it MONTH-ind, with the emphasis on the month. Perhaps people would somehow associate it with calendar month and industry? Not much better, but at least they lost the be-hind bit!

Peter was feeling good. Two weeks without chemotherapy and he was keeping food down.

He felt ready to put more feelers out. After his tentative approach to the Chamber of Commerce, he now approached the Institute of Directors and the Small Business Federation. He never failed to come up with a contact who might help.

Christine had always been amazed at his methodology – he had immaculate address books for every continent, cross referenced by country, company and contact, and several different categories for the UK. Once or twice she had pettily wondered if he had a special one for women worldwide too and, if so, how they were categorised: Blond, brunette, Essex or Suffolk, Ecuador or Sweden? No, my husband's not like that! She chastised herself and hastily dismissed the thought.

Peter had managed to find out that one of the cleaning contracts for a large BComm building in the centre of Ipswich was due for renewal. Tenders were being invited and Peter eventually secured a meeting. She was to see the Building Manager, a Mr Canning.

Two days later, she sat in reception patiently waiting. Eventually a secretary appeared, "Mrs Chapman, Mr Canning hasn't got time to see you. This is the specification which you might like to read. I'll get someone to show you round as soon as I can."   Christine sat anxiously reading the specification, looking up occasionally to see if anyone was coming to her.

Finally after about twenty minutes, she went to reception. The security guard on the desk looked at her sullenly. "Yeah. Ok. OK. As soon as someone takes over here, I've got to show you round." With sinking heart she went back to her seat. Eventually, the receptionist returned. The security guard nodded at her muttering, "Ok. This can't take long though."

Christine held out her hand. He took it with a handshake which made her wince inwardly. She managed a smile and said "Christine Chapman." He looked at her and said in a way which sent a chill down her spine, "I know. I am Security."

He glowered at her and strode ahead, giving her no chance to take notes. "Sorry," said Christine "It would be such a help if I could ask you some questions as we go."

"Look I'm not here to do guided tours. We've had loads of you guys round. I don't know why they want to change – the cleaners we've got are perfectly OK. Bloody waste of time. We'll go up in the lift and come down the stairs."

Eight floors, Christine noted. She had to break down his guard. "I'm new to this and don't want to mess up totally. Can you tell me how many cleaners they have?"

"Varies. About 20 I reckon but you never know."

"What are their hours?"

"Look you'd better ask Building Management."

This was getting her nowhere.

She tried to concentrate "So this is the top floor. How many staff work here." "The bosses are on this floor but they come and go. You can have a look at the board room if it's free." But it wasn't. Down to the floor below.

"Can I have a look at the ladies," asked Christine. She counted the cubicles – just four. She took a few moments to compose herself.

She emerged and smiling at her guide she said, "Well that gives me some idea of the number of loos."

"Hardly," he replied. "The top three floors are the same but then it spreads out. Look you can see from the fire escape plan."

Horrified Christine realised that it didn't just spread out; it was four times the size on the lower floors.

"Would it be possible to have one of these plans so that I can work out areas more accurately?"

"Doubt it – security, you know. We don't want any Tom Dick or Harry knowing the layout of the building."

"Could we just have a look at one of the lower floors, please? I am totally lost."

"Wait till you see the stairs!" He was obviously enjoying this. "This is the west staircase and there's an east and the main which you saw in reception – that's got carpet."

"So there are three staircases."

"Unless you count the kitchen stairs."

Christine stood, looking at the concrete stairs, in dismay. The familiar smell of disinfectant hit her – like stairs in a public car park. They walked through one floor – again it was difficult to assess size and how long it would take to clean. Offices branched off the corridor in all directions with meeting rooms and a kitchen at either end. One thing; she now could gauge the toilets. Gents at one end and ladies at the other.

Christine said, "Well, it certainly would be a challenge."

She looked at the Security guard. "Over my dead body," was written all over his face.

They reached reception and Christine said, "I think I will just sit here and write up my notes."

"Sign out when you're done," he growled.

How the dickens could she get any idea for pricing from this. She looked again at the pack she had been given. At least there was a modicum of information in it. ...Total floor area 72,000 square feet. Wow. That seemed a lot of square feet. Did it include the stairs? She walked round the outside of the building and could see that the top floors formed a sort of small tower, probably with lovely views over the Ipswich docks.

The drive home on the A12 was tedious, the traffic heavy, and by the time she reached home she was feeling thoroughly despondent. She made a cup of weak black tea and took out her notes and the papers provided. She phoned Ros and asked her to come over. With Peter they sat round the kitchen table, papers strewn in front of them. James played with Poppy, their golden Labrador, and his Lego underneath the table.

"I haven't the foggiest idea how we start to gauge this," muttered Christine. "And the security guy who showed me round was utterly unhelpful and quite horrid."

Peter, undeterred and with his usual logical approach, said firmly "The starting point is that we know the overall area to be cleaned. How many square metres can you clean a night?"

"You can't generalise – it will depend on lots of factors like how many staff, what sort of floor coverings there are, how many toilets, whether you have to do the washing up. Anyway I can't think in square metres. "

Christine was anti in the extreme. She had a bad feeling about this contract. It was far too big.

"Come on – after all, you worked on a BComm contract here in Colchester – that should give you an idea."

"Well, there were twelve cleaners listed on the attendance sheet, or there should have been, but we were never fully staffed. But the Ipswich building is a rabbit warren and doesn't have big open plan floors."

Ros, who had been sitting quietly and listening to this exchange suddenly said, "Why don't we count the cleaners! All we have to do is watch the building when they start and when they leave – that should give us a reasonable idea."

"And what if they have three or four off sick?" Christine was feeling really negative about everything.

Undaunted, Peter retorted, "We should be able to work out a rough formula from the information they have given us and, Ros is right, we should do local research. You never know Francesco might have a cousin working there!"

At that moment the telephone rang. Immediate action stations – Ros shushing dog and child and trying to open the utility room door at the same time; Christine answering the call with their number, Colchester 571696.

A voice said "Could we speak to Mrs Chapman."

"Who's calling, please?" asked Christine trying to sound like a receptionist. "It's AUEW, I have Mr Oliver for her."

"Just one moment please:" – this to buy time, get child and dog out.

Christine put her hand over the mouth piece, hoping Marj had not recognised her voice.

"James, Poppy - out" she said fiercely, pointing to the utility room.

Ros quickly picked up James and grabbed Poppy's collar. "Come on you two."

James immediately started to squeal.

"I don't want to. I want a biscuit. Waaaa."

"Shh" said Ros, "Come on I'll make a house for you and Poppy, and you can have milk and biscuits but you have to be as quiet as a mouse."

This was the usual procedure. Every time the phone rang, the dog and the children were banished from the kitchen. James had got wise to this – with luck he'd get a chocolate digestive and if the phone call was a long one, a Penguin too. Sometimes he shared it with tail-wagging Poppy.

When Auntie Ros was here she always had good ideas about tunnels and houses AND she always paid up with a biscuit. When "Mum" was in a bad mood, she'd put her hand over the mouth piece and shout. You'd be lucky if you got a measly stick of carrot.

It wasn't easy working from the kitchen table, trying to make it sound as though they were in an office. It was going to be an improvement when the details of the registered company, with the frightful name arrived. At least they could then pick the phone up and answer "Month-ind Limited, good morning."

Christine was suddenly on her feet. "Yes, that's wonderful, Mr Oliver. I am sure we can. Yes. Tuesday at 11.00 is fine. Thank you so much."

She put the phone down with a whoop of delight. She stuck her tongue out at Pete, "Heee. Heee. Aheee. Heee. We've got the AUEW cleaning contract, how about that!"

She opened the utility door and swooped James, complete with well sucked biscuit, up in her arms. She danced around the kitchen, Poppy jumping up and barking with excitement.

"Chocolate biscuits all round. I've just got to go over, sort the details out and sign a contract. Oh what a lovely man."

Peter was shaking his head. "I just can't believe this one – true blue works for commie red. I don't know how you pulled that off. I thought you didn't do Unions! "

Christine felt slightly ashamed. She would never be able to tell Peter but she suspected Mr Oliver had given her the contract out of sympathy, because of her circumstances. Instead she looked at him and grinned, "Fatal attraction – opposites attract. All we need are the right coloured cleaners! How about purple?"

"We might just impress the TUC and go for chocolate brown. Plenty of West Indians in Ipswich. Just have to make sure they are reliable and honest," muttered Peter.

"Now you ARE being naughty. Seriously, how do we find staff?" Ros asked. "You would be in such a strong position if you could tell Mr Oliver, you have the perfect couple." Should they advertise, put a postcard up in the local shop or … easiest of all, ask Francesco and Maria?

"We know they are totally dependable and as straight as a die."

Peter was the first to voice their fears – were they in danger of being too dependent on the Italians, a Cosa Nostra family operation? And what happened when they all went down with flu?

Christine thought for a moment and said, "I really think we could do with a couple of "Joans" – the lady I worked with on Mrs G's contract here.

Still, I'm going over tonight to see Francesco and Maria. There's no harm in sharing the good news with them and asking if they know anyone. Then, I'll go and sit outside the BComm building and count cleaners."

"Fine, now come on," said Peter. "We still have to try to put together a quotation of sorts for this BComm contract. The deadline for the tender submission is two weeks on Monday and we haven't even got a company yet. Then we need a letterhead and a really good sales pitch." Peter was good at driving them on. When he was feeling well, there was a sense of urgency in everything he did.

Slowly things began to take shape. They now had two contracts under their belt. The big break was yet to come but Christine felt they were becoming more professional. They had chosen the uniform.

They couldn't afford anything too elaborate but she and Ros had decided at the very beginning they must have a corporate image. Green tabards for the ladies and green jackets for the men.

That evening when Christine left for Ipswich it poured with rain. Traffic on the A12 was horrendous – there was no way she was going to be in time to do her stake out of BComm and by the time she had driven back across Ipswich, Francesco and Maria – or F & M as they had become known in the "office", were already hard at work. "I'm so sorry I am late. I wanted to go and count the cleaners at the BComm."

"Notta worry. Why you come here to work? We Ok. You getta more business."

"Well actually, Francesco, we have got another contract – just a little one."   She proceeded to tell them all about AUEW.

"Eez good. We do. Morning OK."

"But it is the other side of town for you."

"We 'elp you."

They worked together, Christine whisking through the toilets, and they met in reception with fifteen minutes in hand, but Maria had her eye on the glass partitions. She would never leave a minute early.

Christine turned to her and asked, anxious to leave, "Are you sure about the morning clean, Maria." "

"EEZ OK, Three mornings. Teresa 'elp me. We needa money."

Christine wanted to talk but she had to go if she was to catch the cleaners leaving the BComm building, "Maria, are you doing all the inside glass, the windows too?"

"Certo!" she said with a shrug, "And why you do counting cleaners?"   Christine just laughed and dashed to the car. That was another thing they needed to sort out and perhaps charge for – the window cleaners were charging no doubt for the internal glass. That would be another saving for Halls.

She managed to park outside the BComm building and she had a good view of reception. She could see people standing round. Suddenly two young girls came to the door,

84

looked at the rain and made a dash for the bus stop. A group of three older ladies emerged, heads down, and crossed the road to a waiting van. Two climbed in the back and another into the passenger seat – that made five. Then three men came out, one putting on a crash helmet. He disappeared round the back of the building. Was he a cleaner?

The other two flipped their anorak hoods up, lit cigarettes and stood chatting. Four more ladies emerged and joined them on the pavement. They huddled together against the rain before breaking up and hurrying away in different directions. The car was misting up badly as Christine tried to see how many people were still in reception. There was one lady at the desk writing in a book and about six others queued up behind.

Eventually they too emerged putting up umbrellas.

Christine wiped the car window with her sleeve. The condensation was making it really difficult to see clearly.

One had a brief case – was she a cleaner or a member of staff working late? This was hopeless. Finally the lady who had been writing, put her clipboard in her shopping bag and waved to security. A man joined her and they came out together. Almost immediately, the lights in reception were dimmed and a security guard came forward to lock the doors. That must be it.

There was a sudden knock on her window. Christine nearly jumped out of her skin. She wound the steamed up window down a little. A uniformed policeman was looking in at her with a serious 'Hello Hello Hello' face on: "Are you waiting for someone, madam? I presume you know you're on a double yellow line."

"Oh I'm so sorry, I'm just on my way, officer." Christine gave him her best 'little girl lost' smile and he appeared to be satisfied.

"Just move along then please madam," and he turned to carry on with his beat.

Switching off the interior light of the car, Christine started up the engine and headed for home. The whole thing had been a waste of time anyway. She couldn't be sure how many were cleaners. It had to be somewhere between 17 and 20 but that was a fat lot of good.

Oh well, she at least had an idea – she could have picked any number between 8 and 20 before her undercover spy work but it was hardly a reliable way to do market research or whatever professional name Peter chose to apply to her sitting in a steamed up car and being asked to move on by the local law.

There must be better ways to get information about the competition. At least she had picked up that some of them were wearing a maroon uniform…. ACS, POCS, or ICS, one of those big national companies and all the more reason for her to harbour an increasingly negative attitude towards this contract.

CHAPTER 10 - PROGRESS

The next morning Peter wasn't feeling too well. He had been in a great deal of pain during the night and hadn't slept much. She phoned Ros and asked her to come to the house. Ros's three children were all at the local primary school, conveniently sited at the end of her road. During term time she was free until about three o'clock.

They needed to talk. James was due to start at the Convent with Anya which would make things so much easier but she also had to take Peter to the Royal Marsden Cancer Hospital for more treatment on Tuesday and Thursday next week. There were undercurrents at the Study Centre and she knew she had to give in her notice – they really did require an efficient full time secretary – and at the moment she was neither full time nor efficient, despite her best efforts. If only she could get a few more cleaning contracts.

Ros was her usual upbeat self. "Let's go flat out for the BComm contract. While you are at the hospital, I will type up the tender papers."

"Great." said Pete, "Come on – let's put our dream onto paper."

Christine was not enthusiastic. She really did not like that building, the people or anything about it.

Ros looked at her "This is not like you, Chris. Come on, you cleaned the BComm building here in Colchester. You were not at all happy with the way Mrs G was cleaning it. That was what convinced you, you could do better. She's not a big national company either. You've got the same chance as she had and you are baulking at it."

87

Yes, she thought later, when Peter had gone for a rest, Ros was right. Perhaps it was meant to be – she had learnt so much working on that contract. Why hadn't she thought of it before? Not only had she cleaned a BComm building but Guy Lattimer works there. She was muttering to herself, "Pete always said we should tell him what we are doing but I didn't want to, especially when he looked straight through me that night. I'm such a snob".

She swallowed hard and took Peter a cup of camomile tea. He immediately jumped on the idea of enlisting Guy Lattimer's support.

"Why don't you invite Guy and Alison to dinner?"

Christine sighed. She was feeling exhausted. The thought of having to do a sophisticated dinner party did not appeal and she liked least of all the thought of telling Guy she had cleaned his office. She blew out her cheeks - needs must and at the moment they needed all the help they could get.

Christine's method of keeping on top of things was to make a list every night before she went to bed, putting the worst things first.

She was not looking forward to phoning Alison but she was top of the list, so get it out of the way now.

"Hi Alison, it's Chris here. How are you?"

"Fine, but how are YOU? I hear Pete hasn't been too well lately."

"Oh, he's not too bad. Look we were wondering if you could come round for a kitchen supper to catch up. Could you manage this weekend sometime?"

"I'll check with Guy and ring you back." A few minutes later Alison rang, "We'd love to. Would Saturday evening early be OK and why don't you come here."

"No, I think it is better if you come to us. Then I don't have to worry about the children. I was just going to do a lasagne and a salad."

"Great!" said Alison, "I'll bring a pud and that'll make it easy. We were only talking about you the other evening. Guy really does want to catch up with you both."

So he had realised it was her cleaning his office, Christine knew it. She went hot and cold. Blast, blast, blast. Pull yourself together. That was the whole point of getting them over, after all.

There was a long pause, "Chris, are you sure that's OK?"

"Sorry. Alison, that'll be perfect. See you about 7.00."

Saturday night arrived.

The children were tucked up in bed. The house looked good, the table was laid and the lasagne in the oven. Pete with his glass of cranberry juice in his hand was relaxed. The doorbell went and Christine anxiously rushed to answer it. Alison immediately hugged her ... "How are you?"

"Fine, fine."

Then she turned to Guy who handed over a bottle and a bag, "That's the promised pud," he said "Alison's made me drive at 20 m.p.h. all the way here so that it didn't slop."

"I just didn't want it in my lap," laughed Alison.

"Thank you so much. Come through to the kitchen and I'll get you a drink." She took out the pudding – chocolate mouse and cream.

"Mmmm. It looks scrummily rich and gooey, Alison. Thank you. Come through, Pete's in the sitting room."

He was standing, looking pale but good. He held out his arms to Alison who hugged him and then quickly turned to Christine, an expression of real concern on her face.

"What can I get you to drink? Come into the kitchen." Christine hurriedly ushered her away, afraid of her reaction to Peter's emaciated appearance.

"Sorry, sorry," said Alison. "I had no idea. It's bad isn't it? Why didn't you tell us?"

"What are you having to drink and what will Guy have? I'm having a G & T – shall I make that three?"

"That'll be perfect," said Alison, "Chris, I wouldn't have recognised him. He's so thin."

"I know, but come on, let's have a good evening. Like old times!"

She handed Alison a glass and they joined the men. Guy turned to her and reached for his drink, "Phew that's lovely. Hope it's a stiff one!"

"It is," Christine smiled, "It's so good to see you both. We must try and do more entertaining. The trouble is you get buried in your own little world."

"Yep," said Guy, "We've a hell of a lot to catch up on. Pete's been telling me the Marsden are on his case and he's back there next week for more chemo."

"That's right – the travelling is a pain, I hate the M25, but they are the best and the consultant is ace. Come on, let's sit down and we can chat in comfort. What's your news? Are you both still working?"

"Not for much longer …. I'm expecting" said Alison. Christine leapt up and gave her a hug. "That's wonderful news. You must be thrilled. When's the baby due?" They chattered on about the joys of parent hood, the need to continue working, and the importance of grannies.

Eventually Christine took a deep breath and said, "Well, we've got some news too. We've set up a cleaning company!" She was watching Guy's face carefully – a mini frown passed across it and then his eyebrows raised. "Domestic or office?" He's quick, thought Christine. "Office", she replied studying him intently.

"Bloody good idea. BComm could certainly do with a decent company. I think we must have had about six cleaning companies and none of them get it right. I think they all try to get the business by undercutting prices and the service deteriorates instead of improving."

There was her answer … he hadn't seen her. Or was he just being clever? Not wanting to go further down the BComm route, Christine leapt to her feet,

"I'll check the lasagne. I'm sure you're ready to eat."

"Let me help. I'd better rescue that pudding." Alison followed her, adding, "You're not still working at the Study Centre as well are you?"

"Yes. We need the money, Alison. It's a long story. After he left VE, Pete tried to start up on his own but this cancer business has been a pig and he's had to close his business down. So I'm still working at the Centre, but to be honest I'm going to have to give it up because I can't cope. I have to take so much time off. The thing about cleaning is that I can do it in the evenings when the children are tucked up. I've got some super cleaners and I actually love it."

Frightened that she was going to well up, she called, "Come on chaps, food's ready ...take your seats. Guy, could you open the wine on the sideboard."

Pete took a while to get himself to his seat at the head of the table. It was noticeable how difficult he found it to walk now. His feet were swollen from the chemo and at times his co-ordination was affected.

Guy proffered the wine "You having some, old chap?"

"Better stick to the soft stuff." said Pete. Guy immediately retrieved Pete's glass of cranberry juice and put it down beside him. He poured for the girls and then filled his own glass.

Christine could see him collecting himself. He sat down opposite Pete and looked round the table. She dished up the lasagne and passed everyone a plate, giving Peter his usual miniscule portion. "Help yourselves to salad, please, and do start before it gets cold."

Guy was thoughtfully forking his lasagne. He cleared his throat before taking a mouthful.

"Well now, we've a lot to talk about. Let's not waste time. We can talk and eat!"

"He's going to run this like a business meeting!" thought Christine.

"OK. Now what's all this about a cleaning business, Pete?"

"Chris has really got the bit between her teeth. She wants to give up working at the Study Centre. We've done a bit of research and we think there's a need for a professional cleaning company in the area. The problem seems to be that management and cleaners don't communicate and the service suffers as a result."

"Do you mean management of the client or management of the cleaners?"

Both," said Christine vehemently and she proceeded to tell Guy about Halls and her Italian superstars. "The difference we have made there is amazing. We've re-written the spec and are providing a completely different service now, anticipating the client's needs and saving him money."

"You are actually up and running then," said Guy in surprise and with more than a hint of admiration in his voice. "But saving money? How do you save clients money? Surely you have a set contract to work to?"

"Well, yes, but that's the whole point. Once we're in, we talk to the client and make suggestions about adapting the specification. So often the specs are written by people who haven't a clue about cleaning. And Guy, you should see the waste, I just know there's huge scope there to save money."

"What companies are you working for?" he paused, something deep down was niggling him. She wasn't cleaning his offices, was she? No, that was impossible – their cleaning company was run by that flamboyant German woman with the red hair.

"Chris is such a snob," said Pete with a wink at his wife, "she doesn't want to clean here in Colchester because too many people know her and she doesn't want her friends thinking she's a cleaner. She bombs up the A12 every night and cleans in Ipswich." How neat was that? The question headed off perfectly. Pete was in his element. His faced was flushed and he had hardly touched his food. Christine prayed he wasn't running a temperature again but he was obviously relishing Guy's questions and certainly wasn't going to let his old sparring partner get the upper hand. Still, looking at Alison, Christine knew by her worried look, that she was gauging their situation.

The truth was that since Peter's appointment as Export Manager at VE, they had been able to take out a mortgage on a nice house, to join the Officers' Club, to play tennis and to enjoy a reasonable social life. Okay, Christine's mother had raised an eyebrow when they moved from Reading to Essex. Essex .....

After all, Essex conjured up pictures of 'Sowfend', 'arlow' and Romford, of medallion man and Essex girl in black tights and 6" white stilettos, all driving white convertible Ford escorts with their names printed on the windscreen – Gary and Tracy - ugh.

Christine had tried to convince her mother that Colchester had its history and its classy side. After all, it is Britain's oldest recorded town and has Boudiccea as its heroine, queen of the Iceni, the town is surrounded by a Roman wall and has a wonderful Norman castle.

Its other claims to fame are admittedly slightly more dubious. Colchester has had the highest number of earthquakes in Britain and is the Ministry of Transport's testing centre for roundabouts, but perhaps we won't go there. Mind you, any system that has a roundabout that is part of a larger roundabout which leads you onto another roundabout before reaching another roundabout for your exit perhaps does deserve to be talked about – and it was, all the time, by all the residents of Colchester!

Her Mother always felt Suffolk had a much more acceptable ring to it. Ipswich was just 20 miles up the main A12 dual carriageway, over the county border where lie the exquisite landscapes of painter, John Constable, still largely unchanged since he painted the Hay Wain. Suffolk is the county of gentleman farmers and much prized post-codes and 'couldn't Peter commute from there'.

Back to Guy, and Pete's 'snob' accusation - "But it's not like that. Colchester's great," protested Christine feebly, secretly knowing there was a lot of truth in Pete's statement. Guy and Alison were cases in point – she hadn't wanted them to know she went cleaning. "It's just that Pete has a lot of contacts in Suffolk!" Now that DID sound pathetic! He had contacts everywhere and even more in Essex.

But Guy was on the business case immediately. "Have you approached BComm?" Guy asked Peter, direct as ever. Men didn't beat about the bush – when they wanted to know something, they just … well, asked.

"Alison, I'll get your lovely pud – it looks delicious." Christine shot off to the kitchen – she could feel her colour mounting. Guy must be putting two and two together. Would he now think they were using him?

Alison joined her bringing out the plates. "Let me give you a hand," and she immediately started to wash up the glasses. "Chris, how an earth are you coping? You're doing this on top of the Study Centre and the children and with Peter as he is. We had no idea. You must be shattered."

"I'm fine but I am dreading next week. It's the trips to the Marsden and the chemo which are hardest. Also the last bout of radiotherapy was so bad. Pete has huge burns on his right side. I'm so worried they are going septic. He's really screwed up about our GP which doesn't help. We still can't get over the fact that three times he failed to diagnose cancer. If only he had done something when Peter was still at VE, we'd at least still have an income and insurance." Christine sighed, before continuing, "Yes, sometimes I am at my wits end but the kids and work keep me focussed and friends are fab. But I've got to give in my notice at the Study Centre before they boot me out. I really am not delivering any more and it's not fair."

"Chris, after all you have done for them, don't even go there! If they want you out, let them make you redundant. You've worked your socks off. You have to think of you and Pete. Promise me you won't do anything rash."

Alison fiddled with the pudding, "I wonder if Guy could help, I am sure he will, if he can." They carried in the desserts to hear Guy saying,

"I've no idea who is handling the Ipswich offices but I can certainly give you information about my building. I know

BComm have a policy at the moment of wanting to smarten up their image. Your timing could be perfect. Look, no promises but I will see what I can do." Peter nodded, "That would be great."

Christine embarrassed, quickly turned the conversation to Alison's pregnancy. "We've a loft full of baby things from toys and clothes to prams, high chairs and stair gates. You'd be more than welcome to take the lot, unless you want to get everything new of course."

"My mother wants to get the pram, but we're saving hard. We're going to need to move and I want to go down to working part-time, so yes please – we'd be grateful for everything!" said Alison enthusiastically.

After Alison and Guy had left, Christine turned on Peter. "I hope you didn't make him feel he has to help us." "God, Chris, he's a friend and he's a businessman. He knows and I know that's what happens. I have given him leads in the past. Sometimes, you are too precious for your own good."

She wasn't sure how to take that, but she was too tired to care.

CHAPTER 11 - REMISSION

The drive to the cancer hospital, the Royal Marsden, was horrendous, the M25 a nightmare as always. Three and a half tortuous hours for a journey that should have taken well under two hours. This circular motorway all around Greater London had been built to avoid the horrendous traffic jams of the previous ring roads, the North and South Circulars. Unfortunately everyone now knew it was there and therefore everyone used it and it became known as The Road to Hell or the World's Largest Parking Lot by all and sundry. Still that's progress.

When they arrived at the hospital there were no parking spaces anywhere near the entrance. She pulled up in the "Ambulance Only" parking and helped Pete out. She eventually put the car on the edge of the grass miles away and walked slowly back to reception, dreading the meeting with the consultant.

Peter was sitting in reception, hunched forward, obviously feeling the effects of the long journey and also dreading the forthcoming meeting. They patiently waited. There was the usual round of X-rays, blood tests etc before finally being shown in to the consultant.

He was smiling. "I've good news. The tumour on your liver hasn't grown and the one on your lungs has actually shrunk a little."

They both sat up. Christine's eyes widened.

"Yes, it is good news. It may, of course, just be remission and I want to keep an eye on you. Let's stop the treatment for a month and see how you do. I have to stress, however, that it could only be remission. The liver is like compost, it fertilises everything, especially cancer cells, so we will just have to watch it closely. We've never cracked this one before – only time will tell." The consultant allowed himself a weary smile.

The journey home was easier. Peter slept and Christine just kept muttering, "Thank you, God" over and over again. She had not dared to ask the consultant how long remission might be but Peter had already beaten the original prognosis by almost a year. She recalled the poem, "If you think you're beaten, you are." Dear Uncle Harold. We won't be beaten.

The children were spending the night with her friend, Simone. Her children, Natalie and Stephen were exactly the same age as Anya and James.

Tonight she and Peter could relax and enjoy a ray of hope.

When they opened the door there was a large envelope on the mat. Christine bent and picked it up. "It's for you, Pete. By hand."

A little later as they sat eating scrambled eggs on toast washed down with the inevitable cranberry juice, Pete asked her to get the package.

As he opened it, his eyes popped out. "Chris, I can't believe this. Guy has given us a complete copy of the existing contract for his building. He's just blacked out certain bits. There's a note too. Hey, he's really pleased with himself – listen to this."

Dear Piss and Crete!

(Peter was shaking with laughter. On a memorable GEC conference trip to Milan together, a slightly sloshed Guy had had difficulty with Chris and Pete's names ....)

Thanks for a grand evening. Loved the lasagne.

'Fraid I can't get you much gen on Stour House or the other Ipswich buildings, but I have the name of the chap you should contact. They are not at all happy with the deal they've currently got and won't be reappointing the same firm. Mark Halliday is a decent sort. He doesn't make the final decision but he's redone the spec so knows what he's talking about. You'll need to move on it. Quotes have to be in next week but he'll free up time to see you ASAP. Ring him… Pronto.

Hope the enclosed helps. Keep me posted.

Regards Guy

PS: I AM sober. Great evening – Thanks again.

"You see," said Pete triumphantly, "I knew he'd come up trumps."

Christine nodded and allowed herself a tiny gasp of relief. Guy really hadn't recognised her, had he? She was almost, almost sure.

Next morning Christine telephoned and arranged to see Mark Halliday, explaining that she'd already had an appointment the week before. She asked if she could take Ros with her and he agreed. While they had been at the hospital, Ros had spent the day working on the tender documents. This would be an enormous help and she was thrilled at the prospect of being involved. Christine knew two heads were definitely going to be better than one when assessing this complex building.

The same surly security man was on reception but this time it was different. Mr Halliday responded promptly and greeted them with a friendly, "Mr Canning was sorry he didn't get to meet you when you came before. He hopes to pop in later. Let's go to a meeting room for a chat and I'll give you a guided tour en route. That way if there is anything you want to re-visit we can do so on the way out."

"Victor, please can we have visitor passes for Mrs Chapman and Mrs Barnum." As Christine expected, the request was greeted by yet another scowl but the passes were handed over.

This time they both made copious notes from the direct answers to their queries about numbers of staff and timings. In reply to Christine's question, "Is this a routine tender exercise or are you looking for something different in your cleaning service?" Mark replied, "To be honest the cleaning of this building has been a headache for years and I am spending hours sorting out problems and complaints. We really need a company who will manage it well. We know the difficulties of getting good staff, but what we are not getting is decent management. This building needs a dedicated manager not a cleaner cum supervisor. I need to do my proper job looking after all building contracts and not have to constantly be worrying about cleaning."

This sounded just like the kind of changes Monthind wanted to bring about so by the time they had left, both Ros and Christine were marginally happier. They had even been briefly introduced to Mr Canning, disinterested though he seemed. "Maybe he was just preoccupied," said Ros, generous as always. They both agreed it all depended how much sway Mark had as to whether they stood a chance.

Their big problem would be staff. There is no way F & M could solve this one – "You'd need the entire Italian mafia on board," muttered Christine.

"We can advertise," said Ros. "Why don't we give it a whirl? I'm sure it's probably illegal to advertise for a job you haven't got, but hey ho, we don't need to give details." This from holy Ros who would never do anything underhand!

Using minimum words to keep the cost down, all they did was to advertise "Evening Cleaning Ipswich Town centre. Top Rates. Cleaning and management positions. 01206 571696."

On Friday, Christine had taken Maria and her sister, Teresa to AUEW. Marj, the secretary, was delightful. She showed them round, told them what was required before organising the key and the log book for them to sign in and out. They were due to start the following Monday morning. Again Christine had no option but to trust them – there was no way she could be in Ipswich at 06.30 a.m. to hold their hands. She looked at Maria's open honest face and knew she needn't worry.

Monday morning. It was James's first day at the Convent. Up and ready at 07.00 in his new school uniform with Anya, fussing over him like a little Mum.

Peter had organised putting on James' tie, already done up, so all he had to do was put it carefully over his head, but there was Anya straightening it neatly. His shoes were polished but within minutes one sock was down over his ankles. He was so excited. Christine had to take a photograph.

She left them both at the convent holding hands, James with his cap crooked and both socks down. Christine had a lump in her throat. How quickly they were growing up. She turned away and drove home, holding back her tears.

Ros arrived at 9.30, thrilled to find there were already two replies to the ad on the answer phone.

Just as Christine was settling down ... the phone rang again. Ros answered it. "It's AUEW for you."

What was this going to be about? Maria's first morning. Christine apprehensively took the phone. Mr Oliver was chuckling at the other end,

"Oh man, I just love your Maria. She was still here when I arrived. Made me a coffee and left a gorgeous slice of Italian cake for Marj and me. Talk about bribery, Christine. You and your staff sure know how to win the customer over. The place looks and smells fantastic."

Tackling Maria that evening at Halls, she grinned, "Maria, Mr Oliver loved your cake this morning." Christine could just imagine Maria accosting the boss – "You like Maria pannetonne. Eez good, No?"

"Signora – book eez no good. Better I see 'im. Ee like pannatonne. Eef I make coffee, ee talk. No cleaning problem. No book." Maria was shaking her head vehemently.

Making coffee was certainly not in the specification but Christine could see the benefit of Maria's being there when Mr Oliver arrived and even making the coffee but there was no need for her to provide cake and Christine told her so in no uncertain terms.

"Signora – you geev me and Francesco presents. I geev Signor, boss, pannetonne – not every day. Justa Monday. Monday bad day, nobody lika Monday. He contento. We 'appy."

There was no arguing with this! Dear, dear Maria. They say the way to a man's heart is through his stomach. If only they could charm every male like this!

Christine had taken two days' holiday from the Centre in order to finalise the Stour House quotation which Peter and Ros had drafted. She needed time to make decisions and if she were to give in her notice, the cleaning company would have to grow and grow fast. Suppose they didn't get Stour House?

Christine kept looking at the piece of paper she had propped up on the telephone in front of her working area – Ring Mr Parnell at Duyfken Line 01473 223333. This was Mr Barton's referral and it had now been about five days since he had given it to her. She knew she should have followed it up immediately but she was terrified that BCOMM might take off. How much more could they cope with? Peter had frowned and said she should hedge her bets – "The chances are you will only get one or the other so you really shouldn't look a gift horse in the mouth!" were his actual words.

Reluctantly, she picked up the phone and dialled the number. She asked to be put through to Mr Parnell but the receptionist, doing her job properly, wasn't having any of that. "Who's calling, please? ..... From which company? ..... Could you repeat that?" "It is a little difficult... I'll spell it," said Christine resignedly, "M O N T H I N D Ltd., Monthind Limited."
"What is your call in connection with?"

"I understand Mr Parnell is interested in discussing Duyfken Line's cleaning requirements – Mr Barton asked me to telephone." Even that didn't shake the receptionist. She just said firmly, and with a sort of grim satisfaction, "Well, Mr

Parnell is engaged just now but I will tell his secretary you called. Can I take your number?"

"How kind, thank you," said Christine sweetly, but secretly she was thinking, "Great, that is that!" She had made contact and with luck that would be that.

OK … if they didn't get Stour House, she could telephone again but if they were successful, she could forget them. What was important was that, with Stour House, she could afford to give up working at the Colchester English Study Centre immediately.

How she would miss the intellectual challenge, the fascinating students from all over the world, the teachers and, most of all, Uncle Harold.

It was such a gamble, a financial gamble too, but what would be best for Peter? Whatever happened he would need her more and more. Yes, she would give in her notice and see what happened. She was sure the Study Centre would take her back as a temp to help out during the holidays. After all she knew the place inside out and could do most things, except teaching.

Even teaching she could perhaps help with, although she did not have a teaching qualification. She thought fondly of her childhood in Cornwall constantly correcting her Polish father's charming English mistakes – mainz peas instead of mince pies was just one of his many such errors. He always got his "i's" and his "e's" mixed up with glorious results.

Language to her was fascinating and she knew from years of practice how to articulate clearly and how to pick her words so that they were easily understood.

CHAPTER 12 – THE SEARCH FOR STAFF

Peter was upbeat. She gave in her notice at the Centre, asking if she could have an appointment with the Chairman, Uncle Harold's nephew, Tony Abrahams, on his next visit to Colchester. Two days later he was there and to her amazement, he was charming. He understood why she felt she couldn't do her job as School Secretary and offered her a position in his subsidiary company, The Centre for British Teachers, in Colchester writing materials for teachers. "You write well and would be a great asset to the team. You could choose your hours there."

Christine was so grateful.

The perfect solution you would think. Certainly, financially it was a godsend. However, it didn't work out as it was meant to. Christine hated it. The man in charge quite rightly resented having her foisted upon him. He didn't include her in any way and she felt like a spare part. She felt totally useless and indeed was totally useless.

Possibly this was meant to be. She resolved to concentrate on the cleaning company and getting things sorted at home. She was unhappy. She felt she was taking advantage of the Abrahams' kindness, but maybe not for long. She threw herself more and more into working in the evenings.

She loved working with Francesco and Maria, their broken English and their arias. She mused about who had taken whom under whose wing. Francesco told her about his sister's brother-in-law who ran a cleaning company in Milano and who had an Aston Martin and two Porsches and "maka lota money". Christine laughed and shook her head.

Maria had told Mr Oliver that Mrs Chapman "needa more work," and Mr Oliver had apparently told Maria to tell Mrs Chapman to phone him.

Feeling slightly steamrollered, and not at all sure if Maria had got it right, Christine decided to ring Mr Oliver to see if this had any credence.

"Mr Oliver, I hope all is well with Maria. She is so enthusiastic about getting more work for her family that I am afraid she may be pestering you."

"Not at all. We love Maria and I just wondered how things are going for you. How's your husband?" Christine gasped. What had Maria been saying? Then she remembered her outburst about Peter when she first came to quote for AUEW. "He's OK," she said tentatively. "We've got our fingers crossed, but the chemotherapy is tough." She couldn't believe she was saying this to a client. "Thank you for asking," she added humbly.

"Did Maria tell you? I have a lead which I think may be of interest. One of our members is a shop steward for the Eastern Water Authority. They want to appoint an independent cleaning contractor. Up till now they've used their own staff but the powers that be want to outsource to save money. His wife works as a cleaner there but she's going to lose her job. I told him they won't get anywhere by going on strike. But then I thought you'd be just the person to take the contract and possibly the staff on." He paused and Christine taken aback gasped her delight, "Gosh, that's wonderful. Thank you so much, Mr Oliver."

"I can give you the name of the guy at EWA to get in touch with. Don't quote me. A referral from a trades union won't do you any favours, but I think you should go for it. You need to speak to Mick first – he's the shop steward, and he'll give you the low down."

Christine wanted to burst into tears and say "You darling man, thank you sooo much." Instead she just said, "Thank you. Can you give his name and number, please?"

Mr Oliver carefully dictated, "Michael... Riley ....Telephone number 01473 292034 and the guy at EWA is Mr Arnold Henson. Good luck."

Christine had just chance to mutter, "Thank you. Thank you," before she heard the receiver click at the other end of the line.

Without a second thought she picked up the phone and dialled the number. A female voice with a deep Suffolk accent answered, "Yeah. Oo's that, then." Christine smiled, "Is that Mrs Riley? My name's Mrs Chapman. Mr Oliver at AUEW has told me to telephone and speak to Mr Mick Riley."

"Oh yeah, I know .... the Union. He's out the back with Willie. I'll just get him."

Christine could hear her yelling "Mickie, someone's on the phone from the union fer you."

A few minutes later, the phone was picked up and a deep male voice said, "Yeah."

Christine wasn't sure where to begin but she launched in, trying to keep her voice as non-plummy, as possible. "Mr Riley, Mr Oliver has told me you work at Eastern Water Authority and that things are about to change with regard to the cleaning."

"Yeah, we're pretty worried about it. They are bringing in flaming contractors, out-sourcing they call it, and all the cleaners are going to lose their jobs. Why are you asking?"

"It's a long story but I am a cleaner and I run a very small cleaning company. We clean AUEW for Mr Oliver but I am trying to get more contracts and to build up a team of ladies to work with me."

"Well, I don't know that I can help. I work there on the electrical side and Lou, my wife, is one of the cleaners. I mentioned it to Mr Oliver, on the union side, because all the cleaners'll be getting the shove, Lou being one of them. We are pretty peed off because the hours fit in great for Lou – she has my tea ready when I get in and then she goes round the corner to clean so we don't have to leave our son, Willie on his own."

"Do you think it would be possible for me to get in to quote for the cleaning – I would love to keep the cleaners working there if at all possible?"

"Well, I don't know about that. Lou could tell you more but you would have to speak to the guy in charge. He's generally OK but at the moment he won't talk to no one."

"Perhaps I could try. What's his name?"

"Yeah, well. I can give you his name but I don't know about you doing the cleaning. It's pretty filthy, all the mud from the linesmen and the gents is, well, not the sort of place for a lady to clean …"

Christine burst out laughing. "Mr Riley, that's not a very wise thing to say about your wife. I hope she didn't hear that. If she can clean there, so can I! I think she and I may have one or two things in common."

"Aw gawd, I've dropped myself right in it, ain't I." He was laughing too. "Maybe you should speak to her. Hold on…"

Christine could hear them talking and the phone was picked up once more. "It's Lou speaking. Mick says you want to take on the cleaning at Anglia."

"Yes, but I don't know anything about it. I wonder if you could help at all, please, Mrs Riley? I run a very small but very happy family cleaning business and this sounds just the sort of contract we could do. Mr Oliver at AUEW told me to contact Mr Henson but he said to talk to Mick, or better still you, first."

"Trouble is they don't tell us anything. We just know we get paid to the end of next month. But we're not daft. Mr Henson don't clear his desk so we've seen the letters. We aren't happy cos these big cleaning companies they pay the minimum rate, cut the hours and expect standards to be bloody brilliant."

"Don't I know it." said Christine with feeling, "That's why, Mrs Riley, I know we could do it. I clean myself, not like the bosses from the big cleaning contractors, we don't have a fancy office. We work from my kitchen table and keep costs to a minimum so we can look after the cleaners – pay them well and make sure they have the hours to do the job properly. The trouble is I haven't even spoken to Mr Henson let alone persuaded him to allow me to quote – we're very small and I haven't a clue how big the contract is. He might not even talk to me."

"Reckon Mick can sort that,… can't you Mick?" There was a pause but Christine couldn't hear his reply. Lou continued doggedly, "He bain't a shop steward for nothing. He can have a word in certain ears, can't you Mick?" In fact, Mick was renowned for his ability to have a few words, believing that if a few words were required a few more from him would do no harm, all of which led to him being generally known as Gobby, a nickname of which he was actually quite proud but again there appeared to be no response from Mick.

Undaunted, Lou continued, "Well, if you want to know about the hours an' all, that's easy … there're ten of us and we do two and a half hours each … well, we're supposed to …."

"Mrs Riley, I really would love to come and talk to you and your husband. I think you would like how we work and I know you could be a great help to me – you could teach me a lot!"

"When do you want to come? Trouble is that me and Mick aren't home together until, well … after 8.30 p.m. when I get home from me cleaning. He's only here today because we had to take Willie to hospital for one of his check-ups and I can't do that on me own – he autistic you see and has these funny turns."

"If your husband is home today, could I come over, like right away for a chat?"

"Cor, you're keen, ain't you? Just let me ask Mick. I reckon he should go back to work by rights but he did say sod them." There was another pause. Lou came back quickly. "Mick says he was due to work over Beccles way today so by the time he gets there, it'll be time to come home. If you can come over this afternoon, it'll be great. I have to go cleaning at half past five though."

"So do I!" said Christine with a laugh. "Can you give me your address? If I get to you about 3.30, would that be OK?"

"That'll be fine. I'll have the kettle on. We're the far side of Gainsborough – you know, the painters' estate." "Painters' estate?" Christine queried, slow in the uptake.

"Yeah you know … famous painters. We're 200 yards down the road from the entrance to Anglia. 36 Monet Road, the house with the caravan outside." She pronounced it "Munnet" … obviously French impressionist painters were lost on Lou. Christine wondered how the locals would pronounce other artists, Van Gogh and Gauguin. Could be interesting. Still, Christine vaguely knew where Monet Road was and promised to be there at 3.30.

She arrived on time, Lou's description made it easy to find and she was impressed as she opened the white gate and walked up the narrow path beside the caravan. Bright red Salvias and orange French Marigolds lined the path with military precision. They weren't colours which Christine would have put together but there wasn't a weed in sight and the spotless, cream caravan would have graced a car showroom as it gleamed in the sunshine. Crisp white net curtains hung at the windows.

Before she had chance to push the doorbell, the door opened and Lou stood there smiling, "Mrs Chapman, you found us all right, then. I've got the kettle on. Milk and sugar?"

"Could I just have it weak and black, please? They laugh at me in the office, saying you can get three cups out of my tea bag. Ah Mr Riley. I am so pleased to meet you." She held out her hand and shook his outstretched hand. Mr Riley was in his late forties, his jet black hair was receding fast but he looked tanned and pretty fit, although there were signs of a slight tummy where it stretched over his Ipswich Town football shirt. Christine looked round the immaculate sitting room. Sitting at the table in the corner was a young lad. "You must be Willie?" Christine smiled at him and he peered at her through his fingers. "Are you an Ipswich Town supporter like your Dad?" she asked gently.

Mick immediately defensive said, "He don't say much." Then raising his voice he added, "You come with me to matches, don't you Willie?" The fingers closed completely but the fair head inclined slightly. Christine smiled and turned back to Mick.

"This is very kind of you, Mr Riley. Mr Oliver said you could perhaps fill me in with some background. Why, for example, is the Water Authority going out to tender? I gather they've always employed their own cleaners."

Mick nodded, "It's the same old story - wanting to save money. Mr Henson's due to retire. He had a minor stroke a couple of years back and they've downsized his job. He used to look after staff but that's all changed and now they've got a Personnel department, he's just in charge of the cleaning and health and safety and that sort of thing. They reckon outsourcing's the future so all they have to do is give the cleaners notice and appoint a contractor. Everyone's pretty much up in arms about it."

Lou appeared with a tray of tea and biscuits. Everything about her was no nonsense – no make-up, her tightly permed hair was just beginning to go grey at the roots, her black T shirt faded from regular washing and her jeans worn at the knees - no fashion statement this, merely wear and tear from kneeling, probably scrubbing floors by hand.

She handed Christine a weak black tea. Christine thanked her before turning back to Mick and replying, "I don't see that that's necessarily a problem. Surely the cleaning contractor can take on the staff and everyone will be happy?"

Mick's reply was to the point: "These cowboys don't work like that – they bring in their own people, paying them peanuts with no holidays or sickness pay. That's how they cut the costs. What's more the bosses here don't have to pay redundancy because the cleaners ain't got a union. I should know, me being a shop steward."

Christine's mind was working overtime. She knew Monthind hadn't fully addressed these issues yet. Their contracts only costed in for one weeks' paid holiday and she allowed 5% for sickness. It was important to find out exactly what these cleaners were taking home each week and what their terms and conditions were because this was exactly where she needed to be if she was to fulfil her dream.

"I think we may be able to help, if I can get in, of course. You see we don't have big overheads and if we can operate the contract efficiently with good cleaners who work hard because they are happy and are rewarded properly, I think we can do it. Do you think there is any way we can work this out together so that we put in a competitive quote but still give the cleaners a fair deal?"

Mick was nodding. Lou said, "The trouble is the engineers' buildings are filthy. The toilet block and the canteen are the real buggers. Nobody wants to do them. The office block isn't so bad."

"You said 10 of you work two and a half hours a night. What rate of pay are you getting?" Lou interrupted her. "Look here's a copy of my contract. You can have that if you like –

114

it won't be any good to me after the end of next month. I've done a rough sketch showing who works where to give you an idea."

Christine, her eyes wide, thanked her and asked, "Lou, is there any way we can cut down on the amount of hours? - so often there are people who waste time because they haven't been trained properly or don't pull their weight."

"Too right," Lou agreed with feeling. "The first thing would be to get rid of the non-working supervisor. Mind you, I reckon she'll go anyway. There's no way Fanny will work for a contractor – she must be due for retirement anyway. She's been there since the ice age and spends most of her time in the gate house chatting up security. Never lifts a finger to help even when we're short."

Christine smiled to herself, wondering if Fanny was really her name, or something Lou called her.

"Mmm. That's interesting. I believe all management should roll up their sleeves and be part of the team. I wonder what we can do about the engineers' facilities. How about crew cleaning them to save time?"

"What d'you mean, "crew cleaning"?" Lou looked mystified.

"Well, first of all, we would blitz the area so you get a good start – that's essential. After that the entire team works together in there at the start of each evening. Everybody has to muck in doing loos, urinals, basins, cleaning two each. Six people, say, then move on to the canteen and do the tables etc. and the other two stay behind and sweep and mop the floors. You work it as a team, that's all it means but it makes it much more fun. Everyone gets to know each other and can have a chat while you tackle the worst bits, and then you move on to your own areas in the office block. Would that work?"   Lou nodded cautiously.

Mick was laughing.

"What so funny?" Lou asked him.

"I'm just thinking of you lot descending en masse on us guys and booting us out. No more sitting round chewing the fat after work."

"Too right," retorted Lou. "You've all got homes to go to." She turned to Christine and said seriously, "I think that could work. Mind you, one or two wouldn't like it. But then, there are a couple we could do with seeing the back of anyways."

"I've found we can save such a lot of time crew cleaning areas like that but as you say, it may not be popular."   This wasn't strictly true – she had read something, (was it about aeroplanes being crew cleaned?) and thought it sounded a good idea.

"You're saying … muck in or do the other!" Lou's eyes were gleaming.

"Precisely. It's their choice. I think we could make this work, Lou. I've just got to try and get asked to quote. We are very small and I'm not sure they would even consider us."

Mick was looking unhappy. "Well, there's not much I can do to help. Everyone knows Lou's cleaning there and that she's my wife. Old Arnold Henson regards me as trouble anyway. He doesn't hold with unions. Mind you he has got a soft spot for the ladies – the girls all love him. Can't help though. Sorry."

"Never mind. I'll just ring Mr Henson. You never know, I might just be lucky. Thank you so much for seeing me today and, Lou, thank you for this." She tucked the contract into her briefcase. "I will return it, of course. It has been a great help talking to you. If I do get the chance to quote, I'd love to go through it with you before I commit to paper. I'd hate to get it wrong."

"Oh Mrs Chapman, if you could get it and I could keep my job, we'd be ever so grateful. You see, with Willie it's not easy and we'd have to let the caravan go because we couldn't afford the repayments. That'd mean no weekends at Yarmouth."

Christine thanked Lou for the tea, gave Willie a little wave and shook hands with Mick, before driving the short distance along Monet Road and pulling up opposite the entrance to EWA and the gatehouse where she could see the office block. She started to make a few notes. The sound of a lorry changing gear made her look up. A large lorry, half loaded with huge bags of aggregate, sand or cement was pulling away from the gatehouse. Halls … why did that name ring a bell?

CHAPTER 13 – FOLLOW THAT TRUCK

Of course, HALLS, delivering here, the builders' merchants, Mr Barton. "I wonder ….. I just wonder." She still hadn't managed to speak to his contact at Duyfken Line, despite leaving her name. She really should have chased that up.

Looking at her watch, she quickly started the engine. There was nothing like striking while the iron's hot. It was almost 4.50 p.m. and Halls was the other side of Ipswich. With the rush hour traffic she probably wouldn't get there until well after 5.00. Still it was worth a try. As Peter always said, "You make your own luck."

The traffic was impossible. She pulled into Halls' yard just after 5.20 to see Mr Barton, briefcase in hand, standing in the doorway chatting to Maria. She beamed: trust Maria a) to arrive early and b) to be bubbling away to the guy who probably desperately wanted to get home. Well, now it was her turn. She hurried across the yard.

"Mr Barton, I am so glad I caught you, please, please, could I have a quick, a very quick word with you? Maria, you are a star – early as ever. Can I catch you up in a minute?"

"Si, signora. Donna worry! I go do toilets!"

Christine smiled. "Mr Barton, remember you very kindly gave me a lead into Duyfken Line."

"Yep, any joy?"

"I am hopeful but Mr Parnell's quite tricky to pin down! I shall persevere but I suddenly have another opening. I feel really bad asking you this but I have just seen a Halls lorry leaving Eastern Water Authority. I really want to get the chance to quote for their cleaning – they are going out to tender right now but I am worried that they won't even countenance us because we are so small."

"You want a reference – absolutely no problem. Just give them my name."

"Actually, Mr Barton, could I be even cheekier? I was wondering if you knew anybody there. I don't stand a chance of getting in "cold". You see, the cleaners working there want to stay on but they are all going to lose their jobs. I know we could do it and do it well, keeping the existing staff - the cleaners just need managing. When I saw your lorry, I thought I bet Mr Barton knows who to contact. I know this is very cheeky but I was wondering if you know someone there who might be prepared to talk to me. If you could put in a word ...." Christine paused, anxious that she had overstepped the mark.

Mr Barton hesitated for what seemed like an age and then he looked at her. "You know, you could charm the hind leg off a donkey. You and Maria! When I put you two together I should have known it was going to be trouble!" He was smiling.

"Sorree," said Christine, anything but sorry. She looked at him winningly and pressed on, "Well, actually I just wondered if the person you deal with is Mr Arnold Henson?"

Mr Barton nodded. "I know Arnie but, better still, I know their Procurement Manager, clever chap. Was an engineer. He's Polish with an impossible name … A..a. and, and..jay Koron ..ovski, or something like that."

Christine was so excited she could hardly suppress a giggle as she corrected his pronunciation. "Andrzej .. Oh Mr Barton, you are amazing. My father was Polish and he studied engineering at Gdansk University before the war. Gosh … I'd love to meet Mr Koronovski."

Mr Barton grinned, "You are incorrigible, young lady. OK, I'll see what I can do. Sandwiched between you and Maria I don't stand a hope in hell. One thing though, I don't want you taking Francesco and Maria off my contract … promise me that."   He was serious now.

Christine matched his look and responded with absolute sincerity, "I promise, I promise sincerely we will never neglect you, but Francesco and Maria are always keen to get extra work at weekends and, of course, for the rest of the family."

"Right. Leave it with me, young lady! But if you start to get too big, I shall be asking for a commission."

"No problem! But please … Can I ring you to find out how you got on at Eastern Water Authority?"

"Just leave it with me and I'll do what I can. Meantime, don't forget about Oliver Parnell at Duyfken Line." He said firmly and strode purposely off across the car park.

Christine found herself crossing her fingers as she looked after him. Pete was right – you can make your own luck, or at least help it on its way. Thank goodness she had gone to see Mick and Lou, then the Halls lorry, catching Mr Barton and finally learning that the procurement guy was Polish.

She was dying to get home and talk to Pete but she was also worried that Maria needed help. Mind you, she could do with some exercise and she hadn't seen Francesco arrive. Maria had already done the ladies and was busy polishing the mirrors in the gents, humming away to herself.

"Maria, can I help you? Is Francesco OK?"

"Si, signora, he had rapture but 'e come. Arriva poco tardi."

"Rapture? Maria, do you mean he's had a rupture? A rupture? Do you mean he has pulled something?" Christine was suddenly concerned.

"No, no, he had rapture in 'ees macchina. ... In 'ees automobile. You know rapture. Psssssst..." she made a long noise like air escaping.

"Oh ... puncture! The word is puncture, Maria. Puncture. Oh, that's OK."

"Puncture – oh zees ingleesh." They both laughed, Christine more out of relief. She had been going into minor panic mode at the thought of Francesco with a hernia. She had always been aware that if either Maria or Francesco were incapacitated in anyway, she would have to work to cover them. She tucked a couple of plastic bags in her waist-band and began to empty bins.

She was just starting on the second bag when she heard Francesco... "Maria, OK. Sono qui, e tutto va bene. OK." He caught sight of Christine with her bag of rubbish. "Who eez zees new cleaner? She taka my job, eh? You no taka my money, Missus ..."

Christine was laughing – dear Francesco. She handed him the rubbish bag. "Sorry, Francesco, I was only trying to help. Is the car OK?"

"Eez only rapture, Signora. Eez OK. Alberto fix it domani."

"No eez rapture, Francesco. Eez punture!" Maria proudly corrected her husband. "Puncture," she repeated firmly, giving Christine a knowing smile.

"Ok, I will leave you two to it. I am really trying hard to get more work for you."

They waved her on her way. "Arrivederci, signora…
More work ees good. Alberto wanta more work."

There were several things in the pipeline now and the future looked a little more encouraging. She must have another go at getting past the formidable receptionist at Duyfken Line. Peter was so sure their luck was changing but Christine was equally worried that she wouldn't be able to cope.

Next morning, she rang the number and asked to be put through to Mr Parnell. The formidable receptionist picked up the call. This time Christine was at her obdurate best and she didn't mention the word "cleaning". She just said that Mr Barton had asked her to telephone Mr Parnell and "Could I be put through please." It worked. A gruff voice answered, "Parnell". "Mr Parnell, my name is Christine Chapman. I run a cleaning company and I have been referred to you by Mr Barton at Halls. He told me to contact you."

With what sounded suspiciously like a snort, Mr Parnell butted in, "That was months ago." Determined not to be intimidated, Christine said sweetly, "Hardly months, Mr Parnell, just a couple of weeks." She was smiling to herself as she continued, "I have tried to contact you but you have a very efficient receptionist. She does her job superbly! I had to leave a message for your secretary. I have tried to follow up but without success." She wasn't going to be put off by bully boy tactics.

"Hmm. You'd better come and see me. We have a delicate situation here and it needs careful handling. I've seen a couple of representatives from other cleaning companies. More trouble than they are worth. Fix a date with my secretary." He put his hand over the mouthpiece and Christine could hear him bellow, "Deborah, take this call and give this girl an appointment – make it this week."

Deborah picked up the call. "Mrs Chapman, could you make tomorrow at 9.30?" Christine was delighted and agreed, although she wished she had the courage to ask if she could come in late afternoon to save yet another drive up the A12.

She arrived the following morning. What a wonderful old office, wood everywhere, wooden panelling, wooden parquet floors. What a shame it didn't smell of polish. She sat in the reception making avid notes. The brass plaque outside was black and in desperate need of polishing, so were the brass finger-plates on the doors, the intricate staircase was dusty. Wow, this was going to be time consuming. How many staff worked here?

She was quickly shepherded into Mr Parnell's office. He stood up and proffered his hand. He looked like a big bear with his bushy beard, not a cuddly teddy bear, more a black grizzly bear – the sort you had to be very wary of. He gripped her hand firmly. There were pictures of boats all around the office, Duyfken Line vessels and sailing yachts. Mr Parnell was a no-nonsense naval man.

"Right. We need evening cleaning. 6-8 p.m. No keys. We have a caretaker. I've telephoned Barton and he says you're good. D'you agree."

Slightly taken aback at this direct assault, Christine replied, "Well, yes. Mind you, most men would concede that cleaning is an area that women do better than men, but you as a navy man, might not accept that!" Christine twinkled at him. "You need to tell me what your problems are."

"Our cleaning has always been done by our caretaker and his wife but she is finding it difficult now. Hips. She's not happy to have her hours reduced but we now have over 40 staff here, wooden floors which need polishing, and they can't manage. I have told him we need to bring in the professionals and leave his wife to do the teas. She can make her money up doing sandwiches, cakes and things."

Christine nodded, already sensing trouble. "The important thing is to find the right staff and not to tread on any toes."

Mr Parnell ignored this. "Look round. Give me a quote and we'll discuss the implications if you are successful." He bellowed for Deborah, held out his hand – another finger crushing squeeze. "Show this lady round, would you?" Christine smiled and thanked him for his time – all of ten minutes.

Deborah (Mrs Hopkins) escorted Christine, conducting an equally brief inspection of the building and Christine made hasty notes. It would need two cleaners for two hours each,… no, two and a half hours to allow for the brass. There were even copper pipes in the gents. The Managing Director, Captain Parnell, would be a tough task master and she didn't fancy a naval dressing down. Tentatively Christine asked Deborah about the caretaker and his wife. "They live next door and regard this as their second home. Up to now they've done everything." Her voice said it all.

Christine was getting the picture and adding more time by the minute. There was so much more to cleaning than dusting and polishing. People - it always boiled down to getting the people right. Goodness knows where they were going to find the right ladies to do this contract – it would require a very special cleaner, no … two. A husband and wife team would be ideal.

Another quotation to prepare. Sigh! Thankfully, her flexible hours at the Centre for British Teachers were growing less and less. It was hopeless trying to juggle going into their office where all she did was type up current newspaper articles with the demands of the cleaning business. Within a matter of weeks she wrote her letter of resignation full of genuine regret and deep sadness at severing her connection with the Abrahams family and most particularly with Uncle Harold but the cleaning business was beginning to excite them all. Could it really have the makings of a viable business? She had to try but she knew that resigning this time would mean commitment. She certainly wouldn't want to ask for this job back!

She and Ros had started interviewing staff in Ipswich. This was an eye-opener. Remembering her own experience of cleaning – just a phone call, no interview, turning up "cold" with no idea what to expect. She was determined Monthind would be different. They interviewed each candidate in their own home. It gave them a tremendous insight into the person and how she cleaned.

"Mind you," Ros said, "It's hardly fair. Fine judges we are: You have Rebecca cleaning for you and my house is filthy!" "That it certainly isn't," retorted Christine, "Anyway, is any house spotless with three children under seven? A house should be a home not a show piece. An office where the client pays for the premises to be cleaned, now that is different and we have to ensure we deliver."

But calling on people did enable them to find out if the woman had little ones, if her husband would get home in time for her to get to work. Whether there was a decent bus service or did she drive, and yes, how organised and clean her house was.

It also brought them face to face with poverty. The Chantry Estate in Ipswich, where many of their applicants lived, was an eye opener. They quickly learnt to assess a house from the outside. Where there was a window boarded up, the net curtains were yellow with nicotine or where there were mounds of rubbish caught in the corners of overgrown gardens, they looked at each other and moved on.

The roads were bird names – Robin Drive, Kestrel Close, Heron Road. Slowly they analysed the area and found the roads where tenants had bought their council house. Many of these were beautifully cared for and to their delight when they arrived at 23 Goldfinch Road to interview one lady, the house looked immaculate.

Mrs Sharp opened the door to them. "I hope you don't mind, but I've got my mum and my sister here too. We thought it would be easier for you if we were all in one place. Would you like a cup of tea?"

Christine and Ros were ecstatic. They just knew all three would be perfect but it wasn't to be …. Mum only wanted to work in the early mornings – she was too old to go out at night and the buses from Chantry were not right for Gill to get to BComm. Pat would have loved it but she wasn't going to come on her own. All three had worked as cleaners before and were full of invaluable information about other contracts.

Could Duyfken Line be a possibility? Christine wondered. Not that they had even submitted a quote for that building yet and anyway she really wouldn't like to ask such nice ladies to work on a contract where she sensed there were latent pitfalls.

Christine and Ros left the Sharp ladies, reluctantly, saying how sorry they were that the contract wasn't right but

126

assuring the ladies that they would find them the perfect situations as soon as possible. Christine wanted ladies like these – and she knew they too were excited at the prospect of working for her.

"We've got to find contracts for them," she muttered. Peter laughed when she told him. This too was a unique concept – find work for potential staff. Not staff for the job! Yep. They were different.

Time consuming though it was, this was the way to recruit staff. They were amazed, however, to find that no other cleaning company interviewed like this.

The reason of course was cost – it averaged a good two hours per interview by the time they had driven to Ipswich, found the house and gone through their spiel, asked questions and sat in the car writing up notes. Time and time again something wasn't right and they found that only one in ten fitted the criteria.

More interviews – an aggressive husband, every seat covered in toys and junk, a dirty nappy on the stool and a smelly stool in the dirty nappy, a smelly dog which kept sniffing her crotch. She tapped it on the nose with her notepad when the woman wasn't looking and instead of retreating with its tail between its legs, it growled but then that went with the area! Screaming child. House stinking of cats, or just that unwashed people smell. In some houses they could taste the dirt in the air and many a cup of tea was declined, just to be on the safe side. Needless to say occupants of these houses were sharply struck off the list. It was good to have Ros with her to assure her she wasn't just being sniffy and priggish.

Slowly they built up a list of possible staff, all of whom were hoping to hear that they'd got the job. Ros was getting worried. She felt it would be good to telephone every one they had interviewed and tell them they still did not have anything to offer them but Christine was secretly worried about the growing cost of the telephone bill and the time this took, although in her heart she knew how angry she would be if she wasn't told. There was still no news from BComm and she would rather not telephone round to all the interviewees until they knew for sure.

She was certain they hadn't been successful or they would have heard.

CHAPTER 14 – WHO YOU GONNA CALL

Peter was all for contacting Guy. Christine much preferred to ring Mark. Ros said do both!

Peter used the bedroom telephone and Christine used the one in the office. What a joy it was to have the second telephone line even though it was still, of course, registered to Peter's now defunct business. Neither of them had wanted to finally disconnect it and Christine found it so handy when she wanted to talk confidentially to the oncologist, without Peter overhearing.

They met on the stairs, both looking pleased. Guy was going into action and would phone back as soon as he had news. Mark said they had opened tenders, whittled it down to two companies and Monthind was one of the final two. "Be prepared to do a presentation to senior management," were his words.

Wow, a presentation. Christine did a double take – she had never done a presentation in her life but, yet again, for Peter it was second nature.

They decided to focus on all the things that were lacking at the BComm contract Christine had worked on: image, delivering the hours contracted, staff training, working with the client and taking great pride in the job.

Whether THEY could deliver this was quite another matter!

They had chosen green and silver as the company colours. Clean cool colours. They had already asked a local printer to print their notepaper – top quality Conqueror paper with Monthind embossed in silver across the top. Rebecca, Christine's help at home, had modelled, dressed in one of their new green tabards. They took photographs of her vacuuming with a "sort of non-descript office background" featuring the golf ball typewriter plus telephone and file, on the dining room table.

They were all totally engrossed in preparing the BCOMM documents. Christine had put all thoughts of everything else completely out of her mind when suddenly the phone rang. Ros answered it after one ring … "Monthind Limited, can I help you? ……   Of course, I'll put you through to her!"

She then put her hand over the receiver before promptly passing it over to Christine, saying, "It's Mr Barton for you." Christine seized the phone and said with genuine glee, "Oh Mr Barton, I was just about to telephone you. We have been short-listed for a contract with BCOMM and I wanted to ask if I could possibly use your name as a referee. This must be telepathy …."

She was about to babble on when she suddenly remembered that he had promised to try and get her an entrée with Eastern Water Authority. She held her breath and waited. Mr Barton was obviously in great spirits. "Yes, young lady, of course, and I've good news regarding EWA. I got through and Arnie Henson's setting up a meeting with the procurement guy, Mr Koronovski, for you – he's free tomorrow. Give him a ring straight away and have a chat. Meantime, you're going for BCOMM too? Just be careful. Don't bite off more than you can chew. Sure, I'm quite happy to give you a reference but I'm going to want to be taken out for a slap up lunch when you wrap up all this business."

Christine thanked him profusely, promising to let him know what happened. She put the telephone down and took a deep breath. This was crazy – she glanced at Peter. He should be resting not working flat out like this. Thank goodness the children were both well and she was coping, although Ros, forever pushing her to have another biscuit, kept pointing out that she was losing weight drastically. Mind you, no bad thing that. She had always wanted to be a size 12.

She quickly unearthed the notes she had made about the Authority contract and in no time she was smiling. Her briefing with Lou and Mick helped enormously. It was as if she already had a feel for the place. Then she did a couple of mental exercises in Polish – counting to twenty and then listing half a dozen easy phrases, how are you? nice weather today, etc., preparing herself to speak Polish if the opportunity allowed.

She dialled the number and asked for Mr Henson. "Oh yes, you're the Polish girl with the cleaning company at Halls." That was one way of describing her. "Yes," Christine replied. "Mr Barton told me that you have very kindly arranged a meeting for me to possibly come in and quote for your contract." "Yes, any chance of coming in at 12.00 noon tomorrow?" "Of course, I shall be there on the dot!"

While she was on the phone, Guy had phoned back, speaking to Peter and confirming what they already knew – they were shortlisted, but he had vital information about the next step. The panel making the decision were three senior managers – one from personnel, one from contracts and one building management. The lady from personnel should be fine, in fact if "you show how you care for your staff, you should win her vote".

The guy from contracts, Mr Canning, whom Christine had already sussed was dead-anti would be a lot tougher. He would be swayed by price - and finally a Mr Reynolds who was new but whose brief was to improve the BComm company image. Unfortunately, Mr Canning was the chairman and Mark was not part of the selection panel but Guy's parting words were "Go for it – I've got good vibes!"

When Peter regurgitated this to Christine, she stamped her foot and spat out her strongest swear words all together, "Oh, pee, bum, drawers. We'll never get it." Peter looked at her. This was a different Chris.

She knew in her heart it could work if they could find good staff. She set off again for Ipswich, this time finding the journey almost therapeutic. She was getting to know the A12 like the back of her hand and could plan the time it took to the minute, accidents not withstanding. She flicked through the tracks on her hymn tape until she came to "Praise my soul the king of heaven". She happily mouthed the words along with King's College Choir" until she pulled up at the red traffic lights near the large Tesco supermarket. Sensing that the people waiting in the outer lane for the lights were looking at her, she glanced to her right. Sure enough they were laughing. She smiled back, wondering if they had any idea what she was singing! It certainly wasn't the Rolling Stones!

 She must remember to ask Peter if he could record some opera – it would be so good if she could sing along with Francesco and Maria.

Ros had arranged for her to interview Will and Mandy Edgecombe. Mandy worked for three hours a day at the local Co-op and Will was a milkman. He finished work at 11.00 a.m. came home and slept for a few hours.

They were keen to work together in the evening. Their daughter Josie was getting married. Josie wanted a white wedding with all the trimmings and it was going to cost "a bloody fortune" said Will.

Christine was very impressed – the house was spotless. No worries on this front.

Neither Will nor Mandy had worked as cleaners before but they both had attractive personalities.

Mandy worked as a cashier at the Co-op and was unofficially looking after several young girls – "they don't call it training". They had asked her to go full-time but she didn't want the commitment and it bugged her that she had to work Saturdays, especially with the wedding coming up. Saturday was the only day Josie was free for shopping, fittings, and all the things weddings involve.

Talking about the wedding revealed a lot. Mandy might be making the dresses but Josie wasn't having any old village hall. The reception was going to be at the Belstead Brook Hotel, sit down for sixty and then a big bash in the evening with a disco.

The Belstead Brook was THE classy hotel in the area and not known for its low prices. Christine was amazed that they were even considering a venue such as this, until she found out that the venue was not the only demand daughter Josie was making for this "the most important day of my life".

"And she wants a bloody horse and carriage. Carriage, mind you, not a cart. If I had my way she'd go on me milk float. Co-op Dairy would give it fer free."

Mandy was laughing "I can see it, with you at the wheel, Ernie and the fastest milk float in the West! Milk bottles rattling and Josie's veil blowing away. He's always boasting." She was laughing.

"Seriously, Josie's boyfriend, Jim, is lovely – they're helping a bit. But she does have big ideas, my daughter and whatever her Dad may say, she can wrap him round her little finger."

Will was grinning, "Anyway if we both work evenings, Josie can have sixteen bridesmaids, her pink champagne, a horse and flippin' carriage. I just don't fancy paying off a bank loan for this lot for the next five years. Flippin' sharks they are."

With that attitude, Christine was convinced they would be perfect not just as cleaners but to manage the contract – if they got it, of course.

The only problem was, when was this wedding? "We've got nine months!" they said together. Nine months? Christine wondered if this was significant. Surely not, Josie would be in labour. Ah, ah … she was beginning to think like a cleaner.

Christine rose to go. She shook hands with them both and said she would be in touch as soon as possible because she definitely wanted them both! With more and more things in the pipeline she knew they would soon be working together, hopefully at BCOMM.

Back home, an evening with Peter and the children was long overdue but even so she had to prepare for Eastern Water. Peter had drawn up a template, a form with all the right questions they needed to ask in order to be able to cost a contract, and sitting down with her notes from the meeting with Lou and Mick, she was amazed at how much she could fill in without even having seen the place.

In the car en route she talked to herself in Polish, hoping against hope she would get to meet Mr Koronovski. To her surprise the reception area was modern with a central spiral staircase and bright red, but none-too-clean, plastic sofas. The glass encasing the staircase had drips running down – ugh, that was going to be difficult to access. Perhaps that was in the window cleaning specification - another question. Within minutes Mr Henson was standing before her with his hand outstretched. "Arnie Henson, pleased to meet you. You must be Christine!" His eyes twinkled and he looked just like every child's dream uncle, white hair, ruddy cheeks and a large moustache, hardly someone who was scheduled to retire due to a stroke.

He stopped at the bottom of the spiral staircase. "After you, my dear." Then looking at her neat pencil line skirt he added, "On second thoughts, perhaps I'd better lead the way. The guys who designed this didn't think we'd employ women, mind you most of the girls round here seem to wear trousers." Christine made a mental note not to wear a skirt again on this contract!

She followed Mr Henson up the staircase clutching her briefcase. They emerged into a large general office packed with ladies clicking away on machines. "This is where your water bills are generated," said Mr Henson with a grin. "Gosh, how many ladies are there in here?" Christine was trying to count them. "45 generally and then there is another similar open- plan typing pool with 20 girls. After that we have ten managers' offices, each with their own secretary. I'll show you those before we take a look at the MD's offices and the boardroom."

"Could I just get my pad out and make some notes?" Christine desperately needed to get this down so that she could fill in their new costing questionnaire for Peter. "It's OK. No panic." Mr Henson paused while she sorted herself out – not that it helped. She had retrieved her notepad and pencil, but couldn't write anything as she still had her briefcase in her left hand. Mr Henson strode ahead and knocked on the second of two closed doors. "Come in".

Mr Henson opened the door and stood aside to allow Christine to enter. Immediately a man in his forties stood up and walked around his large walnut desk to greet her in fluent Polish. "Dzien dobry pani. Bardzo mi milo." Christine immediately coloured, put her brief case down, dropping her notebook and pencil once again as she attempted to shake hands. As she bent to retrieve them she and Mr Koronovski bumped heads.

"Bardzo przepraszam, Pana Dr Inzynier. Bardzo mi przykro." A highly embarrassed Christine proceeded to apologise in Polish, struggling desperately to remember the formal male vocative case. Polish grammar is impossibly complicated and add to that the consonant combinations – grzm, sztr, pstr, make it a far from easy language.

"You do speak Polish then," Mr Koronovski handed her the notebook. "Yes, a little," said Christine, "although I confess to learning it in the cowshed while my father was milking. I can converse fluently about cows, shitty tails and milk yields and give a firm reprimand if I get kicked but when it comes to business negotiations, I would be at a total loss." She smiled.

Mr Koronovski was laughing. "You didn't speak Polish as a family then?" "No, my mother wanted my father to speak English and it wasn't the done thing for children to be bi-lingual back then. My mother was sure we'd speak neither language properly. She was also very worried that my father might be enticed back to Poland. Not that that was likely given the political situation and our connection with the Jaruzelski family. "

Mr Koronovski's ears pricked up. "Not General Jaruzelski, the President." "Yes," said Christine, "General Wojciech Jaruzelski - my aunt married his first cousin, Boleslaw, during the war, but there is no love lost between the two sides of the family and we always try to steer clear of politics. Still, that's enough of me," she said laughing "I'm not here to tell you about me."

"On the contrary," said Mr Koronovski, "It's good to meet some one with such an interesting background. Take a seat and let's have some coffee. Arnold, could you pop your head round the door and ask Jackie to get it organised. How do you have it, black, Polish style?" Christine nodded, "But without the sugar."

Moments later they were seated round the table at the side of the office sipping the weak, very English, vending- machine, coffee.

Christine decided to plough on: "It is a pleasure to have an opportunity to speak a bit of Polish. I never get chance these days. My father was Adam Labiszewski and his family came from Inowroclaw. He studied engineering at Gdansk, managed to get to England in 1940 and flew bombers over here for the duration of the war but he died two years ago. Neither my brother nor my sister speak Polish so it is up to me to keep the Polish link alive and I'm not doing a very good job, although I am very close to my aunt. She's a professor of medicine at the University of Silesia but my uncle, Boleslaw Jaruzelski, who was a senior advocate for the mining industry got booted out of the communist party for defending the Slaski bread rioters a couple of year ago – he now has a minor job as a lawyer for Polski fiat. Sorry," said Christine, "I could go on for ever. But what about you? Are your parents still alive?"

Christine always had trouble judging ages but this was a fairly standard opening with Polish people of her age.

"My mother is and she lives here in Ipswich but my father died during the Warsaw Uprising. He had sent us here for a holiday - my mother, me and my sister - to stay with mother's cousin, just before Hitler invaded. He told us he would be joining us and then we'd all go home, but that was the last my mother heard. We learnt later from the Red Cross that he'd been shot by the Nazis in Wola with several hundred other resistance fighters. We stayed on here living with Ciocia Basia. Mum did cleaning at the hospital. We went to school and learnt English. My sister's a nurse and I did engineering."

Christine nodding her approval, "Yes, we Poles have a way of adapting, working hard and surviving. I would love to meet your mother – perhaps she could give me some advice about cleaning and do something about my appalling Polish!"

"Yes, I gather you've recently set up a cleaning business here in Ipswich and are causing quite a stir!" He was smiling.

Arnie Henson butted in, "I've been telling him about you. I told him you specialise in taking on the existing cleaners and managing the contract – that could work here you know, Andy. The last thing we want is an escalating union issue over this. "

"Mmm. Does it work, taking over staff?" Mr Koronovski looked at her quizzically.

"The trouble is when cleaning is run in-house it is always the bottom of the pile. No one wants to look after it and it is expected to perform perfectly. Cleaners like everyone else,

138

perhaps more than anyone else, need direction and appreciation. That's where I come in! I am the link between the customer and the cleaner and it seems to work. Because I clean alongside my ladies, I get to know their problems and, just as importantly I manage the specification to make sure things are done efficiently, cutting down on complaints and improving the service."

"OK, Arnie, let's get Mrs Chapman … Krystyna, isn't it? .. to quote. I'm Andrzej, by the way. No promises, mind. I'd also like to meet again to hear more about your father and the Jaruzelski connection. My wife's Polish too and I know she'd be delighted. We'll have to try to fix something up one Sunday."

A shadow passed over Christine's face. How lovely that would be, but it was completely out of the question now with Peter and the children. Inwardly she sighed but to Mr Koronovski she smiled and said, "Bardzo dobrze. Dziekuje." … That's lovely! Thank you.

As they walked away from Andrzej's office, Mr Henson said, "Come into my humble corner and I'll fill you in with all the information you need and then I'll take you over to the engineers department – that'll be a bit of a challenge, I'm afraid."

"Mr Henson, you have been so kind." Christine was wobbling, all sorts of conflicting emotions were welling up inside. "I don't deserve this – I'm only just starting out and I could really mess things up big time."

"Not half as much as some of those cowboys we've seen. What I like about you is that you care about the people. If the cleaners are unhappy, boy does it have repercussions right down the line! And I should know," he said with feeling.

139

CHAPTER 15 – MR HENSON LIKES US

"But I get the feeling you could have them eating out of your hand."

Together they walked across the yard to the engineers' depot. As they entered the deserted changing rooms, Mr Henson, touched her arm. "It's pretty grim, I'm afraid."

Dirty overalls and boots were everywhere. "The guys come in at 07.00 a.m. to get their orders for the day and they return around 4.00 p.m. At the moment it gets cleaned in the evenings but if you wanted to it could be done during the day." They moved on to the toilets and the shower room. The now familiar smell of urine hit the back of her throat. "Not good," she murmured. They moved through to the canteen area. Again the place was a mess, discarded clothing, magazines and dirty crockery. A raunchy Pirelli calendar hung above the sink. "They are supposed to load the dishwasher," Mr Henson, obviously highly embarrassed, muttered, "But they never do." Christine was wondering if there would be scope for a daytime cleaner to pop in and tidy up. They could still do the main clean in the evening, before the offices.

She walked over to the kitchen area – mugs and plates had just been left where they had been used on the tables. The sink was stained dark brown with tea – absentmindedly she scraped her thumb nail along the edge – the tea flaked off. This was not a recent problem. Mr Henson was too busy trying to conceal a particularly explicit magazine with a large blond nude on the cover, to notice her reaction to the sink and her overall dismay at the state of things.

She gestured towards the fridge.. "May I?" She bent down and opened the door. The smell of rancid milk hit her. She

140

noted the yellow crust of spilt, dried up milk on the glass shelves, a sad sandwich growing mould, and various dubious pots of food. In the door itself, was a bottle of milk which had gone solid. "You could almost say this is a health hazard." She ventured carefully.

Mr Henson bent down and took a quick look. He too grimaced. "Oh dear. The tea lady used to look after this but she got fed up. Her hours have been cut and she just does the teas in the office now. The engineers are supposed to clear up after themselves. They bring in lunch packages from home but they make tea and coffee here. We provide milk, sugar, tea and coffee."

Christine was shaking her head, "This has to be sorted before there is a major problem."

Mr Henson nodded. "I hadn't realised it was so bad."

"Well," said Christine positively, "This has to be the perfect time to find a solution. I'll give it some thought and include a recommendation in my quotation. I presume that other companies tendering are aware of the issues too?" Mr Henson nodded hesitantly, "Yes, but whether they address them, is another matter."

They walked back to reception to allow Christine to sign out. Mr Henson was deep in thought. She hoped that she had shown him that she sniffed out problems, literally. She had to convince him that she would tackle them head on, and come up with a satisfactory solution. Something told her no other potential cleaning contractor had opened the fridge.

She smiled at Mr Henson, "I really feel excited about this." He nodded, "If there's anything else you need to know, give me a ring but I have to have your quote in by Friday. OK? Can you do that?"

Christine had no idea how they were going to manage it but they had to try. She had decided not to telephone Lou and Mick for more help. Somehow it seemed unprofessional and time was the essence. She didn't have time to draw breath at the moment, let alone highlight other problems. Dealing with the quotation was going to be enough.

A couple of days later when she and Ros were working heads down at the kitchen table, putting the final touches to the Eastern Water Authority quotation, the post dropped on the door mat. Poppy gave a gentle bark, picked up one of the envelopes, in true retriever style, and sat at Christine's feet, tail swishing across the kitchen floor. "No, no biscuits. You are as bad as James," Christine muttered, aware that even the dog, poor old Poppy was being neglected. She gave her an affectionate scratch behind the ears. Poppy released the envelope, her eyes pleading. Those eyes were so explicit – they were saying WALK.

Needless to say, Ros quietly slipped a biscuit under the table, before jumping guiltily as Christine let out a whoop – "Here it is! BCOMM Presentation date: 23 November at 2.00 p.m. Next Monday. Would we advise them of the names of people attending, equipment we would need, car registration numbers etc. Oh Ros, this coming through on top of the Water Authority, I am beginning to panic inside."

With little idea how long a presentation would take, Ros immediately said the afternoon would be difficult for her. She had to meet her children from school and perhaps Christine's too, although the Convent would happily look after Anya and James until 6.00 p.m. if necessary.

Christine was a bit miffed. She would have been much happier having Ros for support. The presentation was bad enough but it was the questions that would follow which were more worrying. Still if Ros wasn't there at least she could embellish things a little ... well perhaps just "sell upwards", Peter's much repeated expression. Ros's being there might just cramp her style.

She arrived promptly. Miserable Vic from Security was on duty again. He asked her where she had parked. When she told him she had used the public car park, he just grunted. Her visitor's pass was waiting for her. He signed her in and asked, or rather 'told' her to wait in the reception area. Within five minutes a smart secretary appeared. Christine was ushered to a conference room where the adjudication team were seated behind a long table.

The lady immediately stood up and smiled. "Let me do some introductions. I'm Janet James, Head of Personnel. This is Matt Reynolds in charge of Procurement and Mr Canning, Director of Contracts, who will chair the meeting."

Mr Canning looked over the top of his glasses, "Take a seat." He pointed at the smaller table. "The format is that you do your presentation and tell us why you think you can deliver the service we need.... and indeed expect. We then ask you questions. I note you are alone and that you are not using an overhead projector or any slides!" He made this sound like a criticism.

Undeterred, Christine launched into her presentation:

"We are small but we are growing fast. Why? Because we are approaching cleaning completely differently. I make no bones about the fact that women are the best cleaners but cleaning companies are invariably run by men who have

143

never cleaned a toilet, let alone a urinal in their lives." She deliberately didn't look at Mr Canning at this point.

"What cleaning companies fail to remember is that this is a service industry and that we are only as good as our staff. We need to select our staff with care, we need to train them, then we must develop and treasure them. Our company makes them want to come to work because they know they are appreciated. We give them a pat on the back as things improve and we try to make it fun. The result is we develop a loyal team, loyal to you as well as to us."

She tackled those vital areas: Staffing – We have an on-going recruitment programme. We interview applicants at home. If we haven't immediately got the ideal job for the applicant, we can come back to them when we have. It is important that the job suits, is close by or on a bus route. There is no point in a cleaner working for two hours on a job it takes 40 minutes to get to. Our personnel manager (Ros had yet another title!) organises a lift-share scheme wherever possible.

She was now in her stride. She talked about the training, how they made it easy. Blue for Loos. Colour coding. The importance of time and motion.

She then tackled how they would manage the contract with an In-House Manageress. "Me to begin. I will be the role model and will aim to hand over on your contract to Mandy, Senior Supervisor, within two or three months, promoting her to my role. It is essential to have a Deputy Manager – a man and again we have the ideal person in mind."

The presentation ended on a strong positive note: "We would do an initial clean the weekend before commencement of the contract, charging only £500 to cover labour costs. This would enable us to orientate staff, give basic training and start to raise standards. Your staff would notice the difference from day 1."

Then came the questions: "Fun?" said Mr Canning. "BComm don't pay for you to have fun."

"Yes. I know," said Christine, "But it has to be fun. Part-time cleaning is not like a full time job. Cleaners pick up jobs often only intending to stay as long as it takes to pay for a holiday or a new gas fire. We want them to commit long term. We want them to work as part of a loyal team. We do this in all sorts of fun ways - cards and cakes for birthdays, bonuses, shared lifts. They stay if they enjoy the work. Happy cleaners are the best. "

Next question: What is your absence rate?

"Absenteeism is the greatest problem in cleaning. We haven't had a problem because we work at getting our staff to be loyal, to you, to us and to each other. If employees enjoy work, they do their best not to take time off."

But they'll get sick? How do you organise cover?

"When we can work late we do, but where there is a security problem with working after the stipulated hours, I clean." Christine laughed – "that's a great deterrent for a cleaner. If Mrs Chapman does your area while you're off and she's happy, you're in line for a bonus, but if she decides to work with you when you are back, you'll get sorted out."

Mrs James laughed. "I like this hands-on leadership."

"Yes, I don't expect them to do anything I can't. At the same time, I find that working on the contract enables me to make

145

suggestions to the client about ways we can adapt the specification to improve the cleaning service."

"Aren't you a bit ambitious, taking on a building this size?"

"If we are awarded the contract, we would like to interview the existing cleaners here and see who would like to stay. It helps to keep good staff on, integrating them with new people. Maybe you could even give us guidance – perhaps security or personnel, could tell us about the current staff. I have a letter which, with your approval, could be given to them, if we are awarded the contract of course."

Still the questions rolled on. How many staff do you employ?

"Five cleaners but we have interviewed 15 more." Ros would have winced – twelve interviewed 13 more to go. .....How many contracts do you have? "Just two but we wanted to grow slowly."

Far from being intimidated, Christine answered with minimum exaggeration but with maximum enthusiasm. She was in her element, describing the cleaning company of her dreams.

Mr Canning held up his hand,

"We're not stupid. We realise that you are just starting in this business. Maybe that is a good thing. In my book, fun and work don't go together, but you certainly have some different ideas. Whether we are prepared to let you try them out on BComm is another matter. Our problem is that we have had too many cleaning companies extolling the virtues of their service. But they don't deliver and we have the same old problems."

Christine interrupted forcefully, "Why? Because the same old problems are staff shortages, lack of cover, poor training,

146

lack of commitment and high turnover. My answer to that is good leadership. I would personally work this contract every night until I had the team pulling together."

Mr Canning stood up. "Thank you. We need to give this some thought. There would be an initial trial period of six months. We will be in touch by Friday 19th to let you know whether or not you have been successful."

Christine picked up her papers. "I have sample management documents which I would like to leave with you, showing how we train, log and monitor our staff."

She handed each member of the committee a beautifully bound folder. Ros had got a friend to do this for her.

She shook hands with each of them in turn and with a big smile said,

"I so appreciate this opportunity. It would be a privilege to work with you. I would love to make this contract a flagship for cleaning excellence within BComm. Thank you again for allowing me to give this presentation."

She turned away, head high and walked to the door.

"I'll show you out." Mr Reynolds hastily followed. At reception he took her pass, shook her hand again and said, "You've certainly given us something to think about." Christine gave a big smile, "Good!"

As she walked through the swing doors, the cleaners were just arriving. "Heavens, what was the time?" Six o'clock. She had been there for four hours. She looked at the cleaners and shook her head. They were Doris's sad troop at the Colchester BComm contract all over again. She sighed.

CHAPTER 16 – HAVE WE, HAVEN'T WE?

Friday 19th came and went. The morning post contained a formal card acknowledging receipt of their quotation from Eastern Water, but there was still no communication from Stour House. Christine was on edge. Not knowing if they were successful was so frustrating. Fortunately, they had promised to go to see Peter's parents in Bexhill over the weekend. That would keep them from dwelling on the negative – or as Peter would have it – no news is good news.

Both his sisters and their families would be there. Anya and James would love that. They would be spoilt and she wouldn't have to worry about cooking. The only problem was his parents didn't know about his illness and Peter was not prepared to tell them. Still, in the general melee, it should be easy to divert attention elsewhere.

As soon as they arrived Peter made a huge effort but covered himself by saying he felt he was going down with something. Christine was left to field questions from Anne and from Peter's father. Both asked her anxiously what was wrong. With Pa she laughed it off, but Anne was not so easy to deflect. When they were finishing off washing up the pans together, everyone else having gone into the garden, Anne asked again, "Chris, Pete is not well. Is it serious? Please tell me."

"Actually, Anne, Peter doesn't want anyone to know. I have promised not to say anything."

"I am his sister. I can keep a secret. I promise not to tell our parents or even Barb, but I have to know. It is serious isn't it? Tell me it's not cancer."

Christine just looked at her. Anne returned the look as her worst fears were confirmed.

The moment was shattered as just then in burst Anya, "Mummy, Mummy, Jon's got a frog and he wants me to kiss it!"

"Oh YES, do," laughed Christine, quickly pulling herself together. "It might turn into a handsome prince!"

"Mummy, can you kiss it and then I can marry the prince," said Anya.

"I thought you were going to marry me," piped up her twelve year old cousin, Jon.

"Yuck. No way. You've got spots. Anyway you wanted me to kiss the frog."

"Well, go on then. The frog's got bigger spots than mine." Jon was delightful and the children adored him.

'Children – what would we do without them?' thought Christine.

She started to gather up their bits. "Come on Chapmans all. We've a long drive home and it's school tomorrow." She could see Pete was exhausted.

She piled the children into the car, firmly holding the passenger door open for him. "I'm driving!" Anne hugged her tightly in a way that let her know her thoughts would be with her now they shared the terrible truth.

Within a matter of minutes of waving goodbye, Peter and the children were sound asleep. The journey back was uneventful with Christine wondering how she was going to tell

Peter that Anne had guessed. It was time the family knew, however much Peter didn't want to worry them, and in a way she was glad it had come out like this. Somehow it would prepare the way should things get worse and, with luck, tactful sister Anne would take on the task of breaking the news to Peter's parents. She wasn't sure how they would react or cope should things get worse.

Now she had more urgent things on her plate. The BComm contract at Stour House – would there be a letter in the Monday morning post? Somehow she didn't think so, but her intuition told her she should be working on staff recruitment. She had a really good feeling about Mandy Edgecombe and wanted to talk to her further, without her milkman husband's jolly quips distracting them.

Peter, however, had definite ideas. "You must telephone BComm. Show them that you were expecting to hear and ask them if there is anything they need clarified."

Reluctantly, Christine picked up the telephone. She really didn't want to speak to Mr Canning and as luck would have it, he wasn't available so she asked to be put through to Mr Reynolds.

"Thank you for calling, Mrs Chapman. Mr Canning is going to telephone you this afternoon. We would like you to come back for another meeting before we make the final decision. There are a couple of issues he wants to clear up. May I suggest you wait to hear from him?"

"Oh dear, you've really got me worried now!"

"You certainly shouldn't be worried," his voice sounded warm, almost amused. "I promise you will hear from us later today."

Christine relayed the conversation to Peter and Ros. "Dare we hope?"

"You just need to be prepared for anything and everything," said Peter. "I will see if we have any scope to drop the price. You and Ros work on staff."

Christine immediately telephoned Mandy. She was at home, Will wasn't and she would be delighted to see Christine whenever it suited.

"What if Mr Canning calls while I am out?" Christine asked anxiously.

Peter chipped in, "I think it would be good if Ros took the call and dealt with him. It will show him the company isn't just you. She can arrange for both of you to go over for the meeting. The more you both get the feel of the building the better."

Ros was nodding. Peter was so competent when it came to business directives. He seemed to have an inherent sense about how to play things.

When Christine arrived at the Edgecombes, Mandy was busy cutting out bridesmaids' dresses – the material a lovely blue/green colour. Christine touched it admiringly and asked "What colour is it – teal? No, it's brighter. Peacock, perhaps?" Mandy looked up, "Josie would love you. Everyone else has said sea green or turquoise. She's such a romantic. The gardens at Belstead Brook are full of peacocks which she loves – real regal. But Will keeps telling her the bloody things will squawk all through the speeches!"

She pointed to a seat at the table, "I have just put the kettle on. Hang on and I'll make a cuppa and we can chat. Have you got a job for us, then?"

"Mandy, we aren't sure if we have got the contract yet but we are in the running to do the cleaning at Stour House. I have to go back for a further meeting with them and know it would help if I could tell them about the management team we would appoint. I would love it if you took the top appointment to run the contract."

Mandy froze, boiling kettle in hand. "Me. The top job! You have to be joking."

Christine continued, "I plan to be there full-time for at least a month working with you, training everyone and easing you into the role. Together we could build up the team and make sure standards are immaculate."

"What about Will – he'd make a far better manager than me."

"I disagree and anyway I want a woman running the contract. We'd be very happy to make Will Male Supervisor, looking after the men, the polished floors, and the rubbish, that sort of thing. But I want you in charge. I think you have a lovely manner. You would be great with the staff and if your home is anything to go by, the cleaning would be superlative too."

"I don't know. I don't think I could do it and I don't know what Will would say."

"Why don't you talk it over with him? The details of hours, pay, holidays etc are in this letter. What time will he be home? I could come back and talk to you both later if you think that would help."

Mandy blew out a blast of air. "Well I never. I never expected to be offered the supervisor's job." She laughed, "I know what our Josie would say!"

"Yes, something tells me she'd be thrilled. I'd like to meet her!" said Christine.

"She's coming round later to look at lace for her dress, so I reckon I'll talk it over with Will when Josie is here. Is it alright if we telephone you later?"

Christine left feeling fairly confident that things would work out. It was only later that she learnt from Josie what had happened after she left, namely that Mandy was far from happy about putting this to her husband.

They didn't row or anything but Mandy was well aware Will liked to be boss. She had no illusions about him. He flirted with half the women on his milk round. His point being that it helped to sell the extras, put the "cream" in his wage packet. He seemed to attract women like flies – probably his fun personality, certainly not his svelte good looks. He was always good for a laugh but, like so many small men, he liked to throw his weight about.

She could hear him coming up the path chuckling, Josie on his arm. "Guess what I picked up on the road," he called to Mandy, giving Josie an affectionate pat on the backside. He paused on the doormat to remove his DM boots, already half unlaced.

"How's your day been, love?" he asked reaching up in his stockinged feet to give Mandy a peck on the cheek. He was in a good mood.

Mandy grasped the moment: "You'll never guess who's been round. Mrs Chapman from the new cleaning company. She wants to offer us both a job. She's not quite sure but she thinks they are going to get the contract for Stour House".

"That'd be a laugh, I deliver the milk there."

"Well, she wants me to run the contract. I'm not sure I could do that but she wants a woman."

"I thought you said she was offering us both a job. If you're the boss, what's she got lined up for me then?"

"You'll be in charge of the men and the heavy stuff. It's all in writing – take a look at the letter." She passed the paper to Will.

Josie meantime was looking at the sections of the bridesmaids' dresses that Mandy had cut out. "You know Mum, I do love this colour."

"So did Mrs Chapman. She said it reminded her of peacocks. She said it was a gorgeous rich colour. She wanted to know if it was "teal" or "peacock blue."

Suddenly, Will interrupted, "Hey Jul, listen to this – your Mum's been offered a job at £1 per hour more than me. Bloody hell, she wants you in charge, Mandy." He started to laugh. "I'm not sure it'd work me taking orders off you."

"Dad, you really are a pig, sometimes. A real MCP. You've already got a job you love. Mum gets shoved around at the Co-op and this would be great for her, really running something. Let me have a look at the letter."

She snatched it from him. "Bloody hell the money is really good. You'd be daft not to take it. Honestly Dad, Mum's got to take it. If you aren't happy, you could stay here and cook the supper for Mum when she gets home."

She read some more. "But, Dad, it looks to me as if she wants you to look after the sort of manly side. She's got you sussed. I reckon it could be great – you could back Mum. You'd be a great team. You're always saying you don't have chance to talk – well if you were working on the same job, you'd have plenty to talk about,"

Mandy nodded, "I wouldn't do it, anyhow, if you didn't come with me, Will. You know, I'd be scared stiff. So it's up to you."

"Don't be stupid, Mum. You can do it. You don't need Dad."

"Josie, you keep out of this. I do need your Dad. I couldn't do it without him."

"Okay, Okay. I suppose it does make sense. Dad would take you in the car. The money would be brilliant if the two of you do it. Come on Dad, you'll still be wearing the trousers. I bet you'll work it out that both of you are boss."

Will started to laugh, "Yeah, I reckon you will need me, an' all. They've got one sod of a security guy up there – now he's a real Male Chauvinist Pig. He's fine with me an' the milk, but he don't 'alf give the girls stick. They call him Vic the Prick."

"OK then, who's going to ring Mrs Chapman and tell her we're on?"

"You'd better then, as you're going to be boss!" said Will.

"No ... you do it, dear!"

Josie was grinning! "Come on Mum. I'll dial the number for you!"

"Let your father – he'll be fine! He's so much better than me."

Josie had dialled the number and as it started to ring she forced the phone into her Mum's hand so that she had no option other than to say, "Hello Mrs Chapman? It's Mrs Edgecombe here, Mandy, you know …..about the Stour house job." Then the answer machine clicked on and Mandy put the phone down again, relief written all over her face.

CHAPTER 17 – HAVE WE BITTEN OFF MORE THAN WE CAN CHEW?

Mr Reynolds, however, did telephone from Stour House, as he had promised, that very same afternoon and Ros took the call. She told him she was the "Office Manager" and that she too would like to attend the meeting. They arranged it for 10.00 the following morning.

Peter thought it hugely funny when she came off the phone in a fluster.

"Hey. What am I? I nearly said 'Baby Minder'. General dog's body, more like. Eh .. Poppy?"

Poppy's tail thumped at the mention of her name. Ros continued to deliberate, "No... Secretary? ... No, not if I'm going to the meeting too. Are you happy with me as Office Manager? Or have I promoted myself? It was sort of off the cuff!"

Peter was still laughing "That's perfect. Brilliant title for you."

"Do you think we can get this contract? I don't think Chris is 100% happy about it." Ros went on.

"It's a big step and with everything else, it will be exhausting for her but, you know, I am feeling so much better, with luck we can build it up just enough to give you and her a modest income. Stour House would do that."

"I hope she gets the Edgecombes on board." Ros was putting on her coat to leave. Christine had not phoned to get her to collect the children so she must be on her way back.

"A bit tricky to sign them up when we haven't got the business yet! Still, fingers crossed! I must be away as we

157

have another busy day tomorrow." She gave Peter a cheery wave and left.

Twenty minutes later the door opened and the children burst in followed by Christine. "Any news" she asked eagerly.

"Yes, they telephoned and our Office Manager took the call. You have another meeting at 10.00 tomorrow morning." Peter sounded upbeat.

"Oh God! Who with? So soon. Oh no!"

"With whom," Peter corrected. "I'm not sure, but you are picking Ros up after dropping the children off? She'll brief you – she's just appointed herself Office Manager. By the way, what happened with the Edgecombes?"

"Mandy won't make a decision without asking her bald, bandy legged little hubby. Women who have to refer everything to their husbands really get to me."

"Oh dear," tutted Peter with a broad smile. How his wife was changing! "When are they going to let you know?"

"I haven't a clue." Christine was feeling tetchy.

"Kids, Mum needs a G & T."

"OK. I'll do it", said Anya, "If we can have a Penguin each."

James had got hold of the Beefeaters bottle already. "I'll do it. I'll do it." "No James, you get the crisps and the Penguins. Ok?"

Anya knew exactly how to handle her brother.

What would the Nuns at the Convent think if they could see the two of them now, pouring drinks like accomplished barmen? Sigh! Christine desperately needed to prepare for the meeting tomorrow.

The phone went, G & T in hand, she answered tiredly.

"Oh hello, Mr Edgecombe." - Mandy had lost her nerve after the first attempt. "Have you had chance to see my letter and talk to Mandy? I am sorry you weren't at home when I called."

"Yeah, we've had a family conference and I've got outnumbered. To be honest, I'm not sure about having my wife as my boss but our Josie interfered."

"Well, you could say the problem is two-fold, Mr Edgecombe. I'm running the business and if you've got to work for a woman, I'm sure you'd rather work for your wife than for me! I think you'd agree that women are better than men at cleaning and after all that's what we're doing.

The men who work for us will look after supplies, and the specialist floor cleaning – that sort of thing. They will be heavily outnumbered but much appreciated. My husband rather fancies the idea!"

Will chuckled, "Yeah, I reckon you've got a point. Could be fun, then!"

"Women on mass are far from fun, Will. Seriously, Mandy is going to need your support and so am I. I hope this means your answer is yes. I shall be really thrilled to have you both."

"We'll give it a whirl until the big day and then we'll have to see. Getting spliced don't come cheap these days you know

159

and the way our Josie is racking up this wedding; we may be working for you for years."

"I can't think of anything better," Christine said with a smile. "I'll be in touch with Mandy in a day or two".

She didn't know whether to laugh or cry. She felt as though she was being swept along and the whole thing was getting out of control. All they needed now was the contract!

Next morning she picked up Ros as planned.

"How do you like your new Office Manager?" Ros was grinning.

Ros looked great. It was the first time Christine had seen her in a skirt.

What a transformation. She remembered seeing Ros and her husband in town with their three children. They had looked so alike – she and Doug both with straight short hair, grey trousers and flat black shoes.

Here was Ros looking stunning, a white blouse, beautiful red jacket and black skirt, sensible court shoes.

"Ros, you look terrific!"

"Well," came the retort, "I have to live up to my new title. Office Manager! This is the outfit I had for Elaine, my friend's wedding. Is it OK?" she asked.

"It's perfect."

What an asset Ros was. She always came up trumps. Christine made a mental note. They must always ensure they and their staff looked good.

They checked in at reception with the usual sour faced security man. Christine announced their names, "Mrs Chapman and Mrs Barnum from Monthind Limited."

He looked them up and down. Christine held her head high and raised her eyes at Ros. They exchanged meaningful looks - they would have an uphill battle with him.

Without delay they were escorted to the conference room. Was it just the two men this time? Christine felt this was ominous. Where was Mrs James? Mrs James had talked her language. She was a people person. Mr Canning stood up and Christine immediately introduced Ros.

"Good morning. So what's your function in the company?"

"The solid hub," said Ros with a broad smile. "Christine leads the company and I ensure that we deliver. I am the Office Manager."

"I see. Well. It's good that you are here. There are various things we need to clarify."

They were fielding each question fairly comfortably when the door opened and in came Mrs James.

"Sorry to be late. A personnel problem and they don't wait."

Christine smiled at her. "No, they don't." They were on the same wave length.

"Now that Mrs James is here, let's talk staffing", said Mr Canning. "Where do you stand with staff? I note you only have 5 cleaners in total."

"I know it sounds presumptuous, but we have appointed two supervisory staff for this contract – just provisionally of

161

course. Additionally we have an extensive list of potential cleaners, all of whom we have interviewed." Christine paused.

Ros hadn't batted an eyelid and Christine continued, "Obviously we would like to retain any good people already employed on your contract – it would be awful for them to lose their jobs, especially as we honestly believe that staff respond to the right leadership."

"I've already been working on that," said Mrs James, adding quickly "…for whoever is the successful contractor."

"We have one major issue," said Mr Canning. "You want to charge us for an initial clean?"

"£500. Just to cover labour costs. We feel it is essential to have a weekend to orientate ourselves, train staff and to improve standards so that your staff immediately notice the difference."

"No other company is asking for this."

"We do this because we feel it benefits both you and us. It ensures that you get a smooth service from Day 1. If we don't devote a full weekend on the contract, it can take up to a week to get routines in place."

"I accept that, but it should be your company's investment."

Christine felt sick inside, "We already have to invest in new capital equipment – the vacuum cleaners and the floor machines. We have to finance two month's wages which we pay fortnightly before we receive any payment from you. We are still very small and this will be a large outlay for us." Smiling sweetly, she added, "I was really hoping you could make this concession".

162

Mr Reynolds looked up, "Will the time all be taken up training or will you be able to actually clean?"

"It is essential that we train as we clean and that we clean effectively. If we are awarded the contract, the incumbent contractor will certainly let things slide the moment he knows he has lost the contract, and standards will fall significantly. An initial clean will be vital."

"Mmm," said Mr Canning. "We still need to talk things over before making a decision. As you rightly said there is a month's notice period so you will be informed of our decision by the end of this week, latest."

Christine and Ros, smiled, shook hands with each member of the panel and left silently. It wasn't until they reached the car that Christine worried, "Did I blow it by not conceding the cost of the initial clean? It's just that I'm worried about having to borrow the money as it is." Ros shook her head, "I really don't know."

When she anxiously asked Peter the same question, he grinned and said "I'd have done exactly the same. When you've got a strong argument, don't give way. Never be a push-over. Let's see what happens."

The following morning they received a call from Mr Reynolds, confirming the contract and that BComm would pay for the initial clean, keeping it as a one off charge prior to commencement. He was obviously delighted.

"Yippee!" – So were they! Christine and Ros danced around the kitchen with Peter clapping like mad. They all laughed more than any of them had in a very long time, they were a team and they were winning.

CHAPTER 18 - ALL HANDS ON DECK

Mandy and Will were drawn in. Christine couldn't help smiling when she saw them together. Mandy was slightly taller, her blond hair always neat. She loved to wear crisp white blouses and trim pastel coloured cardigans. Will was chubby with ruddy cheeks and a shiny bald pate. His grin and twinkly blue eyes endeared you to him immediately.

His legs were bowed and the turn ups of his blue overalls folded thickly over his black DM boots. Probably years of carrying heavy milk crates had bowed his legs. His walk was a waddle, albeit a chirpy waddle – he covered the ground like a mallard drake on a mission.

They responded to Christine's plea for help and Will, in particular, amazed everyone with his enthusiasm, even offering to recruit ladies on his milk round. An offer Mandy was quick to shoot down.

The Italians were asked to help with the initial clean. Christine wanted them to tackle all toilets and kitchens so that these would be sparkling on Monday morning.

They jumped at the chance although when they learnt that there were no weekend rates, they checked their enthusiasm somewhat. Francesco visibly cheered when Christine said there could be a bonus if they hit their target.

This would allow her, Mandy and Will to concentrate on organising the allocation of areas and to train staff. Josie asked if she and fiancé Jim could come along and help on the initial clean too. Christine was touched at this show of backing and happily agreed.

Slowly they built up the team. The next thing was to meet the incumbent cleaners. This was arranged a week before the contract changed hands. Christine and Ros had asked those that were interested to come in 20 minutes earlier than their usual starting time and here they were now sitting in the canteen waiting to see who would show.

Mrs James had given them a list of staff who might like to stay – just ten, including the supervisor. Eventually the door was thrown open and in strode a heavily made-up lady. "I'm the supervisor here. Mrs Wilks is my name. We just want to hear what you're going to be paying. Our company are offering us other work but some of us are used to this contract and if the money's better we might stay."

Milkman Will, chuffed with his undercover research, had already warned Ros that Mrs Wilks was related to the surly Security man. This did not bode well. According to Will he was referred to by one and all as Vic the Prick. So Mrs Wilks was Vic the Prick's sister in law.

Her staff trooped in behind her, heads down. Christine smiled and gestured to them to sit but they lent against the wall looking resentful.

Christine introduced herself and the company, Monthind Limited. She outlined their plans and invited those that wished to stay to come along at the weekend to help with the initial clean.

"Well, that won't be necessary. We know the contract backwards," said Mrs Wilks.

"We would welcome you all because your knowledge of the building would be invaluable. We will be appointing our own manager, although I will be running the contract for the first few months."

"We just want to know about pay, and terms and conditions. Then we can turn up if we want."

Determined not to have a confrontation, Christine asked each of them to give Ros their name, address and telephone number, in return for which they received a letter of welcome answering all their questions.

She asked Mrs Wilks to wait until she had spoken to the others so that they could have a private chat.

Mrs Wilks was bristling. "Here we go again. I've worked on this contract for five years now and I've been in charge for nearly two. People like you always think they can do better but you don't know the half of it."

"Take a look at our letter and then give me a ring if you are interested in joining us, Mrs Wilks."

On the way home, Christine said to Ros, "Mrs Wilks would be destructive in the extreme. We've got to make sure she doesn't stay. I can imagine her plotting our downfall with Vic the Prick." They laughed tentatively.

Peter arranged a meeting with their bank, manager, Mr Clough. It helped that he lived two doors away in Elm Drive and both he and Peter had belonged to the same tennis club. Christine was worried about borrowing money but armed with Monthind Limited's business plan and a promise to pay the money back in one year, she secured a loan of £2,000 without a problem.

They had been so engrossed in the excitement of getting the contract that they had quite forgotten to contact Guy. Feeling very shamefaced, Christine picked up the phone early on Saturday morning and rang their number. Guy sleepy voice answered - he was obviously still in bed – but the moment he heard her voice, she could hear him yelling, "Alison, Chris is on the phone".

The next thing she heard was the sound of them both singing, "Congratulations, felicitations…."

"Thank you so much, Guy. We so hope we won't let you down! Who told you?"

"I've got my spies but I have been following progress. It's brilliant and we just wanted to tell you we are routing for you, big time!"

"How can we ever thank you enough," Christine said. "Peter is over the moon – this is our big break and it's all down to you."

"Rubbish," said Guy. "I think you are going to take the cleaning industry by storm. If I can help any further, please just give me a ring and in the meantime I hope all goes well with Pete. Give him my regards."

Christine relayed this to Peter who looked at her and said, "He's a really nice guy."

Supplies started to arrive by the lorry load, causing quizzical looks from the neighbours. The title deeds strictly forbade having a caravan let alone the running of a business in Elm Drive. Ros and Christine were stacking boxes shoulder high in the garage when Mr Pryke, her sad neighbour with a disabled wife from No 14, asked what they were doing. Christine told him they were unloading vacuum cleaners for a cleaning contract. "Going to run a business from here then?" he wheedled.

"Oh no, just very temporary storage. They'll all be moved at the weekend," said Christine, smiling sweetly. "I hope it hasn't inconvenienced you."

Under her breath she was muttering about the joys of neighbours who have nothing better to do other than spy on everyone else.

Ros laughed, "Talking about neighbours, I must tell you about Claire." Claire was Ros' incredibly supportive neighbour. Right from the very beginning when Ros had told her about the cleaning company, she had offered her help.

Claire originated from Durham and had known tough times in the North.

She wasted nothing and when she heard Ros was trying to source cotton cleaning cloths, she took herself off to every church jumble sale going and bought up all the left-over cotton clothes. She sifted through them with a choosy eye – only the softest pure cotton would do. Invariably she would get the lot for no more than £2.

She then brought everything home, cut off all the buttons and zips, washed the lot and hung the weird selection of men's vests, voluminous knickers, pyjamas and T shirts on her long washing-line.

Concerned about quizzical looks from passers-by and comments from her neighbours down the street, Claire hung a huge sign in the middle of the washing.

~ THIS WASHING HANGING ON THE LINE
YOU NEED TO KNOW IT IS NOT MINE.
IT'S HANGING HERE BUT JUST BE'COS
IT ALL BELONGS TO MY FRIEND ROS! ~

Once the rags were dry and sweet smelling, she proceeded to cut them into perfect 8" x 8" squares, making ideal dusters and cleaning cloths for initial cleans.

Ros even selected the white and blue cloths for regular evening cleaning.

Her dear neighbour saved Monthind pounds over the years and when Christine tried to thank her, she just chuckled and said, "Pleasure, pet. Gives me an excuse to rifle through the jumble. You'd be surprised what I come up with!" She stuck out her ample bosom and pointed proudly at her exquisite plum coloured cashmere twin set … "Jaeger – how about that! Got it at St John's church jumble last week for 20p!"

Nothing had been heard from the existing BComm cleaners so one by one Christine and Ros telephoned them. It was hard work. The parrot answer to each question was "Dun know."

"Are you interested in staying on?" "Dun know."

"Would you like us to come along and talk to you about the job?" "Dun know."

"Have POCS offered you another job?" "Dun know."

"Something tells me they've been got at," said Ros.

They deliberately hadn't called Mrs Wilks but Christine decided it had to be done.

She dialled the number. It was answered by an aggressive male "Yeah."

"Could I speak to Mrs Wilks, please?"   The same, "Yeah."

A long pause. Same male drawl, "Who wants her?"

"Mrs Chapman."

An even longer pause. Then a female "Yeah".

"We were just wondering if any of your staff want to stay on at Stour House."

Pause. Then the explosion: "Not bloody likely. You won't be there fer long, you'll see. You don't know the half," came the truculent reply.

"That's fine. We will take it that you are all happy to leave." Then with heavy sarcasm, "Thank you for your co-operation, Mrs Wilks. Good bye."

Christine came off the phone shaking. She was angry.

Brainwave – she would speak to Mrs James. She was after all Head of Personnel on the contract and they had seemed to be on the same wavelength at the initial interview.

"Mrs James, we have tried to speak to the POCS cleaning staff but I feel Mrs Wilks is blocking us, perhaps even intimidating the staff because we have not offered her the position of manageress. I just wonder if there is any way round this. We are particularly keen to keep on anyone who wants to stay and of course anyone who is good."

"I'm so pleased you have called" was the instant reply "Off the record, we are delighted you are changing things at the top. The last thing we want is the same staff with the same problems. However, can I suggest that you speak quietly and in private to Ann Parker and Janet Williams – they clean the directors' floors and are particularly good workers.

I'll also have a word with Jane who does my floor and suggest she telephones you. She is really lovely and I know she doesn't want to leave. There may be a couple of others as well but POCS will try hard to make sure they only leave deadwood."

"Thank you. That is such a help. May I call you again if we have any other queries?"

"Of course, I'll be pleased to help in any way I can!"

They now knew whom they should try to entice and this time when Christine telephoned she used a completely different approach.

"Mrs Parker, we have been planning the contract with BComm and they have been telling us how wonderful you and Mrs Williams are. They are very keen for you both to stay on. We'd love to have you and think you would be such an asset to our company. If you are able to come along for the initial clean we would pay you "Trainers rates" on top of the weekend rate."

"Oh. Thank you so much" Mrs Parker replied "I'll have to talk to Janet of course so can I call you back as soon as I can get hold of her?"

"Of course you can and I do so hope you will both stay. I look forward to hearing from you," said Christine.

171

Half an hour later, Mrs Parker called back to say that they would love to stay on because they were both very happy with the news "but only as long as we can continue to do the same area and" she continued with a harder edge to her voice "as long as no one tells Mrs Wilks".

Christine was quick to reassure her about the areas they would clean "because the customer wants you to stay too" and to promise that "We will certainly not be giving Mrs Wilks any information at all."

"That's good then ….and there are a couple of others who we think would want to stay but we reckon they're just too scared to say. Do you want me and Janet to talk to them on the quiet like?"

"That would be so kind of you and if they come with your recommendation that would be fine with us. We just feel it would be sad for anyone to be pushed into moving if they don't want to. Please ring me and let me know. And thank you again for being so honest and helpful. Together we can really make a success of this contract into the future, I am sure of that."

Christine had heard tales about cleaning companies in London intimidating staff, particularly immigrant workers. This surely wasn't going to be an issue in gentlemanly Suffolk, in Essex possibly, but surely not in Suffolk.

On paper the workforce was looking good. The arrangements for the initial clean were in place. Peter was determined to come too. They arranged to deliver all the equipment and cleaning materials early on Saturday morning. The cleaners were due to arrive at 10.00. Will rushed his milk round to be on time.

CHAPTER 19 — VIC THE PRICK

Unfortunately, when they arrived the Security Man on the early shift was none other than Vic the Prick. Ros groaned. The equipment and materials had been unloaded and were stacked in reception.

Christine took charge "Just sign everyone in Ros, and with Mandy and Josie helping, start to issue each cleaner with a bucket of equipment and a Henry vacuum cleaner. Once you have done that we will allocate areas and go through the training schedule with everyone."

With that she went smartly up to scowling Victor. "Victor, I know you didn't want a change of cleaning contractor and I recognise it is going to cause you a few problems as we settle in, but POCS were never going to keep the contract. If it hadn't been us, it would have been someone else. We really need your co-operation."

He glared at her and seemed unsure how to respond. Before he had time to open his mouth, Christine continued in her no-nonsense voice, confident as a result of the useful information she had received from the cleaners who were staying on and in the knowledge that she was well within her rights.

"I understand the departing cleaning company have not removed their equipment from the cupboards. They are therefore in breach of contract. I intend to remove everything belonging to them and put it on the loading bay, clean out the cupboards and then ask BComm to pass the charge for this on to them."

"You can't touch their stuff."

"Well, then I suggest you do it. They were instructed to finish last night and no longer have access to the building. I cannot allow them to impede my cleaners at any time today or tomorrow." By now they were glaring at each other.

Christine suddenly felt a presence at her side. "You wouldn't be giving Mrs Chapman no trouble would you, Vic?" She looked round and there was Mandy's Will, all 5' 3" of him, puffed up like a penguin.

"Don't you worry, Mrs Chapman, Vic'll show us where the cleaners cupboards are, won't you Vic, and we'll get the gear sorted." Putting two fingers in his mouth, he issued a piercing whistle, "Over 'ere chaps."

Christine looked in amazement as Francesco, Julio, Alberto and Jim (Josie's 6'2" fiancé) arrayed themselves in a perfect arc either side of wee Will in front of the reception desk – if they had had stetsons, the scene would have been a picture straight from a western. The marshal, although Will was no Wyatt Earp, had one hand at his hip, poised to draw, and his posse alongside, all slightly threateningly lined up at the bar. Vic was weighing them up. He opened his mouth to protest but Will got there first, "Thanks mate. You lead the way. We'll be right behind you. Come on lads; take them vacs and some of that gear while you're about it."

Christine thought she detected a Suffolk-cum-Texan drawl and would not have been surprised to hear the sound of spurs as they headed off into the sunset.

Jim picked up four Henry's, just to show his prospective father-in-law, and Vic too no doubt, that he was a man of substance. He in turn gestured to the Italians.

174

The procession, led by a grumbling Vic the Prick, headed for the lifts. Second in line was Will, sparkling new Henry in each hand, next came giant Jim with his double load, Alberto and Guilio followed, with Francesco whistling happily in the rear. The Italians had somehow managed to take not just two vacuum cleaners each, but a variety of mops, buckets and brooms as well.

"Hey, Vic," called Will. "Don't go empty handed, mate." He tossed him one of the mops that Francesco had dropped.

If looks could kill!

Christine could hardly contain a giggle as she called out in her most sugary voice "Victor, thank you so much." To anyone else and she would have added "You are a star!" The star should be pinned on Will's chest!

Ros in the meantime was pacing anxiously up and down – where were the promised staff – the ladies from BComm. Then she spotted a gaggle of ladies hovering outside on the pavement and pointed. Christine nodded, "Must be them." She opened the door and said "Good morning ladies, I'm Mrs Chapman, thank you so much for coming."

She picked up immediately that something was wrong.

"Are you alright? Which of you is Mrs Parker? Ann?"

A rather pretty lady with lovely blond hair stepped forward and smiled nervously.

"We didn't come in because we saw Vic on Duty. We're a bit worried, you see, cos he'll tell Mrs Wilks and that'll cause trouble."

"Please don't worry about Vic. I think you'll find he's more co-operative now and Mrs Wilks has decided not to join us. But if there is anything at all troubling you, I want you to tell me. BComm are most anxious that you do not leave. Come in and have a chat."

Ros took over, making a big fuss of them and assuring them they would be cleaning on their old areas. From her limited experience Christine knew how important it was to clean an area you knew. Cleaning ladies like their comfort zones and cleaning somewhere new takes much longer to cover, by the time you have located the bins, the sockets etc. She had impressed on Ros and Mandy not to rock any boats at this stage.

Ros gave them each a list of Monthind's cleaning items and talked them through the routines. "Don't worry too much now but by the end of the day, we will check that you are completely happy with the products and our cleaning system."

"Walk your floor, organise your cupboards and then check your areas. Come back here if there is a problem. Coffee will be at 11.00 when Mrs Chapman will be talking to everyone and introducing Mandy who is going to be the supervisor."

Everyone was visibly more relaxed and there was still no sign of Vic. Christine began to wonder if Will had locked him in a distant cupboard. She asked Peter to do a recce. Ten minutes later they all returned, Vic looking a fraction more cheerful. Obviously Peter had done his diplomatic bit.

Will almost saluted. He was clearly enjoying himself. "THEIR stuff's on the loading bay. What a load of crap! The

Italian boys are cleaning out the cupboards. Where do you want 'em next?"

"Sweeping and mopping the stairs is the next job. Can you organise that?" She lowered her voice, "Thanks for your help with Vic, but watch your language, Will."

Will winked. "We'll win him over, don't you worry," and then added slightly sheepishly "Sorry boss."

At that moment Mandy arrived and gawped – Will saying sorry!

Had Mrs Chapman got the measure of him? That would be something to chalk up.

"Just to let you know, Mandy, Maria and Teresa are doing toilets."

"Will, when they've finished we need to machine scrub the floors. Francesco is a wizard with a scrubber so get him on that. And, I want everyone in the canteen on the first floor at 11.00 for coffee."

Christine felt organised, she sounded organised but were they really on top of things?

At 11.00 precisely everyone trooped into the canteen where Ros had mugs lined up with generous spoonfuls of sugar, and chocolate digestive biscuits at the ready. Ros believed in stoking energy levels.

"Cor," said one of the ex POCS girls Christine hadn't yet met "We've never had no coffee and biscuits before".

"No we ain't," said another in her broad Suffolk accent, "and have you seen the 'Enerrrys – they'rrr bootiful."

"Yes, brand new and the latest model," said Christine "Each of you will be given name labels so that you can put your name on your equipment. That way, we know you'll look after it!"

As soon as everyone was in and had settled down with their hot drink and a biscuit – or two – Christine stood up in front of them all and spoke

"And now I want to tell you a little bit about us. I have started a cleaning business because the bosses in cleaning are always men with clipboards. They've never got their hands dirty and most have never cleaned a loo in their life, not even at home." That raised a nod and smile before she went on, "What's more they don't seem to realise their business is only as good as their cleaning ladies, ...oops ....as their cleaning staff," She hastily corrected as she noticed Will out of the corner of her eye, was wagging his finger playfully at her.

"Now, beginning from today I am going to make you all a vital part of this business. I'm going to clean alongside you. If the business does well, you will do well. Your pay packet will reflect this. Everyone will get a bonus.

My challenge to you is that we are going to get ALL the BComm contracts in Ipswich because we are going to make Stour House the best - a happy, sparkling contract. They are going to see just how cleaning should be done and be the envy of all BComm buildings."

Will piped up, "Mrs Chapman, do you know how many BComm buildings there are in the Ipswich area?" Christine shook her head. "About three, at a guess?"

"Well, there's at least four in town but there are 56 at their huge research centre in Worthingham. I guess, you mean all 60!"

Everyone laughed. "But of course!" answered Christine with a grin. "Let's show them!"

She looked at their faces and to her amazement they started to clap. She could have hugged Will.

"We'll concentrate on this one just now and, on that note, it's back to work. When we break at two for tea and sandwiches, I shall ask each of you how you are doing. Go for it! Mrs Barnum, Mandy and I are going to see who needs a bit of help."   Ros and Mandy had already identified those who needed training, four at least, including one, Kathy, who seemed totally clueless.

Will in the meantime was once more marshalling his men and away they trooped in line, this time resembling the Seven Dwarfs, Jim, the tallest in front. She was mildly surprised that Francesco wasn't whistling "Hey ho hey ho, it's off to work we go!" but then Will in the rear, was anything but Dopey!

Christine went to reception to check the cleaning there – she wanted the first impression as people entered the building to be spot on. Vic was sitting behind the desk, his eyes glued on The Sun newspaper. Determined to engage him in conversation she asked about permanent badges for the regular staff.

"Don't know. I finish at one. Ask Terry when he comes, if you want to know."

What was his problem? - Women, POCS and Mrs Wilks going or was he just plain anti-social?

She feared that despite Will's bravado, they weren't out of the woods with Vic.

Nevertheless, the day ended up a success. Two of their new recruits were not coping well but if everyone came back for three hours on Sunday morning, the building would be looking good and they could do a further assessment.

Peter was worried that they would overrun the £500 labour bill but agreed that it was more important to make an impact – the building had to look good.

On Sunday morning Christine drove into the car park ten minutes early. The A12 had been blissfully clear of container-lorries on this sunny Sunday morning. The security man on duty was Terry and he was obliging in the extreme. What a contrast to Victor! Will and Mandy were already there talking to several ladies.

Christine had hastily grabbed a packet of sticky labels. As everyone signed in, she hastily wrote their name on a label and stuck it to their lapel. "I need to get to know you all!" She made a mental note that they should invest in name badges for everyone.

Numbers were down and Christine had promised they would finish at 12.00 today. Neither Peter nor Ros had come but the steadfast Italians arrived, Maria with a basket and something which looked suspiciously like another panettone! Oh pee, bum, blast, Christine realised she had brought the milk, but forgotten to bring the biscuits, and Ros had reminded her too. Thank goodness for Maria! Seeing Christine's face, Maria grinned broadly. "Eez 'ungry work. And my panettone good wiza coffee."

Today was going to be much easier. She and Mandy checked the building and tried to gauge who would come back on Monday and whether they would have enough staff. The Italians couldn't come of course, but daughter Josie and fiancé could come and at a push both of them could clean. Not ideal but they could.

Coffee at ten and sure enough there was a good hunk of Maria's panettone for everyone. The new ladies loved it and Maria beamed with pride when Christine told everyone that Maria always did this and that she was the most popular lady in the company.

They left at 12.00 on the dot, fairly confident that things were off to a good start. The reception floor gleamed, the toilets smelt fresh and the offices literally sparkled. Unfortunately, they had not reckoned with Vic the Prick.

CHAPTER 20 - THE MISSING VACUUM CLEANERS

On Monday morning Ros was busy preparing name labels, and sizing the new uniforms for each of the staff. Christine was telephoning Ann, Janet from POCS and as many of the new staff as she could to thank them for their weekend work and to ensure they were on track for this evening at 6.00 p.m. Had they sorted out their bus routes, etc.?

It was essential that bus times fitted in. No one wanted to be waiting for 30 minutes in the rain at 8.00 o'clock at night.

She had just put the phone down for a breather when it rang again. She answered it.

"Mrs Chapman, Canning here, BComm. I'm afraid we've got a problem. Have you any idea where your people might have put the kitchen cleaning equipment because two vacuum cleaners have disappeared from the catering cupboard and the manager is a bit upset, to put it mildly."

Christine immediately went into conciliation mode "Oh I am sorry. Obviously we are still settling in. That's worrying. I am afraid I have no idea though about your vacuum cleaners. I wasn't aware that we had access to that area as it is not part of our schedule. May I look into it this evening? In the meantime, please tell your catering manager to use our vacuum cleaners – those on the restaurant floor, until I can sort this out."

"Please apologise profusely and assure him we will replace them if we can't find them. Can you give me his name? Have there been any other complaints?"

"No on the contrary, the feedback's been complimentary apart from this, but ….", he added rather sourly, "…. time will tell."

After all their hard work over the weekend, this was all the thanks she was going to get from Canning. Welcome to the harsh world of business, Christine.

Christine decided to go in early that evening and asked Will and Mandy to do the same. Although somewhat bossy and full of himself, Will had realised by now that an 'ask' from Christine was anything but a request to be declined lightly!

Fortunately, nice Terry was on duty when they arrived, but even he could throw no light on the missing equipment. He told them, however, that Joe, the second in charge in the kitchen, was still working in the canteen. Christine introduced herself and then Mandy and Will. She immediately apologised and asked if they had managed with Monthind's vacuum cleaners.

Joe still immaculate after a day's work in his chef's whites, grinned. "Can't understand it – we locked our stuff up on Friday night as usual and the vacs have just disappeared. One's a wet pick-up an' all. We've always kept them separate from the cleaners' – food hygiene and all that."

"We'll look into it this evening Joe." Christine assured him. "In the meantime, please don't worry. Will can let you have one of our new vacuum cleaners for the time being but I can't help with a wet pick up I'm afraid. Can you manage?"

"Good old fashioned mopping will have to do until we get it sorted."

They left him to his pastry and closed the door, with Christine quietly thanking the patron saint of cleaners that Joe was a different character from Vic the Prick. She then vaguely wondered if there had ever been an official holy backer of hand maidens and made a mental note to find out. Peter might know. There did seem to be a Catholic Saint available for just about everything so surely cleaners wouldn't be left out.

Christine was worried about this missing equipment, even though Will was adamant they weren't responsible. Christine knew what he was thinking: "There was more to this than meets the eye."

There was no time for further discussion as the cleaners were arriving and they had to concentrate on the evening duties.

Twice she came back to reception and twice she found Will, floor-machine in hand, talking to Terry. On the second occasion, Mandy was there too.

She wasn't going to rock the boat. She would find out what was going on later and anyway she was needed on the third floor working with Kathy who was in floods of tears when Christine reached her.

Christine then started getting it all. Kathy was a single mother and her Mum was looking after the baby temporarily. She needed the money and "she weren't claiming no benefits but she was fed up of living at home .....". Her boyfriend, Dean, had promised to get a place for them but she'd had her name down for a council place for six months and nothing "had come up".

The whining just went on and on until eventually Christine snapped, "Come on Kathy. There are a lot of people worse off than you. We'll do everything we can to help, but you've got to pull your weight. Finish this vacuuming and start your toilets." Kathy's mouth went down at the edges and that teenage sulky look settled over her face.

Christine hastened off to check on everyone else, praising as she went. There were no major panics but she had a feeling Kathy wouldn't be back tomorrow. Christine couldn't help thinking it would be a lot better than having to sack her. Her whining would get on everyone's nerves. Well, it got on Christine's nerves anyway!

So quickly, oh so very quickly, the clock showed 8.00 and time to finish. How the time flew. She hadn't checked on Ann and Janet. When they appeared, looking happy she immediately went up to them and apologised. Their reply was to beam, "You don't need to worry about us. We're fine and we thought you might like to know that the office staff are singing your praises. They've really noticed a difference."

"Not "my" praises – "our" praises! You are a very important part of our team now, you know. But that's lovely! We are having a few worries but we will get there. I so want you and Mandy to get to know each other."

The cleaners emerged from the lift and from the stairs, chatting happily. Even Kathy looked a little brighter although she scowled as she signed out and didn't respond to Christine's, "Goodnight ladies, thank you. See you all tomorrow!"

Feeling better, Christine turned around to see Will again having a whispered conversation with Terry. Time to find out what's going on. She joined them, extending her hand to Terry.

"I am sorry, we haven't really met. I'm Mrs Chapman. Any thoughts on what might have happened to the missing restaurant equipment? I'm going to come in tomorrow morning and see Mr Canning about it. We can't have this hanging over our heads. I take it you have checked all our cupboards Will – and nothing?"

"If I'd found anything, I'd have come and told you on the double, so I would. Terry here has a theory about what's happened but he don't want to say nuffink. Don't you worry about it none, Mrs Chapman. We'll get it sorted."

Mandy nodded with a sort of "that's my boy" proud look on her face.

Christine hesitated, not sure whether to be heartily grateful or downright worried. "Well, we'll see. Come on now, it's time to go home."

Next morning she was on the telephone to Mr Canning at 09.00 asking if she could come and see him. "Good idea! We need to go over one or two things. Can you be here at 10.00?"

Sighing Christine raced for the car. To her relief the A12 didn't cause her any major problems and she arrived dead on time in reception where Mr Reynolds met her and whisked her along to Mr Canning's office.

She launched straight in "I am so sorry about the vacuum cleaners. We searched high and low. There was just a faint possibility that our driver could have inadvertently picked them up when he delivered our supplies early on Saturday morning but Will Edgecombe, our male Supervisor helped him unload and he swears the van went away empty." She opened her arms wide in a gesture of despair.

"The last thing we want, however, is for this to sour our contract with you. If necessary we would replace them, albeit it rather reluctantly."

"There were minor theft problems before. They have to stop. We have called in the Head of BComm security. He is putting CCTV cameras in, so hopefully we get to the bottom of this. I hear you have already offered to allow the kitchen staff to use your equipment. We'll leave it like that for the time being."

Christine left feeling really despondent. Not a word about improved standards. One thing was clear. She would have to make sure her cleaners were whiter than white and that never ever would they be held to blame for "petty theft".

That evening as everyone arrived they were asked to leave their coats and bags in the ground floor cleaning cupboard. Mandy would have the key.

Christine carefully explained this was to protect them from any accusations of taking things.

"Yeah," said Janet, one of the POCS girls "things were always going missing in this place and it was always us cleaners wot get the blame."

Will immediately piped up, "Well, no way is that going to happen with us."

Each evening for the rest of the week, they steadily became more comfortable with the building and some of the office staff were even beginning to talk to them. On Friday night,

Christine asked all her cleaners to be in reception ten minutes before 8.00 pm.

She beamed. "I want to thank you from the bottom of my heart for everything you have done. I am so proud of the way this contract is shaping up. In just a week it feels and smells like one of our buildings – and it is all down to you. Have a lovely weekend and see you on Monday."

Even the surly Kathy, who somewhat amazingly had kept on turning up, raised a faint smile.

The following week started without incident. Ros pointed out that it was Kathy's birthday on Thursday and gave Christine a large flowery card. "Perhaps you could get everyone on the contract to sign this. It would be good to make it a tradition in the company – we talked about team building!"

"Lovely idea, Ros, … but Kathy? I'm hoping she'll leave before I have to give her the push."

Ros's holy look, "Chris, everyone deserves a chance, and she is a single Mum."

With a sigh, Christine took the card.

Mandy was thrilled and promptly took it upon herself to get it signed by everyone. "If you let me know when everyone's birthday is, I'll organise this. Perhaps I can bring in a cake too – like they do in offices." Christine smiled to herself – it wasn't only Maria, with her Panettone, who thought cake was the answer!

Well, Ros would have crowed if she could have seen Kathy's face when, at the end of the evening, Mandy presented the card! Her smile was from ear to ear as everyone chorused "Happy birthday, Kathy."

"Sorry Kathy, I'll bring in a cake tomorrow and we can celebrate again."

Mandy was getting the idea – "how to win friends and influence people."

The following Friday, Christine's complacency was shattered. Another phone call from Mr Canning, another theft problem. Could she come in?

Yes, it would be fine to come in at 5.00 p.m. so that she could talk to the cleaners immediately afterward.

Various valuable items had been taken from the directors' floor. A bottle of whisky, a calculator and a presentation silver paper knife.

Christine telephoned Mandy. Both of them were puzzled. This was Ann's floor and they both would have vouched 110% for her honesty.

Mandy became more and more indignant – besides, no one could have taken things of that size out of the building without her noticing. She had personally handed out everyone's coats and bags as they left every evening. She was adamant there was no way anyone could have hidden a bottle of whisky from her.

Armed with this, Christine faced Mr Canning. Contract or no contract she was not going to have the finger pointed at her staff. He was stern. "The reason I am having this discussion with you is that these thefts happen overnight when the majority of our staff have gone. Unfortunately, your staff have to be suspects."

"I don't think so, Mr Canning. For a start, we have taken great care to make it difficult for our staff to remove anything from the building. We lock up all coats and bags in the ground floor cleaning cupboard and no one can leave without claiming them from the supervisor."

"Secondly, the things stolen don't add up. It is common knowledge in the industry that cleaners will steal little things - loose cash, stamps, envelopes, even biscuits – but these sorts of things? It doesn't feel right. " She continued,

"And thirdly, you yourself said there were problems before we came."

"But I understand you have taken on some of POCS staff."

"Mmm," said Christine thoughtfully, "But only the ones Mrs James recommended." She was feeling more and more worried.

"Where do we go from here?"

"Well, I have spoken to our Head of Security, Mr Field. Unfortunately, he is dealing with a problem in London and won't be able to do anything about it until next week. Our security men here know about it, of course, and will be doing all they can to solve the problem. I will telephone you again next week and arrange for you to meet Mr Field."

Christine left with a heavy heart. Something was wrong. Terry was on security duty at reception. She would speak to him later.

The cleaners arrived and she endeavoured to act normally. There was no way she was going to even mention the theft to Ann. Everyone signed in, chatting normally. Ann was laughing with Janet – they were going to the Regent together on Saturday.

Mandy looked at Christine, "That's odd. Kathy isn't in yet. After all the fuss we made about her birthday. I even bought a cake. The least she could have done would have been to phone me. Ah ha. …. No worry, I'll do her floor – it'll be good to see what her cleaning's like."

"Why don't we do it together? That way we can chat and decide how we are going to play this theft problem. I take it you told Will not to say a word."

"Yeah, he's not happy. I think he fancies himself as a detective. He's sure POCS are out to get us."

"But they've gone and I for one trust the ladies that have stayed 100%. Come on let's get this floor wrapped up."

Mandy unlocked Kathy's cleaning cupboard on the 3rd floor. "Oh God, look at this. What a mess! This was perfect last weekend. I have a feeling young Kathy and I are going to be at loggerheads before long." Christine smiled.

Mandy began to get out the equipment they needed. She passed Christine a bucket. "Look at this." Dirty cloths shoved in and the spray polish upside down. Something sticky had leaked in the bottom.

"She's even left a bag of rubbish in here, shoved right at the back behind the vacuum cleaner." Mandy passed it to Christine with a bundle of new black sacks. "Hold on," she said. "I think we had better take a shifty at that." She took the rubbish bag and opened it.

"Oh bloody hell. Look at this." Inside was a bottle of whisky, the calculator and several other small items, including the paper knife.

"What do we do now?"

CHAPTER 21 – KATHY ON THE RADAR

Christine thought hard. "Mandy, I am not happy about this."

"Nor am I," returned Mandy with feeling.

"Look, could you do the floor on your own? I'll come and help in a moment. I just want to phone Kathy. I can't believe she would have left things in here and then gone sick. Please keep this under wraps."

She went down stairs and asked Terry if she could make a call to one of her cleaners who hadn't come in.

"Sure, Mrs Chapman. Use the telephone on reception." Just what she wanted. She got through immediately, "Hello Kathy, it's Mrs Chapman here. We are worried about you."

"Oh, I'm ever so sorry. I should've phoned Mandy. Me Mum's got the squits and couldn't have the baby. Me neighbour said she'd 'ave her but she weren't home and I had to wait and then I missed the bus. I'm ever so sorry. I'll be in Monday. Will you tell Mandy? She'll be mad at me, I reckon."

"Don't worry, Kathy. I'll tell her. Just make sure you are here on time Monday. Mandy and I will do your floor tonight."

"Ah, thanks Mrs Chapman. I hope me cleaning's aw right."

This did not smack of someone who had hidden a stash of stolen items in her cupboard. She surely would have sounded worried or guilty. Christine hadn't detected anything of the sort.

"Thank you Terry. Did you hear that conversation?"

"Yes, young Kathy, I guess," he said with a nod. "Mandy's been lovely with her."

Christine then went to find Will – she quickly filled him in. "Will, I have a funny feeling this stuff has been planted. If we show Terry, do you think we can trust him? You see, I don't want to remove the stuff tonight. I want it left over the weekend to see if anyone comes for it."

"Terry don't like this theft business any more than we do, Mrs. I told you he'd got his suspicions and I reckon he'll go along 100%. He reckons Vic wants POCS back in here, Mrs Wilks 'n all. They had a cosy little number going."

"Could you ask Terry to come to the 3rd floor cleaning cupboard? Just tell him we've got something we want him to see. I'll get Mandy. We need to log this carefully."

Fifteen minutes later they met outside the cupboard, Will bristling with excitement.

"Mandy, could you show Terry what we found and where we found it." Mandy produced the black bag.

"Wow," said Terry opening it, "And there's more stuff too." Frowning, he pulled out a beautiful engraved box and read the inscription.

"Oh my God, this is from the Chief Exec's office – it's got his name on it."

"That's on the directors' floor isn't it?" asked Mandy. "That is odd. Ann cleans that floor you know and there's no reason for Kathy to go up there."

Christine explained that neither she nor Mandy thought Kathy was responsible, even though the bag was concealed right at the back of her cupboard. Terry had overheard Christine's conversation with her and he nodded in agreement.

"Terry, we have a niggle that these things might have been planted and what frightens me even more is that it might be "found" sometime soon and a finger pointed at us."

Terry was thinking. He nodded slowly, "….. Like this weekend. Vic's on tomorrow." A pause and then more forcefully, "Right, I'll take the bag. I'm going to phone Mr Canning."

"Wouldn't it be better if we left it there at the back of the cupboard to see who comes to get it. After all, it could be Kathy and if so, we want to catch her red handed on Monday night."

"But you don't reckon it is Kathy, do you? Not after you spoke to her this evening."

"Terry. You just never know and none of us can afford to make unsubstantiated accusations. Why don't you telephone Mr Canning and tell him that we have shown you the bag and that we want to leave it there to test our cleaning lady on Monday."

"But what if someone else takes it at the weekend?"

"It would have to be the person who put it there in the first place and it would rule us out. As long as you report it first and are prepared to vouch for us that we showed it to you tonight, that would be proof enough."

Will was loving this. "Yeah, Terry. Reckon you'll trap the bugger! I bet he'll try and set us up good and proper."

"Trouble is we haven't got the CCTV cameras in yet."

Calmly Christine reassured "Terry, just do what you think is right. It would be very unprofessional of us to get involved. We have just shown you what we found. Come on, Mandy, we need to finish this floor."

As they walked away, they could hear Will saying "Go on, telephone the boss now. He'll be bloody chuffed at you, mate. Then, if Vic reports he found it at the back of the cleaners' cupboard, he'll have a job explaining how he knew where to look."

Christine and Mandy finished the third floor quickly and they put everything back into the cupboard carefully, trying to remember how Kathy, or whoever, had left it. They went downstairs to reception. There was no sign of Terry.

The cleaners, oblivious to the drama unfolding, departed waving their usual cheery "Goodnight". Two of them stopped to ask Mandy if they could have a night off next Friday to go to Bingo. "Bingo! Bingo?" said Mandy. "Bingo doesn't start till 8.00. What do you want a night off for? You'll lose more than you win. I tell you what, I'll let you leave half an hour early and then you can go straight from here – you'll have to come in early and clean the canteen before, mind." They laughed, "You're on!" Christine nodded. Mandy was good, keeping her cool and her humour even with this distraction… and the team was gelling.

Will appeared from the depths of the building, quivering with anticipation. "What's happening?"

"Shh, Will." - this from his wife. "You really are the limit. We can hear Terry in there talking to someone with the door shut." She pointed to the office off reception.

"Yes, Will, we've handed it over to BComm. They have to deal with it now. Come on, … HOME!" - this from Christine.

They left the building and headed for their cars but not before catching sight of Terry, emerging from the office in deep conversation with a tall gentleman in a suit.

Mandy told Christine later that Will was all for sitting in the car outside the building waiting for Terry. She'd had to drag him firmly home for supper. He was furious and grumbled when Mandy reminded him that she was the boss on that contract. He had even wanted to go in on Saturday morning, his nosey nose twitching, but his milk round was the other side of town. "Ha!" said Mandy triumphantly although she too was dying to know what was happening.

Christine heard nothing from BComm on Monday and arrived a little late at Stour House that evening to find a new security man on duty. She tracked Mandy down outside Kathy's cupboard on the third floor. She despatched Kathy to empty her bins and then turned to Christine.

"It's gone. I wanted to make sure so I brought Kathy up with me and made a thing about her messy cupboard. What do you make of the new security guy? Will's spitting mad that Terry's not in!"

"I'm going to go and introduce myself and see if I can find out anything."

Christine went up to the desk, "I'm Mrs Chapman, I run the cleaning company – sorry I haven't signed in yet." She was about to continue when he interrupted. "Oh great, you're the cleaning lady. I have a message for you. Would you go to Conference Room 404 on the fourth floor – Mr Canning is waiting for you."

"Oh. Thank you." Christine went to the lift, feeling slightly sick. She stood and timidly knocked on the door marked Engaged. "Come in." Mr Canning stood up – "Great, Mrs Chapman, you got my message. This is Mr Fielding, BComm's Head of Security and pointing at the other gentleman, "Mr Feering, Personnel Director. I have been telling them about your company and that you have only recently taken over our cleaning. We want to thank you for the way you and your staff have handled the recent problem."

Christine gave a nervous smile, "It was really down to Terry, your Security man, Terry – he was so supportive. We were lucky he was on duty. We would have been at a loss without him. I presume, then, you have resolved the problem. I hate incidents like this, particularly when we have new staff."

Mr Fielding looked at her and nodded, "Cleaners are always the first to be blamed when anything goes missing. We are aware of that but unfortunately this time we think there was a lot more to it than that.

I should tell you that we acted fast on Friday night. We installed a mini security camera inside the cleaning cupboard on the third floor while Terry was still on duty.

There will be a full enquiry but the reason I wanted to speak to you this evening is to ensure that you do not take any further action with your cleaning ladies."

Christine simply smiled and said, "Thank you. This is a great relief. I know my supervisory team here will be relieved too." That was an understatement – she could imagine Will whooping round reception in glee. She shook hands with everyone, and couldn't help noticing that Mr Canning took her hand in both of his – a very different handshake from his fleeting touch when they first met.

"Mr Canning, I would be grateful if you could keep me informed. I am still worried about the cleaning equipment which went missing from the restaurant."

"Of course. We are hoping to get to the bottom of that too."

She went to find Mandy who was working alongside Kathy and very much in training mode. As Christine approached she gave her an exasperated look, "Here's Mrs Chapman. Make sure you've cleaned all the telephones by the time I get back. You know how to do it and I shall check. Remember - Don't spray the phones – spray your cloth. We don't want them all gunged up with cleaning fluid."

Mandy looked at Christine raising her eyes heavenward.

"Mandy, let's find Will. I need to have a chat with you both." Will was polishing the canteen floor.

She sat them both down at a table. "I have just been called into a meeting with the head of security. I don't know any details but something happened at the weekend. Apparently after we left on Friday night, they put a camera in the cupboard. Anyway we are off the hook and there's going to be a full investigation."

Will was grinning "Did they get the sod?" Christine looked severely at Will.

"We don't know and it's none of our business."

"Ah, shit. How can you say that? That sod could have lost us the contract."

"Actually Will, he may inadvertently have done us a lot of good. Now we have to act as though nothing has happened and make sure we carry on professionally. Mandy, I am sure you understand that. BComm were very complimentary about the way you have handled this. You are a great supervisor, in fact you are a great team … but Will, Mandy's the boss, and, mind your language!"

"Yeah, yeah. But don't worry, Mrs Chapman. I'll find out. We've a right to know. I'll get the low down on the bug… I mean, about Vic."

"We don't know for sure it was him. Just be discreet, Will."

Mandy snorted. Discretion was not one of her husband's strong points.

Christine left them, anxious to get to Halls. Ros had told her Maria and Francesco were feeling neglected. Christine sighed. She felt torn in twenty ways.

Needless to say, the first night Terry was back on duty Will and Mandy got the full story. Terry even showed them how he'd put the mini camera on the ledge above the inside of the cleaning cupboard door.

They'd got Vic on film struggling over the vacuum cleaner and buckets to get at the rubbish bag at the back. He'd even taken his torch with him.

Just as they'd thought, he had telephoned Mr Canning. Ha … Terry had got in first. Apparently, after they had shown Terry the rubbish bag in the cupboard, he had gone down to phone Mr Canning. In the lift was Mr Fielding who by chance had stayed late after a meeting about installing CCTV and Terry had asked for a private word. Mr Fielding had then taken over, phoned Mr Canning and authorised the installation of a camera.

"Guess what, our Victor was suspended immediately. He was called before a BComm disciplinary board who suggested that either he resigned or they handed the whole thing over to the police for a full investigation. Needless to say, Vic left swearing that it was the new bloody cleaning company's fault – they had set him up.

Worryingly, however, there was still no news about the missing vacuum cleaners from the kitchen store.

Christine and Ros were sitting quietly mulling over the implications of this when the telephone went - Mr Parnell from Duyfken Line. "Mrs Chapman, unfortunately our caretaker's wife, Mrs Hoskins, has been taken into hospital and we need our offices cleaned urgently. Can you start immediately? This will be a temporary arrangement, of course. I am far from happy about your charges but unfortunately under the circumstances I have no option. How quickly could you start? Ideally tonight?"

Christine was thinking hard. She needed to buy a few minutes. "Mr Parnell, thank you for asking us. I need to talk to one or two people. Can you give me ten minutes? I will come back to you very quickly. I would obviously like to help you out. I do hope it is not too serious."
Christine put the phone down, looked at Ros and said, "Is there anyway we could start at Duyfken Line this evening? It would do us the world of good if we could. I get the impression the canny old fellow has tried several companies and is throwing out a challenge."

"Mandy and Will can cope at Stour House but I can't pull anyone out from there to help. What about any of the ladies we interviewed? I could possibly pinch Francesco from Halls if Alberto would go in to help Maria for a couple of nights. He and I could cover it until the weekend and then we could do a thorough initial clean. What do you think?"

"Duyfken Line's offices aren't too far from those nice ladies we interviewed – shall I see if they could get there? The trouble is no one will want to start tonight. They'll all need time to organise the family, tell their husbands etc."

"But if I go and clean with Francesco, we could do the toilets and the rubbish and tide things over until the weekend. The joy is we don't need equipment or materials, just manpower. It will be easy to keep clean after we've done the weekend clean."

CHAPTER 22 – BELLA BELLA

Christine was buzzing. She had felt an antipathy towards this contract, or was it towards the man? She had had bad vibes about the caretaker and his wife, but when the MD himself approached her cap in hand, it could be a golden opportunity to prove themselves and show that they do indeed offer a special service.

Christine looked up. Ros was looking concerned. "Chris, I am just worried that you will knock yourself up."

"I can manage. I was going to Ipswich anyway. Let me see if I can get hold of Maria … how on earth I am going to explain this to her over the phone, I really need to do something about my Italian."

Maria answered the telephone nervously, "Pronto chi parla?" "Maria, it's me Mrs Chapman. Maria, I have a big problem this evening …questa serra. We start clean a new office. Questa serra. Possa Francesco mi auita? Possa Alberto work at Halls oggi, today, and Francesco come help me with new contract. Capisci?" Talking over the telephone was so much more difficult without facial expressions and gestures. Had she understood a word?

"Si. Capisco. You want Alberto and Teresa come? No problem. Si. Dove?"

"Halls at 6.00 o'clock." Christine wanted to say 5.45 but her mind went blank.

"Eeez good. You want Francesco. And Teresa. I 'ave Alberto. We all 'elp. OK." Christine wasn't going to argue – the more the merrier. She would sort out who worked where at 6.00 p.m.

She picked up the telephone and dialled the Duyfken Line number. She was put through to Deborah. "Mr Parnell said you would telephone back in ten minutes. I will put you through." "Ah. Right. You've got it sorted then?" he boomed.

"I think so, Mr Parnell, but it's not ideal. We can cover for the remainder of the week. I shall come in with one or two other relief cleaners and clean the toilets, remove rubbish and do the essentials. At the weekend we will do a full scale initial clean which will make it easier for Mrs Hoskins when she comes back. I do hope she's OK." Christine paused.

"Mmm. Could be some time before she's back. You say relief cleaners? Do we get a reduction then?"

"I will try. But we will need to work on that basis until we find the ideal team for you. We normally have time to set everything up. I've got to juggle people and pay transport."

"You mean your petrol from Colchester?" He sounded so aggressive.

"Mr Parnell," she pleaded, "I am trying to help you out. My costs are included in the overheads but it takes time to get a new contract settled and we have to work at recruiting the right staff, training and so on. I really do want to help you out. I am sure if you decide you would like to keep us, we could review the costs then."

"Fair enough. Let's see how you perform," he barked. "Tonight at six then." She attempted to say, "A little after six …" but the telephone had gone dead.

That wasn't going to help – they would obviously arrive late which wouldn't get them off to a good start. Oh well, she'd deal with that later.

Ros was frowning. "Are you sure about this? I worry about Peter because if you cave in, it will be devastating for him. Don't you think we've got enough on our plates with Stour House?"

"I have to do this now while I can, Ros. Things aren't going to get any better you know."

Ros went silent, well aware that this was probably the truth. "Let me talk to Peter now."

Peter was sitting in an armchair looking tired. "Darling, we've been asked to start cleaning Duyfken Line tonight. I am trying to get hold of Francesco to come and help but I'm going to have to do the actual cleaning myself for a couple of nights at least. Do you think you can manage the children? We'll have to have supper early and I won't be back until after 9."

Peter gave an almost inaudible sigh. "We'll cope. You've got to do this. Things are tough all round but they will get better, I know. Has Mr Parnell agreed the price?"

Christine explained, crossing her fingers as she spoke. "It'll be fine once we've done the initial clean at the weekend and if we can find the right staff." Weekend cleans were exhausting and she was worried sick about leaving Peter with the children for the bulk of the weekend. Ros was right. She had to be careful. There was so much to think about and the car was almost out of petrol. If she left early this evening before 5.00 p.m. she could fill up and call in at Duyfken Line en route to Halls to leave a message to say that she would be in about 6.15. Better to warn the bearded bully - if only he could be a Captain Pugwash instead of a Captain Hook, she thought wistfully.

The children were playing up. They had refused to eat their cauliflower cheese and Peter looked drawn. Christine hugged them all quickly and left feeling sick inside. She glanced anxiously at the clock – it was 5 past five. She would never get to Duyfken Line by 5.30. Tears of guilt, or was it frustration, were pricking her eyes as she pulled into the petrol station. She paid for the petrol, grimly buying 6 Mars bars at the same time. Back in the car she promptly unwrapped one which she devoured, as she drove, in huge tasteless hunks. The speedometer touched 90mph. She had never driven at this speed before and as the poor old VW began to judder in protest, she eased her foot off the accelerator. She swore resignedly as a flake of chocolate landed somewhere down her front. The chocolate had to give her energy and somehow Mars bars were the ultimate rebellion – she needed both.

She swerved into the Duyfken Line car park and took the stairs up to reception two at a time. The receptionist looked up enquiringly. Christine gasped, "Please could you tell Mr Parnell I have to pick up my staff and we may be a little late but we will make up the time at the end of the evening. Sorry."   Without waiting for a response she gave a little wave and rushed out.

Ten minutes through the traffic and she arrived at Halls. She gasped with relief there was Maria deep in animated Italian conversation with Teresa. She HAD understood. Christine just hoped Francesco would be along soon …. but at least she could take Teresa with her.

As she got out of the car, Francesco's old blue Fiat drew in beside the VW. "Questa serra laboro con la senora." Francesco was wiggling his hips and grinning at Maria. "Tonight I'm working with the boss. You only got Alberto… so there!"

"Si, Teresa go wiz you also, you bad boy." She took a swipe at him but he ducked. Christine loved their easy sexy teasing.

Hastily, they agreed that Teresa and Francesco would work that evening and the following one, at Duyfken Line, and then they would all come for the weekend clean. "Mucha money?" Francesco asked. Christine nodded – she would have paid them anything they asked. "Come on guys," she said! "We have a job to do."

They crawled back to Duyfken Line in the rush hour traffic and arrived at 6.20 to find a scowling Mr Parnell standing in reception. "I hope you got my message, Mr Parnell." He nodded, "Mr Hoskins normally locks up at 20.00 but as he's at the hospital, I have arranged tonight that one of the Managers will come back and lock up at 20.30. I know tonight is the first night but I need timings to be precise."

Christine apologised quietly, "Tomorrow night we will be here at 6.00." She really wanted to say "Oh, come on … We are doing you a favour here. Give us a chance for heaven's sake."

She could feel Francesco tensing at her side and immediately clapped her hands and laughed.

"Chop, chop! Come on … we workers need to get organised.
Thank you Mr Parnell. I will telephone you in the morning
because there are bound to be things we've missed on the
first night. But we learn fast!"

It was difficult to see his reaction – all that ridiculous facial
hair but his eyes seemed devoid of warmth. She was going
to have to stand her ground and somehow it was becoming
easier. She needed to reward Maria and Francesco, and
Ros, and it was high time she asked Peter to go through the
accounts with her.

Francesco and Teresa were talking rapidly in Italian. Judging
by their looks they had not warmed to Mr Parnell. What were
they saying? …. Something like "What a pig… We'll show
him." No, that glare from Francesco and the growl in his
voice spelt something far more sinister, something like
"Perhaps we get the Mafia to sort him out. A nautical man
like him would be happy sleeping with the fishes."

She smiled and walked along the corridor to the cleaners'
cupboard, taking off her jacket as she went. Oh botheration,
that's where the chocolate had landed … there was a nasty
brown blob on her blouse. Without thinking she pulled it up
into her mouth and sucked hard.

Her shoulders sagged. Life was getting tougher. She felt
two hands on her shoulders. Francesco was gently moving
her out of the way. "Permesso, signora". He reached into
the cupboard for the vacuum cleaner, the broom and various
cleaning materials and gave her a big wink as he started to
sing "O mio babbino caro". Christine couldn't help but laugh.
The translation was "Oh my beloved father!"

"OK 'Papa', can you take some bags and empty rubbish, per
favore?" She extracted four black sacks and, grinning,

handed them to him. "Teresa and I will tackle the toilets so if you need me that's where I'll be. Start with the offices upstairs. Is there only one vacuum cleaner? I can't see a floor polisher either?"

Francesco looked at her blankly. Christine realised that she was forgetting to talk their 'lingo', or rather their 'lingua', albeit it was a corny mixture of simple English and basic school girl Italian. Teresa butted in, translating perfectly, and shooing Francesco in the direction of the stairs.

They worked quickly, Christine doing the toilets and the urinals and Teresa the basins, taps and mirrors. Christine was wondering if they needed a weekend clean after all.

As they emerged from the toilets, Francesco, who had collected the rubbish, done a thorough recce of the building and then taken the bags to the outside bin store, was obviously itching to show them something. They followed him into the staff canteen and watched as he knelt in the corner. To Christine's alarm he took a knife out of his pocket, flicked open the blade and began to scrape the polish off the parquet floor. It peeled off like slices of mature cheddar cheese. "Needa macchina". Francesco made scratching gestures with his fingers. "Halls 'ave macchina. Molto work. Saturday, Sunday?"

Christine shook her head. That would be a huge task and she certainly didn't want to get involved in stripping a parquet floor but Francesco was right layer upon layer of polish had built up and looking at it closely especially in the corners, layer upon layer of polish had been applied to layer upon layer of dust.

Still, that was not her idea of office cleaning. She wasn't going down that route. Francesco took the vacuum cleaner and began to hoover like a man possessed, pulling things out that hadn't been moved in years. Christine shook her finger at him, knowing they needed to pace themselves. As they worked, she realised that deep clean at the weekend was going to be needed.

She was making a note of everything that would put their stamp on the place – nice smelling polish, removing the lime scale build-up around the taps, polishing the wooden floors but most of all cleaning the brass. Then there were the less obvious things like pulling out the desks and cleaning the telephone hand-sets which were caked with face grease and make-up. She remembered Joan's insistence that they be disinfected weekly.

They were finished by 8.15 and had begun to put the equipment back into the cupboard, stacking things neatly when a voice made them jump. "All done then? I'm Dirk. Mr Parnell asked me to come and lock up. Is everything OK?" Christine didn't introduce herself. She was very conscious that her hair had come down at the back, her face was red and sweaty and there was a disgusting brown chocolate mark on her camisole top. Putting her hand up to cover it she replied, "Yes, I think so. No doubt we'll be told in the morning but we've done our best this evening. Is there any news on Mrs Hoskins?"

He shook his head and answered, "Not that I know of. Can I lock up then? Are you here again tomorrow night?"

"We plan to be. G'night." Christine was equally brief, anxious to get Francesco and Teresa back to Halls and herself home.

Thanking her Italian team, she opened the car door and produced a couple of Mars bars. Maria shook her head but

Francesco took one and gave her a big wink. "Domani? Teresa and Franco", (he pointed at himself), "we come new place, alle sei, …six o'clock?" "Si per favore. Yes, please."

Her thanks were heartfelt and noting she still had three Mars bars for herself, she handed one to Teresa who promptly passed it to Alberto. Why were these Italian guys so slim and their wives so plump when all they seemed to do was look after the men?

Christine climbed wearily into the car. Before she pulled away, she peeled back her Mars bar wrapper, took a huge bite, and vaguely waved the diminished chocolate bar in the direction of the departing Fiat. A string of melting toffee dribbled onto the steering wheel. Oh God what a mess.

She made a mental note to phone Mr Barton in the morning, perhaps after her call to Mr Parnell.

The house was in darkness. Peter was lying quietly in bed. He rolled over as she crept into the bedroom. "You can't keep this up, you know, Chris." "Don't you believe it! I've had three Mars bars and I'm just off to make myself an instant coffee – can I get you anything? Have you taken your sleeping pills?" He nodded his head against the pillow.

Christine was up again at five, clearheaded and anxious to look at the figures before she spoke to Mr Parnell. She dropped the children off at school, and as she opened the front door on her return, Peter was standing telephone in hand. "I've just had the Duyfken Line on the phone, Mr Parnell's secretary. Apparently you missed four offices last night. He wants you to phone back straightaway. Chris, don't let him push you around."

She dialled the number and was put straight through. He picked up his phone, "Parnell" and before he had chance to say any more Christine took the initiative, "I am sorry about the rooms we missed last night, Mr Parnell but we ran out of time and there were three of us working flat out. Tonight will obviously be much easier and we will give those offices our special attention. There are lots of areas which will have to be picked up at the weekend." He interrupted her, "Yes, I was going to come to that. I don't think that's going to be needed now."

"Mr Parnell," she could see Peter out of the corner of her eye, "I think you need to take a good look around you. For a start, we didn't touch the brass - it's black with tarnish. I so wanted to have that sparkling for you. And then there are the telephones – they are appalling. Poor Mrs Hoskins obviously doesn't have time to touch them and in a shipping office where staff are on the telephone all day, they should be disinfected at least weekly."

She paused expecting a rapid-fire response. Nothing... Had they been cut off? She sensed he was still there. "Mr Parnell?" Was he inspecting his own phone? Christine had personally cleaned his office last night, and to be fair, his phone, although not one of the worst, was none-the-less far from clean. She had been tempted to clean it, but resisted on the grounds that if she did one she should do all. The hole in the mouth piece was pretty gunky but then he did spit out his words! The ear piece wasn't too bad at all, no doubt polished clean by the bushy bristles in his beard.

Suddenly, he was back with her. "Just looking at the figures you quoted for this weekend clean..." Again, Christine took the initiative. "Would you agree to us doing half the time I have proposed. If we leave the wooden floor for now. I know it needs stripping back but we could just go over it with a polishing machine and see how it responds and tackle the other areas I have highlighted, like the brass and the phones – then it will be more manageable for Mrs Hoskins when she comes back. Is there any news?"

Ignoring her enquiry, Mr Parnell barked, "Very well. Carry on and do the reduced clean at the weekend. Put it in writing. Better come and see me on Monday morning and we can decide where we are going from there." He put the phone down. Christine felt exasperated. The man had absolutely no manners.

Christine turned to Peter and exploded. "He's impossible. He just put the phone down despite the fact he'd told me to make an appointment to come and see him on Monday morning. Grr. I hate him."

"Chris, you make me laugh. He's not there to be all sweetness and light to you – he's got a business to run and cleaning will be the last thing on earth he wants to spend time on."

"Well, why doesn't he just delegate it to someone nice then," she replied petulantly.

"Because he's very much in charge and runs a tight ship."

"I thought all captains in the navy were gentlemen and dishy." She was really out of sorts.

"Well there is a difference between the Royal Navy and the Merchant Navy and even more when you are running a modern shipping company."

"Yes, I bet I can guess which he was in."

"You're much too romantic and you've been watching too many Deep Blue Sea films. Real life's a bit different – they don't all look like Peter Finch and Kenneth More. Anyway, just take a look at his pictures, when you dust them, and you'll be able to tell!" Peter was teasing her now.

"Well, he wants everything ship shape, and he doesn't want to pay for it. And I don't like him."

Peter snorted, "Darling, welcome to the world of business."

CHAPTER 23 – TORN IN TWO

Together, Peter and Ros were calmly getting the administration side of the company organised. By now thepayroll was quite impressive, with 50 staff on the books already, and every Wednesday Ros would have to walk into town to collect the wages money from the bank. That done, they then began the weekly ritual of the wage packets - little brown envelopes with exactly the right money in each were divided up into the different contracts and held together with a pink elastic band.

For 'security' reasons Ros would then put all the little envelopes into a Tesco's carrier bag, convinced, as she kept telling Christine, that she was less likely to get mugged with an old carrier bag in her hand than with her smart briefcase (one which Peter no longer had use for).

For her part, Christine didn't like the idea of Ros walking to and from the bank so she determined to get her a car as soon as possible. As they now had money coming in promptly from three contracts, plus Christine's admittedly ever diminishing salary from the Study Centre, Peter too was adamant that they could afford to get Ros a car.

Peter telephoned Lofty, the garage owner, who serviced their own cars giving him a brief specification. "Lofty, it needs to be an estate and it must be apple green." "Apple green? Apple green – you've got to be joking. ...k'nell. Won't just green do?"

"The lady said "Apple", Lofty."

"Your missus, you mean?"

"No, my Office Manager."

"…k'nell," said Lofty, "You got two of 'em then! You poor bugger. Why don't we just spray one?" He was presumably referring to the car.

A week later he was on the phone. "Got a snip. Vauxhall Cavalier Estate. An' I've got the price knocked down fifty quid cos nobody in their right mind would buy a bright green, poncey monster like this. I told him straight, you'll ave to drop your price, mate! Ain't got a clue what sort of green it is. You'd better bring the missus."

Ros and Peter went to see it – the two men purred over the engine and the mileage - just 20,000 on the clock. "She's a beaut. Smooth as silk. Tyres'll do you for a bit too. And the colour, what do you reckon on the colour?"

Even Ros was slightly taken aback, it was hardly Apple, more like Lime Green but Green it was and she was getting a car!

She was over the moon and promptly arranged to take a short refresher driving course. It had been five years since she had driven and she was incredibly apprehensive about driving on the A12 with its huge container-lorries.

But she was now a mobile Office Manager. She was doubly over the moon when Christine said, "Of course you can use the car for your personal travel." What a difference this was going to make to her and her children's lives. But Ros, honest as ever, had the last word … "I'll pay for my private petrol – I promise."

To their delight, BComm had confirmed their contract at the end of the probationary period. Mandy was over the moon, indeed they were all over the moon. This was a wonderful endorsement that they were getting things right. Complaints were minimal and although Kathy was still an unpredictable headache, everyone seemed genuinely fond of her. Guy too was the first to applaud, although he and Alison were preoccupied with their gorgeous new baby, Damian.

Maria and Francesco regularly chided Christine that they didn't see her enough, but Duyfken Line had changed that. After only two nights, she and Teresa were really getting to grips with the building and on Friday night, Christine allowed Francesco to start pulling out the furniture. She had brought over a good supply of Monthind's own cleaning materials, including things like Brasso and specialist oil for the lovely wooden furniture – they had almost exhausted Mrs Hoskins meagre stock of Sainsbury's own brand products. She knew they would need vastly more of everything for the weekend clean and then the building would begin to smell better.

She and Teresa started to tackle the brass. They put masking tape around the plaques and fingerplates – Christine didn't want tell-tale white Brasso building up on the wood. She then gave Teresa a quick lesson on cleaning the telephones, remembering with great affection how Joan had shown her.

Francesco was a marvel and yet again, he shooed her away, saying that he and his team would look after the weekend work. Christine was very twitchy about this and in the end she agreed to work with them on Saturday and come in at lunch time on Sunday to do a final check.

It wasn't that she didn't trust her steadfast Italian team but she knew Mr Parnell was going to be a tough task-master. He would pick holes in anything and everything. For her own peace of mind, she needed to be there, in charge, at the weekend. She was dreading the meeting with Mr Parnell on Monday. Everything was so up in the air. Even if the weekend clean went well and he wanted them to continue,

216

she hadn't found the right staff to work here. It was pretty obvious that Mrs Hoskins wasn't going to be back in the very near future and Christine was certain Mr Parnell would try to shave the regular evening cleaning hours down. She couldn't keep pulling Francesco out of Halls and it wasn't fair on Peter and the children, or on Mandy. She needed to spell it out to Ros – they must find new staff.

Christine slept fitfully. The whole Duyfken Line contract was becoming a nightmare. She woke at 7.00 to find James at her bedside, bouncing up and down, "Can we go to the park? Please, Mummy, can we go to the park?"

She crawled out of bed feeling awful. "No, darling. I've got to go to work." "But Daddy said we'd go to the park and we could have a picnic..."

Peter was sitting on the side of the bed. "Sorry old boy," he held out his arms to James. "Mum's got to work. We'll have to have a picnic in the garden." James' lip was trembling, "You said we could. I want to go to the park. You said we would have a picnic and an ice-cream. You promised." He ran out of the room into Anja's bedroom where he lay on the floor, his sobs getting louder and louder.

Christine looked despairingly at Peter. His head was hanging down. "Sorry, Chris. I should have realised." Christine touched him on the shoulder, before heading across the landing. James was now in full tantrum mode. She bent to pick him up but he pushed her away and proceeded to lash out wildly. She raised her voice but he rolled over on his tummy and pounded the carpet with his fists. Alarmed, she tried to stroke his head but he turned, his little face red and contorted with rage, and shouted, "I hate you, I hate you, you spoil everything!" He banged his head violently on the floor.

Anja was sitting on her bed, tears streaming down her face. At a total loss, Christine sat next to her. She reached out to comfort her daughter, but as Peter came wearily to the door, his pyjamas loose against his thin frame, Anja ran to him, hugging his legs.

This was affecting them all – it was tearing them apart. She was utterly crazy to think she could hold the family together and run this business. Something would have to give.

James' tantrum was beginning to lose its passion and his hysterical anger gradually subsided into heart-rending sobs.

Christine gently picked him up and rocked him backwards and forwards until he eventually put his arms around her neck and offered his tear stained face up for her kisses.

"Come on," she said quietly, "Let's all get dressed quickly and then we can have a special breakfast together. Would you like boiled eggs and soldiers, James?" He produced a long, final, sob and then gave a big nod.

She glanced anxiously at the funny little fairy clock beside Anja's bed – she'd never make it to Duyfken Line for 9 o'clock. She carried James to the bathroom, "Come on, let's just have a lick and a promise," she poked her tongue out and bent to lick his face. James squealed and wriggled out of her arms. "OK, here's the face cloth. Then I'll race you to get dressed! The last one to get all their clothes on will be a smelly monkey." Not so inappropriate, she thought grimly, as there was no way she had time to shower this morning.

Downstairs she hastily put eight eggs in the pan, fishing four out after five minutes, and leaving the others to hard boil. She was still worrying how to fit in the promised picnic.

They all sat down to breakfast. James now grinning and chanting, "Mum's a smelly monkey." She hastily cut the toast into soldiers as she looked up she saw all three of them were holding their noses and grinning. "OK, well, you three are all CHEEKY monkeys, so we're a one big monkey family." She thought better of doing a monkey impression – James would just get carried away – she passed him three toast soldiers and indicated to his egg.

Dippy eggs – the yellow yolks were just right. That was a miracle.

She cast yet another glance at the clock. What on earth was she going to do? There was no way she could get hold of Francesco. Even if she did manage to telephone, the thought of trying to communicate in broken Italian was more than she could face, especially as she needed to give specific instructions to them all.

She now fully understood the expression torn in two. She looked across at Peter who had begun to stack the breakfast plates. They really should be spending the weekend with the children having a fun day. He winked at her, "I've got an idea why don't we all go to Ipswich. Mum can go into work and we can go to the park. I haven't met Maria and Francesco and if I remember rightly there is a park just across the road from Duyfken Line. Perhaps you could come over and join us for a bit and we could still have a picnic."

She threw Pete a look of gratitude. He was so good at finding a solution. This could work especially as he had wanted to meet F & M and although it wasn't ideal, she could at least explain face to face to the Italians why she was late and brief them thoroughly. They had after all made good inroads into her weekend cleaning schedule last night and the children were already scrambling down from the table to find things to take.

She quickly put the eggs, some tomatoes, a slab of cheese, four rolls and a large bottle of lemonade into a bag. Anja was holding open a large shopping bag and encouraging James to put in books and balls. Christine slipped in some plastic plates and beakers, remembering as she did so to get the "Cleaners Break Box" and add biscuits and milk. That would do and it was a nice day! Her spirits lifted.

As she piled everyone into the car, she remembered to put two folding chairs and a rug in the back. She pulled out of the garage just before nine – she was going to be very late. Peter put his hand on her knee – "It'll be all right. You're the boss, you know." She flashed him a look of gratitude, but HE didn't know Mr Parnell!

They pulled into the car park behind Duyfken Line's offices. The only other car was Francesco's little blue Fiat but Christine suggested they wait in the car while she made sure there was no one from the company working in the building. She could imagine Mr Parnell's reaction to her turning up with hubby and children.

She took the steps two at a time. Where would they be? She opened the back door and listened. Praises be, they were already working! She could hear a machine. Following the sound to the canteen, she found all the tables and chairs had been cleared, Alberto was vacuuming the parquet floor and young Julio was on his hands and knees scouring the edges. Francesco had his back to her and she watched him manoeuvre the machine in a graceful arc. The wood gleamed – wow, what a difference!

220

She walked up behind him and touched him on the shoulder. He jumped and the machine cut out. Alberto too had spotted her and switched off the vacuum cleaner.

Her face said it all – she was beaming. "You are fantastic. What time did you start? I can't believe how good the floor looks." Francesco beamed with pride, "Halls macchina eez good." Christine had a brief flash of guilt – poor Mr Barton, we're borrowing first his staff and now his equipment.

"Yes, the machine is good, but Francesco is super good!" and she beckoned him to follow her. Francesco spoke quickly in Italian and Alberto grinned and took over the polisher – you'd have thought he been handed the steering wheel of a Porsche! "I learn 'im good," said Francesco with pride. Christine was impressed.

"Where is Maria?" she asked. "She and Teresa do telephones. Ssh." He cocked his head as they walked up the stairs and she picked up the faint strains of singing.

Following the sound, they tracked the ladies down. Both were armed with toothbrushes and a pile of Ros' white cotton cloths. They stopped as Christine opened the door.

Maria immediately looked concerned, "Signora, why you 'ere. We OK? We 'appy you no come."

Christine smiled. "I want you and Francesco to meet my husband and children." She cast a quick look around but there was no sign of anyone from Duyfken Line. "Come."

They followed her to the back door. Peter and the children were sorting things out in the boot of the car and James quickly came running to meet her shouting. "Mummy, can we play football here?" He dropped the ball and kicked it with all his might. Francesco neatly intercepted it and deftly dribbled it back towards James, who with a big grin ran towards the ball and taking a huge kick managed to kick it off at an angle of 90 degrees. Peter ruffled James hair and pointed to the ball which Anja was already running to retrieve. He held out his hand to Francesco, "Buon giorno, sono Christine's marito."

Francesco shook his hand and gestured to Maria, who wiping her hands on her tabard, gave a little bow and also shook Peter's hand. She then turned to the children who were skipping back with the ball, her facing relaxing into a broad smile, "Aah bambini!"

Christine picked up the box with the milk and biscuits and looked at Peter. "Darling, I'm just going to explain a few things to Francesco and Maria. I won't be long. Will you be OK with the children? I think it will be alright if they kick the ball around here. I won't be long." and she walked back towards the building.

Christine started to apologise for being late. "We had a problem …" but Maria cut in worriedly, "Signor Chapman, 'e sick?" Christine nodded. Maria was sharp. She exchanged a look with Francesco. Francesco took the box resolutely from Christine's hands and said, "Why you 'ere? We OK. Eez OK. You go with children. I telephone you."

Christine could have embraced them. What did it matter if the place wasn't perfect? After all, she was doing the 'Captain', 'Captain Hook' more like, a favour. The place was looking a million times better than it had and it would be so much easier to clean from now on. She would battle with him on Monday, but as long as they didn't lose money and she could go to the park with the children, that was all that mattered. Who the dickens was going to clean from then on, she didn't know, but what the hell. She was going to forget work and have a weekend with the family. She quickly thanked Francesco and Maria and gave them vague instructions to do as much as they could in the time, before rushing back to the car.

"Tada" she trilled. "Come on, we're off to the park." She held the car door open for the children. Peter was smiling.

CHAPTER 24 – NOT A NICE MAN

Christine woke on Monday realising she hadn't heard from the Italians on Sunday. She should have telephoned them but presumably no news was good news. Still, she really needed to know when they had finished.

Immediately after 9.00 a.m. she telephoned Mr Barton and started to explain that she had "borrowed" Francesco and his floor machine for the Duyfken Line. Mr Barton, who obviously had far more important things on his mind first thing on a Monday, dismissed her with a "Great. No problem. Can we talk another time?"

Feeling a little sheepish, Christine put the phone down. Monday morning was obviously not a good time to talk to customers about cleaning. She decided against phoning Mr Parnell.

Ros arrived and they began to discuss how they could find people to clean regularly at Duyfken Line. The problem was not knowing when Mrs Hoskins would be back and that they hadn't interviewed anyone who lived nearby. They agreed, however, that Christine couldn't keep doing the cleaning herself. As they were chatting, the telephone rang.

It was an incensed Mr Parnell. "Mrs Chapman, I have arrived this morning to find the place in a total mess. There's a floor machine by the back door, a tin of what appears to be oil on the board room table and the brass everywhere is covered with masking tape. What the hell went on at the weekend?"

Shocked, Christine immediately went on the defensive, "I am so sorry, Mr Parnell. I am afraid I didn't come in to check everything yesterday. I can only apologise. We will, of course put it right this evening."

"This evening, this evening. It can't wait until then. I need it sorted now. Get someone over here straight away." He put the phone down with a bang.

Christine put her head in her hands. Ros said nervously, "What did he say?"

"He's far from happy – things were left out and he wants someone over there like now to sort it." Peter came into the kitchen and she explained again. "Pete, he's so angry. He was spitting the words out, straight into his beautifully clean phone." She shuddered. "He hasn't noticed anything good, just that we left the masking tape round the brass, and he wants someone over there immediately to sort it out." She was close to tears.

"Right, I'll prepare the invoice for work to date. You can take that with you. Don't let him bully you."

"Francesco left the floor machine right by the back door and Mr Parnell wants that moved too. I'll never lift it into the car on my own." She bit her tongue. They both knew Peter couldn't help her. The chemotherapy had left him so weak. Ros looked from one to the other, and said, "I'll come with you, Chris. We can manage to get the machine in the car together and in any case you need moral support. I tell you what, I will bring a couple of postcard adverts – perhaps we can find a post office or shop and put them up. We might find someone to take on the cleaning that way."

Christine was shaking her head at the injustice of this. "I've had enough. After all the hard work we've put it for that beastly man, I don't want to carry on. He can clean the place himself."

Peter picked this up quickly. "That's the whole point, Chris. After all you have done, it'll be easy to run the contract now."

"Not with that man, it won't. Anyway with luck, they won't want us because Mrs Hoskins will be back fairly soon. We've done the dirty work and they'll be able to manage now. Ros, it'll be great if we can pop the machine back to Halls, perhaps I can see Mr Barton then. He's the sort of man I want to work with, not unpleasant bullies."

Peter was laughing, "Chris, you are going to have to learn that the customer is always right. There are times when you have to work with crooks and people who don't like you, when things are unfair or you get taken for a ride, but you have to just swallow hard and take it on the chin. You can't afford to walk away from Duyfken Line now."

Christine was furious. "It's alright for you. You haven't had to work your socks off there night after night for the past week ...." She stopped, realising what she had just said. "Oh, darling. I'm sorry." She put her hand to her mouth.

Peter wasn't looking at her. He had thrust an invoice into the typewriter and was typing in the price for the cleaning, hitting each key with such ferocity that it cut into the carbon paper and copy below. She immediately put her arms around him, mortified at her insensitivity. He shrugged her off and carried on typing in Duyfken Line's address.

Ros, trying to be helpful, said, "Peter, let me do that while you work out the figures." He threw her a dirty look and snapped, "I can manage. I'm not a complete invalid yet."

Later as they drove to Ipswich, she and Ros resolved to keep stress levels down as much as possible but as they pulled into the car park, Christine muttered, "I feel sick, Ros. He's going to eat me for breakfast."

"Well, breakfast's long gone; it's almost lunch-time so you'll be fine," said Ros, matter-of-factly. "Come on, I'm right behind you."

The floor machine was there by the back door so together they carried it to the foot of the car park steps before reporting to reception. While they were waiting for Mr Parnell, they began to peel the masking tape off the plaques by the front door and in reception. Christine produced the Swiss Army pocketknife which she now always carried, to trim the awkward bits.

She was just folding the blade away when Mr Parnell came down the stairs. He noted the knife and the pile of screwed up masking tape. "You came yourself?" Christine nodded before turning to Ros and saying, "This is Mrs Barnum, my Office Manager." Ros, stoically, didn't wince as he shook her hand but nor did she smile. He continued curtly, ""We need to talk. Come upstairs."

Christine quickly picked up the masking tape, thrusting it in her pocket as they followed him up the stairs. Christine was making mental notes - Maria had spent time cleaning the intricate scrolled banisters. She surreptitiously ran her finger along the top of one of the photographs – that too had been done, and the whole place smelt so much better. He opened the board room door. There standing on a white cotton cloth was the tin of furniture oil.

Mr Parnell gestured for them to sit. Before she did so, Ros removed the offending tin and used the cloth to give a quick wipe to the immaculate table, in case it had left a smear.

Christine pulled the invoice from her briefcase and put it on the table in front of her. She looked at Mr Parnell and waited. "Your people left the place in a mess," he barked. Christine could feel her anger mounting. There was no appreciation of anything and she was not going to allow him to criticise her team like that.

She took a deep breath and began, "I'm totally to blame. I should have come over yesterday afternoon to check when they finished but I had a family commitment I couldn't break. You must remember we have stepped into the breach, quite literally.

I apologise but the masking tape was left on because I wanted to discuss with you the possibility of lacquering the brass before we removed it. The floor machine was left here because my operative wanted to buff the parquet flooring with a finer polishing pad. Unfortunately, it wouldn't fit in the cleaners' cupboard. I am sorry though about the tin of oil."

Keeping her anger under control, she added more gently, "I so hope Mrs Hoskins is better and can resume her cleaning duties soon."

"She's due home today. How much are you charging me for the weekend? – I presume that's your bill."

"Yes, you've been charged, as agreed, half the original quote and, incidentally, the cleaners were able to work longer because I didn't come over on Sunday. I am sorry, however, that you were not happy." She passed him the bill and stood up.

Mr Parnell was weighing her up. "Sit down, please. As I said, we need to talk."

"Mr Parnell," said Christine still standing. "My cleaners have worked their socks off to bring standards up to a manageable level. I am amazed at the difference. You have no appreciation of how difficult it has been to work on this ad hoc basis. I cannot appoint staff when we don't know if there's a permanent job for them. I cannot continue travelling over every evening from Colchester and bringing in key cleaners from other contracts. I hope Mrs Hoskins is able to return quickly but in the meantime, I am afraid you will have to find another solution. I am sorry."

She picked up her briefcase and nodded at Ros.

Mr Parnell rose, looking slightly taken aback. "You are leaving? Hmm, Well, I will get back to you. Thank you for coming in this morning."

Christine nodded coldly. "You will find our cleaning products in the cupboard downstairs. They have been charged as part of the deep clean but Mrs Barnum and I will remove the floor machine as we leave."

She held out her hand. "You know where we are," she said with a shadow of a smile, "if you should need our services in the future." Mr Parnell took her hand and glanced briefly at Ros, whose face was blank. They left in silence, heads high.

As they struggled to load the floor machine into the car, Christine chanced to look up at the windows on the first floor. Mr Parnell was standing, at the board room window with his hands behind his back, watching them. Christine quickly averted her eyes and muttered fervently, "What a pig. I'd hate to work for him. Come on, heave. " The machine fell on its side in the back of the car and Christine slammed down the lid.

"Well", said Ros as they drove away, "I think he got the point. I have a feeling you've rocked the boat somewhat. Was it true about lacquering the brass and buffing the floor with a finer pad?"

"Well, no not exactly. I just made that up on the spur of the moment. But I think it sounded quite plausible, don't you? I just wanted to make sure he didn't try to cut the price even more."

"Well, I just hope we get paid. I get the feeling he wasn't very pleased. Do you think he will find somebody else to clean it or will he hang on for Mrs Hoskins?"

"I really don't care. One thing for sure, it will be a damn sight easier to clean now but if she does come back, there's no way one lady on her own can manage. It'll go rapidly down-hill again and serve him right. All I know is, I've gone right off the navy – give me builders' merchants and trade unionists, every time! And, I think it's about time we chased things up with Eastern Water Authority. Let's put Duyfken Line behind us and move on."

It was such a relief not to have to have to rush off to Ipswich that night. As soon as they got back, she telephoned Maria to say Mr Parnell was "molto contento with their work (a little white lie wouldn't go amiss) and that she was so grateful for all their help. She explained that the cleaning lady was out of hospital so… "Tell Francesco he can clean with you tonight!"

She knew this would be a relief in many ways, for Teresa too. The extra travelling was a nuisance and it couldn't go on like this forever, but, as always, everyone had bent over backwards to help.

CHAPTER 25 - TIME TO MOVE ON

Eastern Water Authority had had their quotation for nearly three weeks and there had been no contact except that perfunctory acknowledgement on a brown postcard. Surely they must have made a decision by now, after all, Lou had said the cleaners had been given notice to leave at the end of August. Christine decided to telephone Lou to see if she had heard anything before ringing Mr Henson. Deep down though she was feeling quite aggrieved that she hadn't heard from Andrzej – he was so lovely and she really felt he'd enjoyed meeting her.

How pathetic was that? This is business. She had to be rational and look at it from his point of view. In his shoes, would she give EWA's major cleaning contract to an insignificant little company with negligible experience, just because the gushy owner was Polish and he liked her? No, of course he wouldn't, he was far too professional. She smiled. She, on the other hand, probably would! But then women were different.

Anyway, she told herself, no doubt, it would be similar to BCOMM with several people on a committee and they would make a 'sensible' commercial decision. Well, let's just hope Andrzej and Mr Henson were on that committee.

She was prevaricating. Taking a deep breath, she picked up the phone. "Mrs Riley, I am sorry I haven't been in touch. I wondered if you have heard anything. I haven't but I thought I should tell you, we did submit a quotation for the cleaning."

"Oh Mrs Chapman, we knew you had and I was hoping you might get in touch like. There's been all sorts of trouble over the canteen cleaning. All us cleaners were called in last week and we was told we weren't doing our job proper.

Fanny, err, Mrs Perkins, our supervisor like, told the bosses that the engineers were a load of pigs and we weren't paid to clean up their shit. Mr Hicks, he's the boss of the engineers, said if that was the case, why hadn't she reported it. She said it weren't her place to snitch on the blokes and anyways it weren't in our specification to pick up their stinking clothes or to clean out the filthy fridge."

Without drawing breath, she continued, "The two ladies and old Ernie what does that block said yeah it were a waste of time tryin' to clean up - as soon as they done it, the blokes mess it up. Mr Hicks, all toity like, said 'Well weren't that what cleaning were all abaht!'" Lou laughed. "He's got a point, but the trouble is nobody wants to clean that block and the cleaners what's supposed to do it are so pissed off, they just sit around drinking coffee and reading magazines."

Mmm, Christine wasn't surprised. She had seen the magazines!

"When we was asked how it could be improved, I piped up and said 'better management' and they all looked at Fan.., err, Mrs Perkins cos everyone knows she spends 'alf her time in the gatehouse. She got mad and said it weren't fair to pin the blame on her and that she wasn't going to go on working in a shit hole and they could stuff their job." Lou paused, "Only I wasn't really pointing a finger at her. Like you said they need to change how they clean it all."

Christine didn't know quite what to say. "Oh Lou. How dreadful. So what's happening now?"

"Well, Fanny's gone and us girls are cleaning the offices, like before, but they've got one of the retired linesmen cleaning, temporary like, in the engineers block – he normally looks after the car park area. Mick doesn't know how long the old boy's supposed to do in there but it isn't going to work. The engineers have been told to tidy the place up but there's no way any of those blokes are going to clean the toilets and poor old Paddy, he ain't got a clue. If you ask me it's a bloody mess."

Christine started to say "Perhaps I should telephone," but Lou was in full flow, desperate to pour out the whole story : "Mick says for two pins he'd call in the Environmental Health people, it's that bad. That would really shake things up, but they'd know it was him. He says it's getting worse by the day and several of his mates want him to go to the union but that'll take for ever and Mick don't want no repercussions because of my job. Oh Mrs Chapman, I'm terrified I'll lose me job." She paused for breath before declaring firmly, "One thing's for sure, the whole of that block desperately needs a proper deep clean like you said."

"I think I'd better telephone Mr Henson."

"That's half the trouble – he's off sick. He would have got this sorted. He's probably sick of the whole place. I don't know who you should ring. D'you want me to ask Mick?"

"No Lou, thank you. It may be they've already made arrangements for one of the big national companies to come in but I'll ring and see what I can find out. Thank you for putting me in the picture, though."

"Oh, and Mrs Chapman, you won't say it was me what told you, will you? Cos I wouldn't want to get Mick into no trouble."

"Of course, not Lou – this is just between you and me, I promise."

Wow. Christine was reeling when she put the phone down.

She was so glad she had listed, in detail, her proposal for crew-cleaning the engineers' area. She wondered if her quotation had even been looked at and if anyone had picked up her ideas about solving the problems. After speaking to Lou, she was sure she was right. Resolutely she reached for the telephone and rang the Water Authority reception.

"Could I speak to Mr Henson, please?" Despite Lou telling her he was off sick, she felt she should ask for him. "Mr Henson is not in this week. Can anyone else help you?"

"Is Mr Koronovski in by any chance?" Christine gave her name and waited.

"Krystyna, I'm so glad you called! We have major problems here and Arnold is off sick which is why no one's got back to you. I'll be honest, we like your ideas for running the cleaning, but there's quite a bit of opposition to bringing in a small, female-led, company with no track record."

"Mr Koronovski, we are cleaning Stour House, the big BCOMM office block, and they have just asked us to take on another building in Princes Street. We have also been cleaning the Duyfken Line head offices on the Hayleigh Road."

"But our big worry is the engineers' block. It's very different from cleaning offices, and not really suitable for a lady like you."

"Mr Koronovski," Christine couldn't keep the annoyance out of her voice. "Don't you think we might be just what IS needed. Those guys would never treat their own homes like that, their wives wouldn't let them. The trouble is, the place is a disgrace, and it's a health hazard. Have you seen the state of the fridge and the sink? To be honest, I'm surprised they want to sit in there, let alone eat." Christine stopped, horrified at what she had said.

"Oh, gosh. I am sorry, Mr Koronovski. But it's true. It's no wonder the engineers treat the whole facility so badly. It needs a thorough deep clean and then a bossy woman like me in charge to make sure it's kept that way. The engineers would respect it then, just like they do at home."

There was still no response. "I'm not afraid to tackle things like this, you know. I was brought up on a farm and we DO clean Halls, Mr Koronovski. They're a builders' merchants with all the mess that entails – we've sorted out all their warehouses and we clean their toilets and canteen. I believe you know Mr Barton …."

He interrupted impatiently, "Andrzej, call me Andrzej. I think you're right. If we brought in the painters and gave the whole place a coat of paint, would that help? And a new fridge? The fridge seems to be a major issue."

Christine shook her head – how typically male! It wasn't as simple as that. "If the place were painted, ideally in white or pale cream that would be wonderful. It would give it a completely different feel. Those dark orange walls are awful – they'll need more than one coat though, probably three. But there's no need for a new fridge, we can scour and sterilise that. I don't think it's very old. The plastic chairs are grim – I think they too were orange once upon a time! But if we spray them with a deep cleaning agent and leave them overnight, I am sure we can get rid of the dirt and grease. They should come up well, but that old sofa needs to be thrown out," she could feel her excitement rising. She stopped dismayed, realising that she was getting carried away.

"Oh, Andrzej, I'm so sorry, bardzo, bardzo przepraszam. I'm talking as though you want us to do it for you," she hung her head.

She heard him take a deep breath and mutter quietly to himself, "I do, oh, I SO do! The trouble is I've got to get this past the board, but it's fast becoming a major issue, no, a crisis. If I can get the go-ahead, how soon could you start?"

"The ideal would be to get the painters in say on Thursday and Friday, we could come in over the weekend and then when the engineers come in to work on Monday morning everything would be transformed - canteen, changing rooms and toilets. The only thing is I don't want to spend hours cleaning it up, if we aren't given the daily contract because it will just be a matter of time before it goes right back to square one."

"How are you going to staff it?"

"Well, I would manage it, with a working supervisor. I would like to employ your existing cleaners – that's only fair, but it is important that the supervisor isn't one of them. Depending on how many are happy to stay, I may need to bring in a few others, but that's not a problem. Changes need to be made and there may have to be a few casualties from the existing cleaners."

Mr Koronovski said, "Well, I gather there have been a few already. I'll have to check with Arnie. Anyway, you are right – changes need to be made. God, I hope he's back next week," he murmured before continuing, "Look, I'm going to

236

stick my neck out and push to get you in on a two month trial basis. What were you going to charge for the initial clean?"

Christine told him. He whistled. There was a long pause, he was obviously doing a few calculations. Christine took the initiative, "That price was for the whole site, the offices as well. Would it help if we concentrated on the engineers' area? I could do that for half."

"And these figures for the regular daily clean? Are these your final figures?"

"I'm afraid so. If we aren't going to do an initial clean in the offices, I daren't reduce the regular time there in any way. I had quoted to put in new equipment but if we used yours to begin with that would help as we wouldn't have that capital expenditure. Maybe, if we can have a review after the two months, and everyone is happy, it might be possible to reduce hours and cut the cost slightly. I'm always prepared to negotiate, once the standards are right. That's the important thing, getting the standards right and ensuring they are sustainable."

"Krystyna, can I call you back? If I can get our painters in beforehand, could you come in this weekend? Realistically, it will probably be the weekend after but it all depends on whether I can get approval."

"Dobrze. That's fine. Just let me know. The important thing is that the problem is tackled as soon as possible – it's only going to get worse. I'll do everything I can to help. Just let me know."

Andrzej thanked her politely in Polish with a promise to get back to her "without delay". Wow, this could be a real break-through. Christine knew if they could just get this contract, it would be a real feather in their cap, as well as, with luck, helping to substantially reduce their personal debts.

She rang Lou, carefully playing down her excitement, but telling her there was just a chance they might be given the cleaning contract. Lou was pragmatic:

"Good, well, it'd better be sooner than later. Mick reckons the engineers aren't pussy footing around. They're going to walk out if management don't do something like, this week, no messing. It's a real shit hole."

Christine silently agreed. "Lou, what worries me is we need a working supervisor. Would you be prepared to take it on? You know the buildings so well."

Lou's reaction was instantaneous – "God, no way, no way. What with Mick being there. Anyway, I couldn't. I couldn't tell the girls what to do. They're me mates."

Deep down Christine knew this, knew Lou wasn't supervisor material but she felt it was important to ask her. "Is there anyone else among the cleaning team who might be right? Or do you know anyone who might be interested in coming to join us."

"None of the girls would do it, not after Fanny. And I can't think off the top of me head but I'll have a talk with Mick when he gets in. He knows a lot of people round here. Oh, Mrs Chapman, do you really think you might get it?"

"Lou, please, please, don't get your hopes up. I've been talking to one of the managers and there's just a chance. But if I hear any more, I will let you know. Meantime, please don't forget to ask Mick about a supervisor, but warn him to keep it under his hat."

Ros had telephoned Mandy and Will who, as Will put it, were as "'appy as Larry" but "when was Mrs Chapman going to come and see them?" Ros promised it would be before the week was out.

Christine felt as though a ton of bricks had been lifted off her shoulders. What a relief it was not to have to go every evening and personally clean Duyfken Line. Peter didn't begin to understand why she had had such bad vibes about the place from the very beginning. He felt she and Mr Parnell had somehow got off on the wrong footing and told her not to be ridiculous when she said, "I just think he doesn't like women!"

Anyway now she had time to do something nice for supper – she started peeling potatoes. She would make a nice sauce for the left-over roast chicken from Sunday.

Suddenly, Peter called. "It's Mick Riley on the 'phone for you."

Christine hastily wiped her hands. "Hello Mick."

"Lou says the bosses are talking to you and that you need someone to be a working supervisor. Well, first of all, the engineers are about to walk out – if it would help, Mrs Chapman, I'll have 'em walk out tomorrow. They'd make a decision, sharpish, then! "

"No Mick. There's no need for that! Unfortunately, Mr Henson is off sick but they are very concerned about things. I think they would quite like to appoint us but they are worried about our lack of experience. If I could find the right lady to run it with me, it might make all the difference."

"Well, Lou didn't want me to say nothing, but her sister would be brilliant. Trouble is she's on her own and is on benefits. She married a sailor from Indonesia and went off with him but he were a bad egg. She's had a rough time but now she's back home with her two girls. She's a bright lass is our Becky, and a hell of a worker."

"It might be a problem though, surely, that she's Lou's sister?"

"I don't reckon. No one round here knows her. Lou's family come from Yarmouth. We didn't see hide nor hair of Beck for ten years. The bastard dumped her out in Jakarta. She's tough and I tell you she don't stand for no nonsense."

"Perhaps I could come round again and meet her with Lou when I know what's happening. I have a feeling I will be hearing back from them quite soon, Mick."

"Well, if I have my way, you will, Mrs Chapman. It'd be a bloody shame if they don't bring you in."

Christine didn't know quite what to make of this but Becky, Rebecca presumably, could be the answer. Being on benefits shouldn't be too much of a problem because they paid cash. She was much more concerned about Mick stirring things up with the engineers – that could have repercussions. Mind you, she felt he had his head screwed on pretty soundly, plus, of course, they had a lot to lose as a family.

Ah, well. It was out of her hands and she hastily went back to preparing the chicken supper. She had just dished up and had put plates in front of Peter and the children when the telephone rang again. Peter sighed: "Ignore it for once and come and sit down or yours will get cold. Let's start, kids."

"I'd better take it," Christine called back, "It might be Francesco and I want to thank him again."

She glanced at the clock. It was almost half past six. She picked up the receiver, "Colchester 571696."

"Is that Mrs Chapman?" It was a voice she recognised but couldn't place. "Henson from Eastern Water Authority here. I'm sorry to phone so late."

"Oh, Mr Henson, are you better? I'd heard you haven't been well."

"I'm fine now, my dear. Thank you. Came back today. This has to be brief. I'm in the middle of a senior management meeting here and I've been sent out to phone you. Could you possibly come in tomorrow? We're trying to sort out the cleaning and wondered how you'd feel if we were to ask you to start at the weekend."

"That's with the deep clean of the engineers' complex, I presume?"

"Yes, I gather you discussed that with Andy."

"As long as we can blitz that area before we start and I can come in one evening beforehand to meet your existing staff, that should be fine. I'd obviously have liked a bit longer to plan it but I don't see any major problems. What time did you want me to come in tomorrow?"

"Would about 11 o'clock be possible? Can I go back and tell the meeting that you could do it?"

"By all means, Mr Henson, and eleven would be fine. Thank you for calling. You've made my day."

She put the phone down and shrieked, "Pete! That was Eastern Water on the line. I think they want us. We might even have to start at the weekend."

"You're joking? I can't believe that! Crumbs, Chris. That would really be a coup."

"It hasn't happened yet but I've got to go over for a meeting at 11.00 tomorrow. I think being half Polish helped!"

"Come and eat. I think we should celebrate with some ice-cream, don't you, kids?"

CHAPTER 26 - A CHANCE TO POLISH HER POLISH

Christine hardly slept a wink. This was even bigger than BCOMM and if Becky was as tough as Mick described, they could really make it work. She sneaked out of bed before six a.m. to go through the quotation again. How early could she phone the Riley household? She knew the engineers started early and it would be good to get hold of Mick before he made any unnecessary waves!

She rang just after 7.00, praying she didn't wake their autistic little lad. Mick answered the phone with a "Yeah?"

"Mick, I'm so sorry to ring so early."

He had recognised her voice, "That's no worry. We get called out all the time. What's the problem?"

"No problem, Mick. It's just that Mr Henson telephoned me late yesterday to ask me to come in this morning. They want us to start at the weekend and I really do need to meet Rebecca and Lou before I go in to see them at 11.00."

"Lou," he yelled, nearly deafening Christine. There were obviously no worries about waking anyone in this house even at seven in the morning. "OK if Mrs Chapman comes round this morning, around ….?" He paused and Christine supplied, "Around 10.00. And could she get hold of Becky?"

"Lou, can you get Beck here by 10.00?" Christine could hear Lou faintly in the background.

"That'll be fine. Cor, things are moving then?" Mick said, "Wait till I tell the boys!"

"Mick, I think we need to play this carefully. Nothing's been confirmed yet." Christine was slightly alarmed.

"Don't worry, Mrs Chapman. I know how to handle this lot better than most. I ain't Shop Steward for nuffink! You're going to be OK."

"I hope so. But thank you for your help, and tell Lou, I look forward to meeting her and Becky at 10.00."

Christine decided to drive straight to Ipswich after taking the children to school. She left Peter busy working out what supplies they would need and instructions for Ros to see if they had any possible candidates living on the "painters' estate". They would also need all the Italians for the deep clean. When she asked Peter to ring Maria, he cautioned, "Don't you think we might be counting our chickens a bit too soon."

Christine shook her head.

It was only 9.37 when she pulled up outside No 36 Monet Road but Lou had spotted her from the kitchen window and was happily waving a cup in the air. The meaning was clear. Christine locked the car. The front door was open. "Beck's on her way. Have a seat. Coffee OK?" Christine nodded, "Just black, thank you."

Lou had just put the cup in front of her when a loud voice called, "Morning Lou. Saw the girls off at school and got here as soon as I could. Jogged all the way, damn sight faster than the bus."

"Ah! Becky meet Mrs Chapman!"

Christine smiled warmly. This girl had personality. She beamed at Christine and immediately held out her hand.

244

"Pleased to meet you. I'm Rebecca Deago. I gather you might have a job for me. You do know I'm on benefits, don't you? I don't want to be but the trouble is I can't work full-time because of the girls and if I declare any part-time work, I'll lose the lot. The system's daft. It doesn't encourage you to get off your backside and work."

Christine nodded – this wasn't the first time she'd heard this. "Well, Becky, we pay cash fortnightly so we can probably get round the benefits for a while. I'm looking for a supervisor to run the cleaning contract where Lou and Mick both work, EWA. I want a working supervisor, though. Someone who leads by example, like I do."

Becky nodded. "Yes, Lou told me. I've worked in restaurants and had girls under me. Trouble is I haven't got any references over here. But we're grafters aren't we, sis? Not afraid of hard work. You could call us a pair of scrubbers, but then people get the wrong end of the stick. What we mean is we don't tickle at cleaning, we get to the bottom of it."

"Well, there's certainly going to be a challenge here on the Eastern Water contract, isn't there, Lou? I must admit I'm really excited about it. The cleaning has been totally mismanaged and I am itching to get my hands on it."

"Yes, Lou says you do your fair share of cleaning, along with the girls."

"I love to but it isn't always possible. We've now got several contracts in Ipswich and I have to move around looking after them all. But I like to start everything off so that I know what my ladies are up against. Cleaning gives me a real kick though – I think it's something about looking back when you've finished. Making a difference and really taking a pride in it!"

"Trouble is no one ever gives you credit. Waitressing is better; at least you get a tip if you do a good job."

"Rebecca, you've hit the nail on the head. That's why I am so passionate about cleaning. Our cleaning ladies need to know how important their job is. I'm determined to raise the status of the cleaner, to show that cleaning is a vital factor in any business. "

Lou was laughing… "Call her Becky, by the way! Rebecca sounds much too posh! You know, I have a feeling the bosses at Eastern Water are beginning to realise that you are the answer. There's so much bad feeling with the blue collar lads. Boy, do they need you, Mrs Chapman."

"I think they need us all! I have a feeling we are going to be the answer to their prayers." Christine was suddenly exhilarated.

"They don't know what's going to hit them!" - This from Lou. They chatted animatedly for another ten minutes before Christine looked at her watch. It was time to go. She wanted to be at the Eastern Water offices in plenty of time.

She only had a few moments to wait in reception before Mr Henson came down the spiral stairs to greet her. Oh bother, she had forgotten to wear trousers again! He smiled, "I'll lead the way!" Not that she would have cared this morning, and anyway she knew she'd got nice legs!

Mr Henson opened the door – another board room? Not on a par with Duyfken Line but a large table none the less. Mr Koronovski was sitting alongside with two other gentlemen. He smiled warmly at her, "Mrs Chapman, may I introduce Mr Accrington, our Managing Director and Mr Horsfield, Head of Finance."

Mr Henson pulled out a chair for her before joining the men on the other side of the table. Christine was still feeling pumped up and plunged straight in without waiting for an invitation to talk.

"Thank you, Mr Koronovski, for asking me here this morning. As you know, I've been giving your cleaning contract a great deal of thought since we last spoke and I think I have found the perfect person to head it up." She turned to Mr Accrington and smiled. "Am I running ahead of myself? It's just that it's so exciting to have a challenge like this. You really need someone to take the bull by the horns and we'd do that with the weekend clean. But then it's making sure standards don't drop again and that needs careful management. I feel a real culture change is needed – respect on both sides."

Mr Accrington was looking at her. "You're talking about the engineering block, I presume, Mrs Chapman."

"Yes, primarily, but the same principle applies across the board, Mr Accrington. For cleaning to work well, it has to be integrated throughout. My cleaners have to feel part of your organisation, they have to know that what they do matters so that they take an interest in providing the service you need."

Mr Accrington nodded, "I'm very interested in your approach. With Mr Henson retiring we aren't going to have anyone in house to manage the cleaners. I gather you want to take our cleaners on?"

Christine nodded, "Most of them. As I have mentioned, I would insist though on appointing my own supervisor. You've got to have a real leader. That's our forte, training and building the team." She was brimming with confidence - she knew she had won them over.

Mr Horsfield frowned, "I take it you have incorporated their same terms and conditions. I notice that some of the other companies quoting have opted to change staff completely, presumably to cut costs by paying them less."

Christine nodded. "That would be such a shame for the ladies who have worked here for a long time and want to stay."

Mr Koronovski looked at his colleagues. "Gentlemen, I think we are agreed. Mrs Chapman, we'd like you to start as soon as possible. I've got the contract here. It's for the usual trial period but I don't think we're going to have a problem. We can always tweak it later. Mr Henson will sort out the details with you. Thank you again for coming in at such short notice."

They all stood to shake her hand.

She spent another half an hour with Mr Henson, finalising the weekend clean, hours etc. She could hardly contain her excitement and when she finally got away, she drove immediately to Lou's house. Becky was still there playing on the floor with Willie but she leaped up as Lou opened the door and Christine mouthed, "We've got it!"

The sisters hugged each other and bounced up and down like school girls, Willie sandwiched between them, before Christine managed to instil a modicum of calm and asked if they could put their heads together and draw up plans. Within minutes, Lou had cleared the table, sorted her son out with Lego and was telling Christine about the intimate details of her fellow cleaners. Not rude things, you understand, just about their reliability, their punctuality, their cleaning strengths, and who gets on with whom. All the things you need to bear in mind if you are going to organise a happy cleaning team. She and her sister were in their element.

Christine proudly sang the praises of her key staff, Mandy and Will, and Francesco and Maria and explained how they worked the deep cleans. Lou and Becky were keen to work with them but they all agreed it might be better to bring in the Eastern Water cleaners on Monday, once the engineers' block had been transformed.

Lou worried that their reaction to "crew cleaning" could be interesting but hopefully, if the engineers played ball, they could start with a clear playing field.

They planned that Christine would come in, with Becky, to meet everyone on Wednesday evening. Lou meantime would play "stumm". Christine would clear it with Mr Henson and Becky would be introduced as their new working supervisor, with the emphasis on "working".

Christine was pleased that all the existing cleaners came in ten minutes early to meet her and that the over-riding atmosphere was one of expectation. Some of the ladies were a little wary of Christine's exuberance but the majority clearly welcomed the changes.

Florence, a rather prim lady in her sixties who had been cleaning the general office for over ten years, said as long as their wages didn't go down and they got holiday pay, she'd give it a go, adding with a smile it was nice that at last they'd got someone to fight their corner. In the end, three of them, as well as Lou, were insistent that they wanted to be part of the weekend deep clean. Christine was delighted, although she wasn't sure if this was because of the money or purely out of curiosity. No matter, they were keen, keen enough.

As promised, Mr Koronovski's painters did their bit and by the time Christine's whizz team arrived on Saturday morning, the smell of paint had effectively obscured the stale smell of sweaty male bodies and boots. The old sofa was nowhere to be seen. Christine was thrilled. She ticked people off her register as they arrived and competently issued instructions as to who was doing what. She introduced Becky to Mandy – she wanted Becky to learn their routines and techniques. Lou and her fellow evening cleaners, Connie, Pru and Sal, joined them. Maria and Teresa were already sorting out the buckets. "Coffee break at 11.00. Do you think we can break the back of the toilets by then?"

Will was unloading the equipment he'd brought from Stour house. Francesco went over to help. Bending down, he promptly threw his arms around Will and kissed him smartly on both cheeks. Will's face was a picture but he recovered quickly - "Hey, mate, how are you doing?" These two were by now great pals, but arch rivals on their floor machines.

Christine called them over. "Right guys as it's a nice day, I want all the tables and chairs outside so we can get a clear run at the floor." Francesco put two fingers in his mouth and whistled. Alberto and Julio grinned and ambled over. A few staccato instructions in Italian later, and impressive stacks of chairs began to grow.

Four EWA linesmen in their navy blue overalls were slouching over one of the last tables, marooned amid the furniture moving activity, and eyeing procedures a little nervously. Sensing trouble, Christine went over to them smiling cheerfully, "Sorry guys, but we're here to clean you up! How about having a seat in the sunshine? It's lovely out there and I could always bring you a coffee outside. Can we move these chairs?" Their attitude changed immediately and they grinned at her, "That's OK, we're waiting for some cable but we'll be off in a minute. We'll shift our chairs. Are you the woman they're bringing in from Colchester to sort out the cleaning? "

Christine smiled, "You could say that. I'm determined to make this place a pleasanter place for you guys to sit and have your breaks. I'm going to need all the help I can get from your side to keep it nice but I think you'll notice a difference. Who's the best person for me to talk to?"

"I guess, Mick's probably the best one – he's the official shop steward - that's his wife over there. This is long overdue, so good luck, but it won't be easy," said the older, grey haired guy with the moustache.

Christine had collected the overflowing ashtrays from the tables and put them to soak. Realising she needed to sort out the fridge and the sink before her men polished the floors, she went to find Lou.

Working together, they emptied the offending fridge and the cupboards under the sink of absolutely everything. There were three milk bottles, all of which had gone off. One was so solid that they couldn't pour the milk away. They took out the glass shelves and the smaller door trays. Lou unearthed some decent glass ashtrays in one of the cupboards and they agreed to dispose of the sad tin ones. The two sinks were now full of hot water with shelves and plastic trays soaking. Lou in the meantime was working on the cupboards, draining board and taps. Christine was on her knees vigorously scouring every nook and cranny of the fridge, aware that many eyes were upon her and that her face was getting redder and redder. Gosh, it was hot.

"Eh, Mrs C, you're making a hell of a mess of that floor." Will was standing there with his mop. "Well, Will, I'm counting on you to clear up after me!" Christine stood up. His face was redder than hers and his bald pate was gleaming.

"You need to give these lads a job. All the furniture is out."

"Right, the chairs all need spraying with de-greaser and then scrubbing off with hot water. Normally, we'd leave them over night but in this sunshine, I think we've got to work on them individually and fast, using buckets of water."

"Alberto and Julio will love it out here topping up their tans!" Will laughed. "I'll get them organised. What do you reckon'll be best, scourers or scrubbing brushes? "

"It'll be trial and error. Give them both, Will, and keep an eye on them, would you?"

Christine went to see how the ladies were doing in the gents. There was a lovely buzz of chatter and the occasional giggle. Mandy looked up from a toilet pedestal, "They are really bad, Mrs Chapman, especially the urinals. I don't think we'll be done by coffee time." "Don't worry, Mandy. We'll take a break and then we'll have a swap around. I don't want anyone doing loos for too long. Could you and Becky organise the coffee, please."

As they sat drinking coffee in the sunshine, Maria handed round slices of her panettone and company chocolate biscuits. Alberto and Julio, stripped to the waist with bare chests gleaming, came in for a lot of stick about sunbathing on the chairs instead of scrubbing them. Only about ten plastic chairs were now a bright orange – the rest were still in need of attention. Maria decided that the boys needed supervision and opted to join them. She would crack the whip. Christine made it clear that once Will and Francesco had finished the floor, the tables and chairs had to be put back, CLEAN.

Christine got a chance to chat to Becky. She was quite different from Lou. In fact you'd never take them for sisters. When Christine asked her about the existing cleaners they would inherit, she was thoughtful in her assessment. "Sal and Connie are fine but I'm not sure Pru'd be happy working over in this block, even in a team, but it's a bit soon to judge."

Yes, Becky would be fine as supervisor. She had a no-nonsense air about her and was plainly not afraid of hard work. Christine had seen her tackling the urinals and she had a nice, friendly manner with people. "One thing, Becky, please wear rubber gloves." She pulled a face but Christine countered firmly, "You have to lead by example, Becky. Cleaning chemicals are harsh and can cause all sorts of skin allergies. I'm looking at your hands!" Becky looked down at her large, capable hands and turned them over. They were red and badly chapped.

"Oh, they're always like that," she shrugged.

"Rubber gloves and plenty of hand cream!" said Christine firmly.

They worked on until 2.00 p.m. Christine was reasonably relaxed. The lockers still had to be done and the toilet floors but she could reduce the team radically for Sunday. Francesco and Maria were a must and first in line to volunteer. Christine was thrilled when both Lou and Becky asked to come in too. Connie and Sal also put their hands up. That would be great, but they could do with another man. Yes, she really needed two floor machine operators. "Guys," she called out, "I could do with another man?" Alberto and Julio shook their heads – they were off to London.

253

Becky came over to her and said quietly, "Couldn't Francesco teach me how to use the machine? We're going to need someone here who can use a floor machine, aren't we?" Christine looked at her. "Well, yes, Rebecca. You are quite right. The only thing is, they are jolly heavy." Becky made a face as if to say, "So …!" "Well, try by all means!" Christine was not going to stand in her way,

Christine had learnt her lesson from Duyfken Line when she hadn't checked that everything was left in perfect order so she too was coming over, leaving nothing to chance. As it happened, Sunday worked extremely well. Francesco took great delight teaching Becky, who picked up how to use a floor machine with ease. Once she had learnt how to control it, she matched him, moving the polisher smoothly from side to side. She even joined him singing, "When the Saints go marching in," as they moved in unison across the locker room floor, their machines neck and neck.

"Come on Lou," Becky called out, "You come have a go – it's not difficult and Frankie's a great teacher."

Lou was not as self-assured as her sister but she too was game to have a go. Francesco demonstrated the on/off button and the levers for left and right and how to move the handle up and down to increase and decrease speed.

"Now, Lou, you do eet." He stepped aside. Lou grasped the machine and squeezed the levers as she has seen Francesco do. It careered off at an angle across the floor with Lou attached, legs flying. She screamed and let go. The machine immediately died. Francesco laughing, ran to her and put his arm around her shoulders. "Come 'ere. I show you better." He stood behind her, his body close to hers, explaining in his broken English, "Eez lika lady. Slowly …" Lou's face was a picture, as she felt Francesco's muscly body move against her, but after a few minutes she began to relax and then to smile. They were moving like partners in a slow waltz, the machine in front of them gracefully gliding across the floor. Everyone cheered and started clapping as Francesco gradually backed away and Sandy continued to move the machine smoothly from side to side. When she stopped, both Becky and Frankie ran over to her and they had a mini group hug.

"eez good. I like learn ladies." Francesco was beaming. "I learn all ze ladies, eh Maria?" Maria wagged her finger but smiled happily. Christine was impressed. This could be the answer to her prayers.

As they cleared up, she, Becky and Lou walked round carefully checking everything. What a transformation! They surveyed the scene with pride. Lou said, "You know, Mrs Chapman, I'd give my front teeth to be with Mick when them engineers come in tomorrow morning. Wait till I tell him! It looks better than a McDonald's restaurant! " Praise indeed.

Christine knew the weekend clean had been an enormous success and achieved every bit of the result she wanted. Now she had to make sure they built on this. She was fully aware though that they hadn't begun to tackle the offices yet but the key out here was to get the engineers on their side. They could undo all the good work, in a very short time, if they didn't respond. Mind you, she had a good feeling Mick and Lou were going to play a key role here.

The next few weeks were going to be crucial and she knew she would have to spend every evening "ra ra-ing" the team, but this was going to work, and to be fun. Becky was the perfect person to run it!

Mr Henson telephoned shortly after nine a.m. He had been down to see for himself and had found a group of the engineers standing in the doorway "gobsmacked". Some of them had actually taken their dirty boots off before walking across the shiny blue floor. "Gawd, I didn't know it were blue. It always looked dirt coloured before and look at them chairs. Are they the old ones, or have they bought completely new chairs?"

"Hey, have you seen the toilets – come and look at this! They smell like a bleedin' hotel!" A line of engineers were standing in front of the urinals grinning. "Hey! Watch what you're doing, mate. You'll be in the dog house if you miss and pee on the floor."

The guys were genuinely delighted. "They must have worked bloody hard." The older chap with the moustache, the one Christine had asked to move, nodded, "They did that. They're a nice bunch and really want to improve things." He looked at Mr Henson and indicated his approval.

Mr Henson had called a meeting of the linesmen and their managers and explained that they had brought in a new cleaning company. "Their ladies are going to be cleaning in here every evening from 6.00 p.m. They are not paid to tidy up after you guys. If you want it to stay looking nice, you've got to do your bit and I'm going to police that. They are a good bunch and I don't want you upsetting them. So give them a fair chance."

Christine had arranged that all the cleaners checked in that evening at the Gatehouse and then went straight through to the engineers block. Here she and Becky signed them in. She explained that everyone was going to be part of crew cleaning this area. That way, they would take no more than half an hour before most people would be able move on the office areas. She introduced herself, and then Becky as the new working supervisor.

In effect, it took them less than twenty minutes to clean the whole complex, leaving it pristine. The few engineers who were there, had greeted them cheerfully, a couple even thanked them, and then they disappeared leaving the coast clear for the girls.

Over in the offices, Lou was a great help. She knew the areas, she knew who worked where. They let the existing cleaners keep the status quo for the time being but with three new ladies on the team, Becky, Lou and Christine, were able to do some training as well as spend extra time in the toilets – always the first place to hit!

Mick was playing his part too. Naturally, the cleaning was the hot topic of conversation throughout Eastern Water and Mr Henson underlined the need to keep the place tidy and generally treat it with respect, as they would their own homes. Once he had gone, the conversation came round to the cleaners themselves.

Mick, as Lou's husband, was immediately quizzed. They wanted to know everything. The boss, was she married? What was she doing on her hands and knees cleaning out the fridge? You wouldn't get Eastern Water bosses doing that!

"And what about that Becky? She's the supervisor, ain't she?"

"Yeah, a tasty bit of all right, that one. Cor, legs up to her armpits."

"I bet she looks good in her undies." "

Yeah, I wouldn't mind an hour in bed with her."

"You wouldn't last an hour."

"I wouldn't mind trying though."

The banter continued in much the same vein until Mick chipped in, "I'd be a bit careful there, Bill. She's kick boxing champion of Canada."

"Cor, you're kidding now." Bill looked awestruck.

"No, I bloody ain't." countered Mick.

"Wow. How about that? Fancy us having the kick boxing champion of Canada cleaning the toilets! "

The guys were all roaring with laughter. "Back off, Bill. She'd lay you flat - on your back in no time." But Bill was still fantasizing … "That would be fine by me, the position don't matter. Kick boxing though! Well, I never."

Mick, of course, relayed this back to his wife and sister-in-law who gleefully discussed how they could exploit this in the future.

CHAPTER 27 - 0H WHAT A BUILDING

BComm had asked them to take on another smaller contract. Will was thrilled because he was appointed "Manager" of their newly refurbished building in Princes Street. Each night he dropped Mandy off at Stour House and then became Boss in his own right. Christine, felt they owed him this, despite his being a man - a male supervisor was contrary to her philosophy, but if it kept Will out of Mandy's hair and achieved marital harmony in the Edgecombe household then that was a bonus and good man management.

Twice a week Christine and Ros would set about ringing prospective new clients. Peter provided the companies and the details – part of his insatiable drive for new business.

Their cold selling approach was quite different. Christine needed quiet so she shut herself in the bedroom. She had to stand up and would only ring round first thing in the morning when she felt at her freshest.

Peter was adamant you should have warmth in your voice when cold calling. "How do you make your voice warm?" Christine asked Ros, tongue in cheek. "Personally I only make calls when the sun is shining."

"A cup of coffee and a good laugh helps me" said Ros.

Clearly Ros' method worked, because she came jubilantly off the phone one morning with.. "Guess what. I have got us an appointment at Willis Faber & Dumas."

"No… never! Gee whiz. Ros. Not the big black glass building!"

The Willis Faber building was an architectural masterpiece, a modern phenomenum, in the very centre of Ipswich. It was architect, Norman Foster's, triumph. Opening in 1975, it went on to win every award a building could win. It was revolutionary – "a pioneering example of energy-conscious design", heated by natural gas and insulated by the thick layer of turf on the roof.

Shaped like a grand piano, it had been designed to fit an area which had once housed a Franciscan friary. The proud old church which still stood adjacent was reflected in the glass in the sunshine and at night the whole building glowed a wonderful green colour through the black glass.

It had been designed specifically to entice high-powered insurance staff away from the City of London to Suffolk. No expense had been spared - there was a 25m swimming pool on the ground floor and a turfed roof garden where the staff could have coffee or even lunch and even sunbathe in the summer. The views over Ipswich were spectacular.

It was featured on a first class stamp and was the background introduction to the BBC 6 o'clock news. This was the country's first Grade 1 listed building under 30 years old and every square inch had to be cleaned.

Christine and Ros dressed carefully, Christine in her beautifully cut Chanel suit and Ros in her neat black skirt, white shirt and green jacket. They had parked close to the building on a single yellow line. 30 minutes waiting.

"Should be ample time," said Ros. "This is just a preliminary meeting."

They pushed the revolving doors and entered. The brilliant green floor mesmerized them. Their eyes were drawn to the silver escalators leading their gaze up and up past the potted palms to the restaurant floor.

They stood gazing in awe.

"Oh Ros."

"Oh Chris! What have I done?"

They walked across the green rubber studded floor in the foyer. It was like walking on air. The reception desk stretched away in an extended arc. Behind it sat a battalion of uniformed security men, monitoring cameras.

As they approached, one of the men looked up and smiled. "You would be Mrs Chapman and Mrs Barnum?"

"Yes," they answered in unison.

"Mr Trenchard is expecting you. Please take a seat. He will be with you shortly."

"Shall we make a run for it now," murmured Ros. "I had no idea."

"No way," replied Christine, her eyes doing a full circuit. "What a place. Even if we never come back, I will remember this building forever. Ros, it's phenomenal."

Mr Trenchard came down to collect them himself. He was a tall, thin, grey-haired, gentleman with a quiet air of authority.

He smiled and shook their hands. "Follow me. Have you ever been in the building before? No, I thought not. I was watching you as I came down the escalators. We'll go to a conference room on the 2nd floor so that you can experience the building."

Christine's excitement was mounting. "Thank you," she breathed. "It's beautiful, quite beautiful. I've read so much about it, but it's breathtaking. You must love it."

The colours were extraordinary – brilliant yellow walls, green carpet so thick it absorbed every noise and a stainless steel ceiling which reflected brilliant light.

"Well you either love it or hate it. The cleaning contract is very complex!"

He opened the door to the conference room. Coffee was laid out on the table and two other people were seated at the table.

Mr Trenchard introduced them: "Robert Black who is Maintenance Manager and Annabel Prior who is in charge of personnel."

Christine couldn't contain herself. "This is the most beautiful building I have ever seen. I can't believe it. I am so excited. I can't wait to hear about the cleaning requirements." Everyone smiled.

Jeffrey Trenchard turned to her.

"Firstly, tell us something about your company. I gather you have been in operation for only 4 years."

"Yes, we started up when this building opened. I set up my business out of necessity. My husband had to give up work because he was diagnosed with cancer and I decided to go cleaning. I found I loved it. It is so satisfying to leave an office gleaming. I also discovered that there are a lot of things wrong with our industry."

Christine was in full-flow, the usual spiel: Her aim was to bring a pride and professionalism to the industry. Monthind was different. We work with our customers. We mould our service to fit yours. Even our company colours match perfectly – green and silver. Our staff uniform would be perfect.

She talked about how they had started with just one tiny contract and two wonderful Italian cleaners. How BComm had gradually asked them to take over all their other buildings in Ipswich. How they had never lost a contract and were slowly building a sound reputation.

"Why do you think this is?" asked Mr Trenchard.

"It is because of our ladies. We give our cleaning staff a respectable job, a career to be proud of. It's not just a two hour stint they do in the evenings to earn a bit on the side. They make a serious contribution, often a vital contribution to the family income, but also a vital contribution to the client and we make sure they understand that. They come because they are proud of their work and because they want to.

Cleaning can be tremendously satisfying, you know, if the people you work for take an interest and give you an occasional pat on the back. We have Well Done You notes for staff and a bonus scheme. All sorts of little touches which make our ladies feel valued, birthday cards and cakes, flowers when they are poorly.

Absenteeism is a huge problem in the cleaning industry. Some companies have an absence rate of 200% - two hundred per cent - can you believe that? It reflects the massive turnover of staff. I would be asking some serious questions if we were to go anywhere near 20% absenteeism.

You have to give proper holidays. You must treasure your staff and treat them well - after all we are only as good as each and every one of them.

We view the company like a giant jigsaw. There's the right slot for every piece, for every person."

Annabel Prior was writing furiously in her notepad and Mr Black lolled back in his chair with a faintly amused expression on his face.

Realising she was talking passionately, with no reference to her notes. She stopped abruptly and apologised. "Sorry. It's just that I know we've got it right!" She laughed, "Sorry. I am convinced we are what the cleaning industry needs and I am passionate about this."

Mr Trenchard held up his hand, smiling. "I can tell that. You know, you are a breath of fresh air in the industry. We have seen endless guys in shiny suits looking like vacuum cleaner salesmen, all telling us they will deliver a perfect service. You are very different and you certainly don't look like a vacuum cleaner salesman – or woman!"

Christine laughed, "This is my office attire! In the evenings I usually look like a cleaner. I work alongside my staff in my green tabard."

Reaction from Mr Black, "You don't mean you actually clean?"

"We all do," piped in Ros. "That way we get to know the contract inside out. It's so important, not just for the cleaners, but also when you want to make suggestions to the client. The cleaners love it when Mrs Chapman cleans with them. You should see her tackling the gents' urinals."

"Thank you, Ros – that's not something I usually share with potential clients," Christine pulled a face.

"Nonetheless, it means you know what is going on." Mr Trenchard nodded.

She ploughed on, "Working with staff is the best way to train them. You can't give them a manual to study – they would never read it. Half of our cleaners are probably semi-literate. You have to show them what to do, make it routine, and make it fun."

Mr Trenchard was twinkling: "You really are coming at things from a completely different angle." He glanced at his watch. "My goodness, we have run dramatically over time. You realise that this is the preliminary selection process. Those who are successful will be invited back for a tour of the building. They will then be given a full manual on the contract including plans and a specification.

It is quite a long process because the contract is very complex.

Thank you so much for coming, ladies. I look forward to seeing you again."

Annabel Prior took them down to reception chatting to them about the building. She stood in front of them as they descended the escalator. "There are a couple of cleaners arriving now. They do the lunch time shift."

Ros looked back at Christine. "Lunch time too!"

They handed over their visitors passes and thanked Mrs Prior for the coffee and for their initial meeting. Christine still bubbling told her how much they hoped they would be called back.

Outside the building they raced to the car, conscious they had grossly exceeded the half an hour waiting time in Elm Street. Sure enough a huge pink parking ticket in a plastic bag was stuck under the windscreen wiper.

"Blast" said Christine.

"It could have been worse", said Ros – "you could have had six tickets. Do you realise we've been there for nearly three hours?" How green, how utterly naïve were they?

Half way down the A12, Christine came down from Cloud Nine. "Do you think we could do it, Ros? I am suddenly having serious doubts."

Things were going well at home. Peter was doing a little consultancy work for VE and had even started having piano lessons. He was spending a lot of time with the children, which was a great help, especially during the school holidays.

They now had six contracts and over sixty staff. Mr Oliver and Mr Barton were effusive in their references and Maria continued to bake cakes. Christine felt the company should give her a cooking allowance. Instead Maria topped the list of bonuses – Well Done You notes were lost on the Italians. They revelled in extra work, especially weekend initial cleans and Francesco boasted "zat 'ee knew every contract".

Christine and Ros tossed their thoughts about the preliminary Willis meeting backwards and forwards between them.

"I know they liked us," breathed Ros.

"But I think they saw us more as a comedy act. Mr Black was amused but also obviously highly sceptical."

"They are probably thinking, the theory sounds fine but can they deliver."

"Can we? I have my doubts, Ros. How on earth would we clean the escalators, that computer room? – No liquid allowed. We know nothing about cleaning swimming pools either."

"Even the basic floor. All that green rubber flooring – I bet that's tricky."

They decided to put it behind them and concentrate on BComm. They were now very comfortable with those contracts and confident that Mr Canning and his fellow managers would give Monthind an excellent reference whatever they did. The Vic the Prick episode had certainly worked in their favour.

Life returned to relative normality with Christine driving to Ipswich each evening to clean and to visit her troops. Ros was busy improving the administration. Even Peter was researching chemicals and sourcing cleaning equipment companies.

Imagine the reaction when a month later they received a huge package from Willis Faber & Dumas by special delivery. The next stage in the selection process, the tender, had arrived, weighing 3lbs 4ozs. That might make it sound like a premature baby, but it was weighty in the extreme compared to anything else they had ever received for their other contracts.

"Just reading it will take a week," muttered Christine. Ros too had serious misgivings. Peter was excited and kept saying "This is the sort of challenge I love." He was in his element, methodically researching exactly what they needed for what.

They had two weeks to study the papers and prepare before the official viewing of the building.

They worked on formulae. They calculated how many square metres a cleaner cleaned in an hour. For Ros and Christine metres meant double brain power - they could only see things in feet. For Peter it was natural. He had been working in metric for years – all those quotations for ventilating the underground Metros of Europe.

How long it took to scrub and dry a floor. How long it took to clean a washbasin, a toilet pan, a urinal.

Mandy and Will, Francesco and Maria were all involved, each trying to outdo the other. Maria could do a complete set of four toilets in 15 minutes but Mandy took 20. Will won the floor polishing hands down but Francesco was a wizard with stairs.

Christine was in despair – that wasn't the idea. They needed to get an average cleaning time, allowing time to organise equipment and materials and to get to the area. So she timed herself. Hmmph! She needed to get fit.

In the end they added 10% to the best times to allow for less capable cleaners plus a further 10% in case there was a dirty patch and to allow the cleaner to blow her nose or ease her aching back.

Christine looked at the list of timings which was supposed to help them work out the hours they needed, a sort of fool-proof formula, and snorted. "We've never done this before – I've always just walked the area and gauged by eye how long it would take me to clean it."

But this was different, oh so different. Perhaps viewing the building would make things easier.

The day of viewing arrived. This time they parked the car in the NCP car park, carefully taking the ticket with them.

They arrived punctually and were horrified to find the reception area full of men, every one in a shiny suit. They all had clipboards. Five other companies were represented - Initial, POCS, TICS and Excel Clean.

Many of the reps obviously knew each other and several cast quizzical glances in their direction. One man came over and introduced himself, "Sidney Ronson from TICS. Where are you from?"

"Colchester", replied Christine with a smile.

"No, no," he tutted, "I meant which contractor."

"Oh, Monthind Limited."

"Sorry, what did you say?"

Christine repeated "Monthind Limited."

"Oh… Colchester based, did you say?"

He sauntered back to his colleagues, said something and they all sniggered.

Christine had never come face to face with the competition before – how right Mr Trenchard was. Vacuum cleaner salesmen, of the door to door kind – they all had that look about them. Essex man personified, one even had white socks and his hair slicked back; another, fat and greasy in a large all-enveloping, yes, shiny… suit. The odd tattoo was visible and a couple had shaved heads and gold medallions. She shuddered. Yes, without a doubt she was different and she was being snobby. Looking hard, she wondered unkindly if any of them ever did any cleaning.

Mr Trenchard welcomed everyone and thanked them for coming. Was Christine imagining it or had he put a special emphasis on "Ladies" – he certainly included them as he addressed the group, "and gentlemen. We are aware this is a unique building. You will need to assess the requirements carefully. We are here to help and answer questions as you tour the building and indeed later when we give you coffee there will be an open opportunity to discuss any aspects which need clarification."

He introduced Mr Black and his colleague Ted Ryan who would show them round. Visitors' passes were presented to everyone and they were divided into two groups for their guided tour.

Christine and Ros trailed at the back of their group listening to the questions and eavesdropping on conversations wherever they could. In no time they were completely disorientated. Ground floor, loading bay, swimming pool with its changing rooms, showers. Conference rooms, computer centre, boiler room, the chiller plant room, which looked like a surreal modern art exhibit with huge black pipes, wheels, dials, all throbbing and glistening, then gas rooms, electric rooms and more plant rooms.

Then the first floor, endless green carpet – totally open plan. Hundreds –no actually thousands of desks and tables (over two thousand to be precise, they discovered), and every one identical. Mr Black, their guide, pointed out the meeting rooms and the four cores, each containing a stair case. They then moved to the second floor, an exact replica of the first.

They were shown lifts, the toilets in cores 1 and 4 and spacious stair wells, all covered in the bright green rubber flooring.

Finally the restaurant floor, which although smaller, retained the same extraordinary curved-shape, the same bright green carpet and looked onto the green grass roof garden, with the kitchen on the cold, north side.

Raised flooring – sub floor cleaning?

How many acres of green carpet were there? Carpet cleaning - what was the best method? Steam or dry foam?

How many square feet, oops, square metres of Freudenberg rubber stud flooring? - Yes, it is German and top quality.

Questions were being fired fast and furiously. To most of them Mr Black, scornfully replied – "It's in the specification."

Over three thousand staff worked for the company.

Christine and Ros concentrated on writing anything and everything down.

They said not a word.

Others in the group were relaxed. There was the occasional burst of laughter at some male joke - one man in particular constantly grinning and addressing Mr Black in a loud familiar voice. Ros and Christine caught snippets and the odd exchange, "Yeah, Rob, Ipswich Town… home match against the Canaries on Saturday. Local Derby. Never miss a home game. Blues victory? 3-1, I reckon. Should be a good match. Need a ticket? Perhaps we could meet up for a jar?"

They also heard snippets about other contracts "You quoting for ICI? Tenders due in end of the month." "Feminine hygiene – sub contracting, are you?" "When's the hospital contract up?"

The tour of the building took three hours. Christine and Ros were exhausted. Christine had to concede that men did have the advantage of flat shoes. She and Ros were both wearing comfortable court shoes but they had walked miles and Ros was limping. Everyone was shepherded into a large meeting room with coffee provided on a side table.

Questions were invited. Peter had listed 22. Christine and Ros sat silently listening, and ticked them off as the answers became evident. Several questions asked were helpful but the majority were answered with a quick referral to the tender document and a look of impatience from Mr Trenchard.

"It's listed on page 63, Item IV (a)"

Eventually Christine plucked up courage – Peter had been thorough. Christine's first question was: "The high level work, the specification states Willis Faber will provide the scaffolding. Does this mean erected?"

A few sniggers.

"Good question," this surprisingly from Mr Black. "Yes, our maintenance men always erect scaffolding and provide high level ladders. Safety of your staff and ours is of paramount importance."

Feeling braver she ventured, "The lunchtime toilet servicing – does this require two cleaners, a male and a female?"

This again provoked a mild titter.

"Currently it is being done by two ladies, but it might be welcomed by all concerned if we had a man and a woman. I can see that being beneficial."

She ploughed on, until Mr Black said, "Mrs Chapman if you would like to submit your questions in writing, I will be happy to get back to you."

One of the shiny suit brigade piped up with a snarl, "I take it you will do that for all of us not just for … her?"

"Of course," said Mr Trenchard, "As long as you don't waste our time asking something already in the specification."

Eventually the session closed. Christine and Ros made a point of hanging back to quietly thank each of the Willis Faber team for the tour, the opportunity to ask questions and the coffee.

They caught the others up at the escalators – the conversation wafted up to them. "Out of their depth…. That one in green, what a snob she is! Hoity toity. Bet she spends most of her time on a bleedin' horse. Lady muck." "Yeah, imagine her ridin' a scrubber dryer." Another snigger.

Christine and Ros reached the car. Christine was seething. Ros, fully prepared on this trip, handed Chris a sandwich. She bit into it hard.

"I'm so angry. I desperately want to prove them all wrong but I think they may have a point. We don't stand a hope in hell of getting it. I just don't know where to start."

They drove home both deep in thought. "Let's talk in the morning, Chris. Things are always better in the morning." Ros was equally worried and equally exhausted.

CHAPTER 28 – WILL WILL BE WILL

Weeks of calculation and planning followed. Each week they revised their figures. Christine flatly refused to count cleaners but she did make a point of delivering a list of questions for Mr Trenchard at the end of the evening cleaning shift. She stopped in the foyer, standing to one side to let them pass. The language, regularly punctuated by an f... word, the general down-trodden demeanour and the slovenly appearance hit her. Without lifting your eyes from the floor, the feet told a story - dirty trainers, white stilettos, down at heel cracked plastic boots, even a pair of brown slippers complete with bobble on the front. And if you looked up – horror of horrors, one woman even had rollers in her hair, admittedly semi-hidden under a pink chiffon scarf.

Christine sighed. That awful image. Yes, they mirrored exactly the cartoon image of a cleaner – curlers, headscarf, and slippers. She had to invite Mr Trenchard to come along to Stour House and see her ladies at work. Professional, wearing neat new uniforms and name badges, they were well-trained and obviously motivated - they were a very different team to this bunch.

Ros advertised for staff. Now they could do so legitimately. They had a constant flow of new staff coming in for training and Mandy was loving it.

Christine had been really touched. She had been asked to Josie's wedding– just the evening function, mind you. She had explained to Mandy that it was difficult. It was the only time she had to be with the family and she would feel mean leaving Peter to babysit at the weekend, as well as every evening.

Mandy was working her socks off. When Christine tentatively asked her whether she would be giving up work after the wedding, Mandy had emphatically shaken her head, "Oh no, I couldn't leave my girls and I've got used to the money. I don't know about Will, though. Don't think he is too happy."

Rumour had it that Will had been getting up to his old tricks on his milk round. Nothing had been proved, or at least Will hadn't been caught red handed yet, but if the cleaners' grapevine was to be believed, there was one Marlene, "you know, her on Whitehouse with the big tits and red hair" who was mouthing off about her milkman "being a bloody good shag". Several of Monthind's cleaners hailed from the Whitehouse estate, built in the fifties, a huge London overspill development on the outskirts of town, where tongues were wont to wag.

Mandy's ladies were very protective, shielding her from gossip, and more and more often they organised a girly night out on a Saturday, ensuring she was included. Josie went too – the wedding the constant topic of conversation. They even held an Ann Summers party, generously showering Josie with sexy underwear and other unmentionables. Christine felt this bonding was good for the contract but did wonder about Ann Summers. Maybe it was the girls' answer to the male obsession with Ipswich Town and football.

Was the problem that Will was jealous? He would bowl into Stour House to pick Mandy up – she was always last to leave and happy if he was a little late.

Something was not right and one evening there had been a minor domestic. Arriving just after 8.00 p.m., Will, in a foul mood, had started to shout at Mandy "to get a fuckin' move on." He wanted his supper, had had a long day and had to be up at 3.30 to be at the milk depot at 4.0 a.m.

Mandy was trying to work out the hours for the payroll which she had to telephone in to Mrs Barnum. It was complicated this week because they had quite a few extra staff in for training. Will was shifting from one bandy leg to the other, his face getting redder by the second.

"Are you coming or are you going to be here all bleedin' night?"

Terry, on Security, got to his feet. "Will, can't you control your language. Mandy's just sorting the wages."

"Well, I'm not bleedin' waiting. And you keep out of this."

Mandy looked up. "Will, come on. What's upset you now? I won't be a tick but if you shout at me it'll take me longer."

"Christ. Trouble with you is that you don't give a shit about me – if it's not the bloody wedding, it's bloody work."

Terry stepped in, "Will, I think you'd better wait outside."

"Stuff you. I'm off. She can get the bloody bus home."

Mandy burst into tears. "It's the strain of the wedding, you know, that's all. He's not normally like this." She sniffed hard. "It's no problem. There's a bus in ten minutes."

She didn't get the bus home. With Terry's comforting arm around her shoulders, she completed the wages, phoned them in to Mrs Barnum and then took up his offer of a lift home, after he had locked up mind. Instead of going home, they drove to Josie's.

It wasn't only his family who were unhappy with Will – so were his cleaners. Several of them who had worked with Mandy at Stour House moved to Princes Street with Will because their bus dropped them right outside the door. Princes Street was on the main bus route from the town centre to the station and to Chantry. Ladies generally loved his jokey manner and he was renowned for blatantly chatting them up. Virtually all of them fell for his line "Come on me luverrly get those boobs bustling …. Cor that's my gal. You ain't half a tasty bit." But just lately he had become tetchy, shouting for no reason.

He had ruffled the feathers of Janet, his self-appointed second-in-command on the contract. Janet was not known for her retiring nature and when she was roused the colour flooded up her neck leaving her face red and blotchy.

She was a big girl and rumour had it, butch to boot.

When Christine delivered the wages one Thursday evening, Janet collared her and let rip, her face going from pink to red to beetroot, "Mrs Chapman, you've got to sort him out. He's really getting up my nose – he's a real NCP, MTP, whatever… You know, a real male pig. Swanning round reception with the floor machine hanging off his little finger. Thinks himself God's gift. An' him supervisor, Supervisor my arse. Even when we have an office move he never gives a hand. Just a bloody stud – that's all he's good at, if you ask me."

"Janet, steady. That's quite an accusation. I think he's under a lot of stress. His daughter's wedding's coming up. I'm sure things will be better after that. But you're right; I need to look into this because it won't do to have this undercurrent."

"Too right, and it ain't going to be an undercurrent much longer. It's going to be a full scale punch up."

"Come on Janet, you're not proposing to physically sort him out are you?" Christine tried to lighten the situation, but Janet was not playing ball.

"If I don't, someone else will, you see. You don't know the half of it."

"Look, you'd better tell me. Come into a conference room where we can shut the door and talk quietly."

"You won't let on. You won't let on that I told you, will yeh?"

"Of course not… I give you my word."

"Well, Will's always been a bit of a lad with the ladies but this time, I reckon he's proper gone and done it"

"What do you mean?" Christine was praying he wasn't having an affair with one of her cleaners.

"There's this woman called Marlene who lives in the next road to my Mam. Will's always been pally with Marlene – no worry, she can look after herself.

The trouble is she reckons Will's been fooling around with her daughter, Sam, and got her pregnant. We've all been saying his dick was bound to get him into trouble, sooner rather than later."

Christine was horror-struck, "Is this true?"

"Who knows but there's no smoke without fire and Marlene's shouting off about it. Mind you, Sam's a bit of a slut so it could be half a dozen of one and six of the other. Still I wouldn't want to be in Will's shoes."

"Oh God, and the wedding coming up too. Does Mandy know?"

"If she don't, she's stupid. That's not the worst of it though. Sam's Dad, he don't live with Marlene mind, and her boyfriend, are going to sort it. So I reckon Mandy will know soon enough. Will could get beaten up pretty bad with them two and serve him bloody well right."

Phew eee! Christine needed time to register the full significance of this.

"Janet, thank you so much for talking to me. This could explain a few things. Now I want to ask you for your help. We have to handle things carefully; after all it could just be malicious gossip, and I don't want to make things worse for Mandy before the wedding."

She continued, "I hope it's just a rumour, but nonetheless, it is not good. Can I ask you to look after things here for a while? Just keep the lid on things, and try not to let Will get to you. I give you my word that I will take Will off this contract but give me a day or two.

The trouble is he may think he is God's gift to women but you have to admit, Janet, the marble floor here looks ace and that's thanks to Will. He IS a master with a floor polisher – anyone who can control it with his little finger has to be class!"

"Just wish he'd control his other bloody finger…," snorted Janet.

"Look, I'm going to tell him you will be looking after things with the girls to give him a break. We can review the situation after the wedding."

"OK, Mrs Chapman, but you watch him. He can smooth talk his way out of anything. Mind you I'd like to see him try and smarm his way round Marlene on this one."

By all accounts getting round Marlene, complete with big tits, would be tricky. Christine immediately went to find Will. It was never wise to hope problems would go away – better to confront them then and there.

Sure enough there he was with the machine gliding smoothly over the glistening floor. As Christine approached he switched it off and gave her a weary semi-smile.

"Will, I wonder if we could have a private chat?" The smile faded totally. Mrs Chapman's private conversations were becoming notorious.

They retired to one of the offices. She moved straight in,

"Will, you look all in. You know, I am really worried about the strain of Josie's wedding. Mandy doesn't want to take a break but I am looking at taking some of the load off you both. We've only got until the end of next month – just five weeks from now. I have asked Janet to look after things here and I'll do the same at Stour House. Anne will gladly help Mandy there. If you could keep the marble floor looking good as always, but take as much time off as you need, and look after Mandy."

To her relief Will nodded. "Yeah, it's getting to us. Josie's behaving like Bridezilla, the bride from Hell. Feel sorry for Jim. My daughter's had a character change. She's a psychopathic monster. Bloody good job when it's all over. "

Christine felt sorry for him.

"Will, that's oooh sooo normal. All brides-to-be are ghastly – it's the tension. She's not having a change of heart is she?"

"No but I wouldn't blame Jim if HE did!"

"How's Mandy coping? It must be hard enough for her, although a wedding is a woman's thing. But for YOU, you are working very long hours, too long. Try and have a break together after it's all over. I'm going to tell Janet to take over here – take some of the pressure off you. You have to be strong for your ladies, Will."

"Yeah, reckon it would be good to work back at Stour House with Mandy for a while. I could come over here a couple of nights a week, say Monday and Thursday just to keep that floor up to scratch. Trouble is we need the money."

Christine was puzzled. Will didn't seem like a guy in imminent danger of being beaten up for getting hot-headed Marlene's girl pregnant. But was he cheating on his wife? She shook her head, not wanting to believe it. She hoped that after the wedding things would be fine again.

Three days later, just when Christine hoped things in the Edgecombe household were a little less fraught, there was a major incident involving Will. Christine was alerted to this by a call from the office. Terry the Security guard at Stour House had been roused from his usual mid evening pose behind the reception desk where his attention flicked from his mini TV set to the even smaller CCTV screens which captured views of the car park, back entrances, the rubbish bins etc. Several of the cleaners were taking the black sacks out, chatting happily enough when suddenly one of them screamed. A big black figure emerged from behind the bins and put his hand out to Anne who was nearest him – "Where's that b … bloke? That Will? I want a word with him."

Poor Anne was nearly beside herself with fright. "Who are you? What do you want with Will?"

The man seemed to pull himself together. "It's alright. I won't hurt you I just want Will."

"I'll get Mandy – I don't think Will's here tonight. He got transferred to Princes Street to help out there."

"There's no need to tell Mandy – where did you say Will was? Princes Street – where in Princes Street."

"153 Princes Street – the other BComm contract. He's supervisor there."

"Thanks …" and with that the shadowy figure disappeared behind the bins, leaving Anne with hands on hips and several other cleaners crowding round her.

Terry who had picked this up on the CCTV screens and immediately clocked that there was an intruder on the premises, he burst out of the back door – "You alright Anne? Where's the guy gone? "

"I'm not sure." Before she could say any more the man in black had thrust her aside, pulled a helmet on his head and disappeared out of the gate. They heard a motorbike revving up. Anne shook herself. Terry looked at her again, "He weren't your old man, then?"

"No way, just someone looking for Will. He didn't look too …happy neither."

Terry shrugged. "Just as well Will isn't here anymore. I don't want any punch-ups on my contract. That guy just seems to attract trouble. Is all the rubbish out? I'll lock up out here.

We'd better tell Mandy someone was looking for her other half, I suppose."

It didn't occur to Terry that the shadow on the motorbike might be heading straight for 153 Princes Street and that he should perhaps telephone his counterpart on that contract.

Will had settled in at the smaller BComm contract and was enjoying his role as supervisor. He had endeared himself to his six ladies and that evening was busy taking their rubbish bags out to the bins in the car park, whistling away to himself as he did so. Suddenly the peace of the evening was shattered by the sound of a motor bike pulling into the car park. The same man in black motorbike leathers, who 15 minutes earlier had given the cleaners at Stour House such a fright, leapt from his machine and pulled off his helmet.

"You're Will, aren't you?" he shouted.

Will turned round black rubbish bag still in hand. "Sure," said Will amiably.

"Take a good look at me mate… Know who I am? I'm Sam's partner. Hear that … her PARTNER. You fucking keep away from her. She don't want nothing to do with you, you bastard."

"I don't know what you are on about, mate. Just move over, there's a good chap. I've got a job to do."

They stood facing each other, Will's path blocked by the towering giant who had his crash helmet in his left hand but his right one was clenched menacingly. He obviously didn't feel dealing with Will warranted him putting his helmet down. He jabbed his fist in Will's direction.

Will took a step backwards and half-heartedly swung the sack of rubbish he was holding at his assailant. The response was instant. The black giant unleashed a hefty punch catching Will on the side of his face. There was a dull thud and Will crumpled to the ground, rubbish strewing everywhere.

"That'll teach you and next time I'll break your bloody neck. Keep yer hands to yourself you dirty bugger." He pushed his crash helmet up his arm and picked up Will's rubbish bag emptying the remaining contents over Will. "You're just filth, you are!"

The back door of the building burst open … "Will, Will, are you out 'ere?" It was Butch Janet looking for her supervisor. She caught sight of Will spread-eagled on the ground and a fleeting glimpse of a shadowy figure mounting a motorbike. "Oh my God, what's happened?" Then with a voice which carried above the sound of the traffic and the now revving of the motorbike … "Help, someone help. Will's been attacked. Help! Help."

Within moments two more ladies appeared. "Get security, get help!" Janet bellowed. They disappeared back through the door.

Meantime Janet tentatively rolled Will over. Blood trickled from his temple. She bent over him. "Gawd, I think that bloke's topped him. Help!" she screamed at double volume.

At this moment Will groaned.

"Oh, thank God. He's alive. Speak to me, Will."

Janet bent over Will prostrate body and gave him a shake. "Come On Will. What happened?"

Nothing. No flicker of recognition.

The ladies reappeared. "We can't find security. Do you want us to ring the police? Is Will OK?"

"No he's bleeding not …" snapped Janet. "I can't tell if he's still breathing or not. Phone for an ambulance somebody. Where the hell is security?" Then a little more calmly, "What do you reckon, Mel?"

"He looks out cold to me. Aren't you supposed to give the kiss of life?"

Janet looked up at her briefly and nodded. "Help me get this rubbish off."

Mel knelt beside her and together they cleared the rubbish to one side before Janet knelt astride Will.

"Do you know what to do? Mouth to mouth? Is it CPR or whatever …?" asked Mel, her voice wobbling.

"Sort of. We had a course at school. Go and find bloody security …. And get him to call an ambulance."

Janet opened Will's mouth. She remembered something about clearing the airways. She took a deep breath and then sealed her lips over his mouth, blowing hard. Will's cheeks filled out but nothing happened. She repeated this for several minutes constantly breaking off to check if anyone was coming to help. There was still no response from Will.

Janet was getting desperate. She had a lesson in life saving at school ten years ago and she wracked her brains to remember what that dishy swimming instructor had taught them.

She couldn't just let Will's life ebb away here between her thighs. She had to do something. Pulling a clean duster from her pocket she patted the trickle of blood, relieved to see that this had almost stopped. She folded the duster and put it over the wound. Still no help.

Then bracing herself, she shifted her position and crossed her hands on Will's chest trying to feel his breast bone but thwarted by the substantial folds of flesh. She began pumping hard, praying she was vaguely in the right area.

Will's eyes flickered. "What the ….?" He spluttered.

Mel burst through the open back door – "It's all right. They're on their way – police, ambulance, the lot and Maisie's found the security guy. Oh thank God."   Will was making a feeble attempt to sit up.

Janet heaved herself off him. "Bloody hell, Will. You didn't half give me a turn!"

CHAPTER 29 - WILLIS – MAKE OR BREAK

At Willis Faber the adjudication board for the cleaning contract had narrowed the contenders down to two. Monthind and TICS: one an unknown local company and the other a highly respected national organisation with a huge track record.

Mr Black pointed out that "Monthind were considerably cheaper."

"Yes, I fear they may have dramatically under-costed, even though their overheads are no doubt negligible compared with the big boys. If we accept their price it would give us leeway to back them." Mr Trenchard was fully aware that they would need support but he added, "It is company policy to support local business."

"Not only that, having them based in Colchester means we can bring in the M.D. herself for a daily bollocking, if necessary." Robert Black grinned at the thought.

"I'd like to see that. I reckon she'd give you a run for your money, Robert. Strikes me she's tougher than she looks. I'm going to telephone Mike Canning for a chat. It'll be interesting to see what he has to say off the record. I like the idea of going and seeing how they operate." Mr Trenchard nodded.

Even before the official request came through to Stour House, the security / cleaners' grapevine had done its stuff. Mandy was already working on it.

The visit was arranged. Mandy had been well primed and Christine asked Will to go back to Stour House to work with her and show off his mechanical skills. The date and time were cleared with Mr Canning who knew Jeffrey Trenchard from the various Facilities Managers courses they had attended together and who was more than happy to talk to the guy in charge of the most iconic building in the area, especially now the cleaning in his building was so much better.

Christine too was proud of the contract. She explained to Mr Trenchard that it was tiny compared with his building but the same principles would be applied - good leadership and happy staff.

The evening visit was a success, Mandy showing off her training schedules, her folder of Well Done You Notes and her attendance records. She introduced the Willis managers to her key ladies, Ann, Barbara and Ethel, all of whom looked immaculate in their green tabards, white shirts and black trousers. They answered questions without prompting and talked enthusiastically about Monthind.

Ethel was happy to tell them bluntly in her broad Suffolk accent that she had worked "fer a lot of them big cleaning companies and they didn't give a shit about their ladies. Now Mrs Chapman, she were different."

It couldn't have gone better. Christine was even beginning to convince herself that they could do it.

The phone call confirming they had been awarded the Willis Faber & Dumas contract, came exactly one week later. They would have cracked a bottle of champagne, but Pete couldn't drink and Ros wouldn't, so Christine begrudgingly made do with cranberry juice.

A further meeting: the contract was signed and everyone shook hands encouragingly. They would start in two months on Monday 3rd September.

This time their request for an initial clean, the weekend prior to their start date, was welcomed, and what was more it would be paid for as soon as the invoice was cleared. Willis Faber's management team, like Christine, were worried that in two months the outgoing cleaning staff would really let standards slip.

Willis Faber would be their flagship and what a flagship, but they were going to have to work for it. Everyone was on a high.

The day of Josie's wedding arrived in the Edgecombe household but not without considerable drama. Two days before the big day a blunt call from the local farmer announced that Daisy, the horse, had gone lame and Josie's dream of arriving at the church in a horse-drawn carriage bit the dust. She was not a happy bunny. She shed petulant tears and stamped her size four feet. Mandy did her to best to find an alternative that would satisfy Josie, however, to source a Rolls Royce or a white stretched limo at this late stage proved impossible. Eventually, after several more tantrums and with bad grace, Bridezilla came round to the idea that it might be fun to take up her Dad's offer and arrive in his milk float, especially when Will told her that her picture would certainly make the front page of the Co-op monthly magazine and probably the local paper. The crisis was overcome!

Mandy who in desperation had telephoned the office to ask if anyone had access to a white Roller, had repeated her request for Christine to come, even if just for an hour. In the end she agreed as Peter's sister had planned a fleeting visit for the day and would be there for him and the children.

Will was secretly chuffed about the issues with the horse. It had saved him a couple of hundred quid and upped his status with his workrmates who cheerfully clubbed together to decorate the newest milk float in the fleet with blue and white ribbons. They filled crates of empty bottles in the back with white roses, and drew lots to see who should drive Will and his daughter to the church. The others put on their Co-op coats and peaked caps and proudly walked alongside the float, forming a very vocal milkman-guard-of-honour.

Milk bottles rattling, the noisy procession ensured neighbours along the route turned out to cheer them on. Josie, looking positively radiant, forgot her airs and graces and waved enthusiastically. Will, who had removed his top hat, which was slightly too large and pushed his ears outwards, was sweating profusely, his bald pate now glistening in the sunshine. He was bursting with pride and good humour, calling out to everyone as they slowly progressed down the road. "Look Josie, there's old Mrs Parsons. Hi, Danny – look at my girl. Ain't she just bootiful." To a lady in a hat on the other side, he called, "See you in church, dearie!"

The crowd accompanying them grew as the procession continued - after all, Will the Milk knew almost everyone. "My daughter's getting married today – come to the church." He wanted to 'shout it from the roof tops' and that he did.

Christine arrived at the church as the photographer had completed the inevitably complicated picture session. She was thrilled to see Maria and Theresa and several of her ladies from Stour House all watching, including Ann and Kathy, whose delightful little daughter was standing on top of the church wall loving every minute. There was much banter and oohing and aahing at the bride and calling to out Will. "Never seen you in a suit, mate!" "Put yer hat on Will!" He grinned in acknowledgment and hastily jammed his top hat on the back of his head. "Don't 'ee look something else!"

"Yeah, but Josie – she's just the perfect bride." "Mandy made her outfit you know and all them bridesmaid's dresses and all." "Yeah, I don't know how she does it!" "Nor do I," thought Christine praying that after the wedding with the bills paid, both Mandy and Will wouldn't decide to leave.

Confetti flew as the bride and groom sqeezed onto the front seat of the milk float, this time driven by Will, to make the short journey from the church to the Belstead Hotel. Christine went to retrieve her car – she had had to park it miles away from the church. Frustratingly, when she arrived at the hotel the car park was full and she finally abandoned it on the grass verge fifty yards down the road. She eventually arrived at the hotel, struggling up the steps with her large package, just as the guests were being ushered through to the dining room.

On either side of the door waitresses stood with depleted silver trays which had held glasses of sweet Harvey's Bristol Cream sherry. Christine hastily slid her package to one side, smiled and asked for directions to the ladies. Emerging with hair tidied, she took one of the three remaining glasses before spotting Mandy greeting the late arrivals. "I am so glad you could come, Mrs Chapman. It really means a lot. I hope you are going to stay for the wedding breakfast after all?"

"No Mandy, I can't do that but I did want to bring a small present for the happy couple. Let me show you. I thought that it would be fun to present it to Jim from the cleaning company."

Christine had hidden her present wrapped in a black plastic rubbish sack behind the front door. She opened the top and showed Mandy the large blue bucket bursting with cleaning materials, Jif, Sparkle polish, dusters, toilet rolls, large pink Marigold rubber gloves draped over the side, and a bright yellow feather duster stuck out of the top.

Mandy shrieked with laughter and hugged Christine. "Oh, that's perfect. Josie will think that's such a laugh and so will Will! Let's show him. ...." Calling to one of the little bridesmaid's who was proudly twirling in her peacock blue dress in the doorway and impeding everyone's entry, she said "Kitty love, could you be a dear and fetch Will over. Mrs Chapman's got something real special to show him."

She returned in seconds with Will in tow. "Oh hello, Mrs C. Good to see you." He took her outstretched hand but cried out "Hell, no! Come here girl. I want a hug!" and with surprising strength he pulled Christine into his arms.

"Oh Will … Sorry Mrs Chapman. He's so excited!" Mandy was looking embarrassed. "Will, just have a look at what Mrs Chapman's bought for Josie."

His response was a huge guffaw. "Cor, yeah, from Monthid like … that's really nifty!"

"Yes, Will. I wonder if you could present it to Jim, rather than to Josie. I am a great believer that men should do their share of the cleaning and he might need a bit of training! There's a cheque in there too Will, so please make sure that doesn't get lost!"

Mandy responded immediately, "Oh that's ever so kind of you, Mrs Chapman, I'll make sure it's safe, don't you worry." Then, ever the organiser, she added, "Look, I know you have to go but just hang on for ten minutes or so until everyone's sitting in their places. You go and have a word with Josie and Jim in the meantime, don't say anything about the bucket, mind. You can see them being clapped in and then when everyone's sitting down, you can present them with the bucket."

Christine shook her head, "No, Mandy, I don't want that. I'd feel very out of place and it's only a silly, fun thing. Will will do it beautifully won't you, Will? And I'd love to watch."

Will was totally up for that. Once everyone was seated, Christine stood discreetly at the back of the room as Will announced that he had a special presentation to make:

"Ladies and Gentleman, before you all get yer grub, I've got a thing or to to say to our Jim here, the brave man who's taking on our Josie. Just so's he knows what's expected of him, Monthind, the cleaning company wot Mandy and me have worked for to pay for all this lot …," he made a sweeping gesture round the room, "have asked me to make this special presentation and to say that he and Josie are welcome to come cleaning anytime but they reckon Jim could do with a spot of training." From under the table he produced the bucket of cleaning materials and holding it high he handed it to a very surprised Jim who grinned and stood up. "There you are, mate" said Will with a wicked grin "from now on you're doing the washing up so you'd better try them pink Marigolds fer size."

Jim duly obliged. As he struggled to pull pink rubber gloves over his very large hands, he looked coyly at Josie and promised to use the equipment diligently. Raucous comments and laughter accompanied this statement. It set the tone for the rest of the day and was the perfect moment for Christine to quietly slip away.

From then on a bucket of cleaning materials became Monthind's traditional present for weddings, retirement and every special celebration in the company. Christine determined that wherever possible the bucket was given to the man, to add to the humour, not, of course, because she was being sexist.

The following Monday back in the kitchen-cum-office, recruitment was now their top priority. Various cleaners already working at Willis Faber for TICS had asked to stay on. Christine and Ros soon realised that few of these were going to be an asset. Indeed, they found that TICS had deliberately left the dross behind in the hope that Monthind would screw up the contract.

Willis Faber allowed them to interview potential new staff in the reception area. Ros still preferred to visit homes but time was short and they had to find well over 50 new staff.

The key was to find a competent manageress. One lady stood out head and shoulders above the rest, literally. She was well over six feet tall, German and beautifully groomed. Christine liked her immediately and felt that she had the stature and the personality they needed.

Hannelou Hammond, who would become known as Hanna as she became a vital part of Christine's management team, was genuinely amazed that they were offering her the key position of manager. She kept saying with disbelief, "But I'm German." "Yes," said Christine, "That's precisely why I want you. I love the German work ethic and discipline. Staff will respect you."

"But my English speaking is not good. My writing is very bad."

"Hanna, we don't need you for your English. We need you to manage and motivate people."

Unfortunately her daughter Gisela was getting married the weekend of the initial clean. Christine was impressed when Hanna said, "If it had been anything else, I would have changed it!" And Christine just knew she meant it.

Her husband, Harry, (eventually nicknamed Taters due to his propensity for holes in his socks with his toes sticking out – hence toes = potatoes = Taters is the cleaners' version of cockney rhyming slang!) was also keen to work.

Christine was over the moon - another milkman and another husband and wife team. These milkmen were characters and their work schedule fitted perfectly. They reported for work at the dairy at 04.00 a.m., did their rounds and were home by 11.00. Some went to bed for a couple of hours (whose bed was a matter for regular gossip on the cleaners' grapevine). Mind you, Christine was quickly learning that, fascinating though it was, the cleaners' grapevine was not always the most reliable source of information.

Many milkmen were ready to work for an extra couple of hours in the evening. They were disciplined time-keepers and well used to dealing with female customers, a huge asset when it came to working with cleaning ladies.

Sadly, there was a limit to the number of milkmen they could source and they ended up asking every male who applied to attend the initial clean at Willis, regardless of age, shape or size. The volume of rubbish alone was a two man task – a minimum of 100 black sacks a night and there were acres of rubber stud flooring every inch of which would need a heavy scrubber over it every evening. She sighed, even essential vocabulary like this was open to misinterpretation, but she was learning.

This contract would need a lot of men, far more than Christine's ideal ratio of 1 man to every 20 women, but slowly the numbers mounted.

Let's take a look at them. There was Harry Hammond – only 5' 5". What is it about Suffolk men – were they all small or was it just the milkmen? Harry had a lovely manner and oozed capability. He worked for Lord Rayleigh's Dairy, always regarded as a cut above the Co-op, and that really got up Will's nose.

Bob Walker – as skinny as a rake, almost 6 foot and with a sharp wit. He worked in business – no one was quite sure what business but as long as "his cleaning pay was cash in hand he was happy."

Dick Sherper, he was 5' 6" with a girth to match, leading to his nickname of Fat Boy, not that this weighed him down. He had a delightful sense of humour, but a wife from hell. He was a professional roof tiler and had all the health and safety certificates you could name. He could erect scaffolding and had no fear of heights. Christine was ecstatic – here was a guy who could look after all the high level work.

Then came Darryl with his teenage spots and head hanging so low that his baseball cap touched his chest. Christine was going to have to implement a uniform code which must ban hats. It was Darryl's fifteenth birthday and he had been pushed to come along by his Dad. Unbeknown to Christine, he overheard her say to Ros, "Oh dear. Look at that poor lad. He won't last the week."

Twenty years later on his 35th birthday, he was still working for Monthind, by now full-time, as a janitor. On that day as they celebrated 20 years' cleaning at Willis, Darryl took great delight in reminding Christine of those words and it was her turn to go red in the face. She looked at him then with deep affection – they had travelled a long road together.

From one extreme to the other - from teenage Darryl to septuagenarian Alf. Alf had long ago retired but wanted to pay for his granddaughter to go to university. Alf had worked for Eastern Water Authority and was a real gent.

Ros had grave misgivings about his health and his stated age, "70 next year, love". "More like 80," thought Ros but, as she said, "Beggars can't be choosers."

There were also two black guys – tiny Mac, unlikely husband of Mathilda, and enormous, Filo Dadzie, built like a heavy weight boxer - very tall, very black, very muscular with long athletic limbs. His Rastafarian hat would have to be removed, although Christine wondered if it would perhaps be preferable to the alternative – were there long smelly dreadlocks under it?

Christine's dream had never included employing men and she was far from comfortable about this. She had always said 'I will never ask my staff to do something I can't do myself.' This was going to be very different.

CHAPTER 30 – THE DAY OF RECKONING

At last the day of reckoning had come. Their dream opportunity and ultimate chance to make a name for themselves. Here they were starting to clean the most prestigious building in the area, maybe even in the country if the awards in the trophy cabinet were anything to go by.

Everyone knew the black glass Willis building – this was going to be the contract that put Monthind on the map. The Willis building was featured on the first class stamp and was the wallpaper background to the BBC Look East Six O'clock news every evening. They had to make it a success.

It was Saturday 1st September, their first day for the initial clean and orientation weekend. They stood in reception waiting for staff to arrive. Christine and Ros were poised, their steadfast crew, Mandy and Will, briefed and ready to organise a team of new cleaners, with Francesco and Maria standing by waiting impatiently for the go-ahead to blitz the 76 toilets.

The team apprehensively watched the revolving doors, unsure who was going to turn up. Slowly and nervously they arrived. This building had a cathedral-like aura and it took courage to enter.

The first to brave it were four ladies who knew each other thanks to Ros suggesting they could perhaps come in on the same bus. In the end they had arranged for one of the husbands to drop them down - they each paid him the equivalent of the bus fare to cover petrol.

They were obviously overawed by the building and stood inside the revolving doors, with expressions of wonder on their faces. Ros quickly went up to them, "Isn't it amazing!

Wait till you see the rest. I know you will love it. Don't worry, in two days you will feel quite at home!"

One of the ladies replied, "I can't wait to tell my children – this don't feel like going cleaning. It feels much more important. I've never seen an office like this."

Christine picked up on this immediately.

The next ladies to emerge from the doors were very large and very black. Christine watched them process across the foyer - that unmistakable African movement, shifting their weight from one hip to the other, progressing like stately galleons on a rolling sea, their eyes taking in the enormity of the building.

Christine had been upbeat about employing black West Indians. There was a large Caribbean community in Ipswich and she was very keen to employ a multi-cultural task force. But her heart sank. They were .... Oh, so slow. It would take them half the morning to get to the second floor.

In sharp contrast, they were followed by Pauline Masters her white stilettos clicking staccato-like across reception; another husband and wife, Lilian and Phil, a little reminiscent of Tweedle Dum and Tweedle Dee hand in hand marching in unison; and then irrepressible Dawn, straight from the market.

Then came the men: Bob, Dick, the two black guys, and Alf, with Darryl bringing up the rear. Phew - They had ALL turned up. Will quickly took them on one side, greeting Dick like a long lost mate – they had been at school together. In no time they had been issued with smart green jackets. The change was startling.

The next group of six rather loud ladies, who obviously knew each other – these cleaners had worked for the previous company, Golden Cleaning Services which Monthind was now replacing. They had decided to stay on, transferring their employment. Christine held out her hand to each one, asking for her name … "You are …?" This was awkward. Shaking hands was obviously foreign, a suspect gesture, to these girls. They tittered and looked at each other. "Which of you is Avril?" Avril had proudly announced over the phone that she was "first floor supervisor" and wanted to stay there. Avril nonchalantly stepped forward, "I'm 'er." Christine eyed her up and down. "Mmm." Avril was in her thirties, her hair peroxide Barbie blond and she was chewing gum - an immediate black mark in Christine's view. Heavy gold bangles stretched her ear lobes and her deeply tanned cleavage was plainly on display. Christine smiled, a cold smile, "Great, Avril. Could you and your ladies sign in with Mrs Barnum, collect your tabards and wait over there. Mrs Barnum will be in charge of your training."

"Training? We don't need no trainin'. We've been here since the building opened."

Christine's hackles were rising. "Everyone needs to learn about the new products, go through the health and safety procedures etc. I am sure you, as an ex supervisor for Golden Cleaning Services, will appreciate that. I also want you to meet the other girls on your floor."

Gradually everyone was split into groups and despatched to their allocated floor and cleaners' cupboard. There were major problems on the second floor where everyone was new – every aspect of it looked identical and the ladies kept getting lost. Demarcation lines between sections were non-existent but Mandy, resourceful as ever, had resorted to putting different coloured buckets with feather dusters sticking out of them on top of the cupboards as beacons.

Christine would ask if they could have numbers on sticks like restaurant tables until the cleaners were familiar with the layout.

Slowly they began to get organised, although Christine, Will and Bob Walker rushed tirelessly from floor to floor, responding to all the questions and cries for help.

Ros was working on the first floor with Avril bossing everyone including Ros with an air of "I know it all." As Ros attempted to divide the areas, Avril would say "Aw no, Doreen won't like that. You can't put Mary next to Jenny. She wants to work with Emily. You'd better cut down my area. I'm supervisor and I've got more desks than anyone else."

Eventually when the areas were semi-sorted, with Ros backing down, Avril began to throw her weight around even more. "Don't expect me and my ladies to do the rubbish. We always had a man to carry our bags and there's no way I'm cleaning the gents. You can get your new women to do that. We had a loo lady before."

"Areas are areas" said Ros. "In this company everyone has to do something in the toilets – that's how we work."

"Well, we don't."

By the time Christine got to the first floor Ros had capitulated, retreating to the gents' toilet which she was grimly cleaning with Maria – even Maria was looking glum, sensing the tension.

Ros off-loaded her worries to Christine. "Avril is trouble. She is insisting that she knows best, refusing to accept the areas

301

we organised. She is upsetting everyone else and honestly I don't know what is going on."

Furious, Christine asked where she would find Avril on the floor. Ros wasn't sure, so Christine decided the fastest way to locate her was to climb on top of the cabinets and do a 360 degrees scan of the floor. Hardly dignified, and certainly not in line with health and safety procedures, of that she was certain.

Sure enough, there due south east towards the reflected church tower, she saw a group of ladies sitting on the desks with Avril in the middle. She hopped down hoping that the security guys had not spotted her.

She headed in that direction, guided by the coarse laughter. As she neared the group she could hear, "And that Barnum woman, all 'please and would you be a dear … Avril dearest'. Not bloody likely. I ain't doing toilets. Never have and never will."

Christine was furious. "What's going on here? Why aren't you on your areas? This floor looks as though it hasn't been touched." She turned to Avril, "I thought you used to run this floor. Everyone should be cleaning and learning her area by now." Christine was pre-menstrual and angry - not a good time for anyone to challenge her.

Avril glared, "That Barnum woman don't know what she's doing. Anyway we ain't got a problem. We know where we want to work. I was trying to tell her what ….."

Christine cut her short, "Mrs Barnum knows perfectly well how WE want to run this floor and that is the way it will be run. From now you will take orders from me. You are all to go back to your allotted sections. I want rubbish to Cores 1 and 4 by11.00 and bins washed out. They are disgusting. Standards on this floor need a lot of improvement. Off you go." Then eyes blazing, she said, "Avril I want a quiet word with you."

Avril glared. Christine waited for the ladies to disperse and then she let rip, "Don't you ever undermine my authority again. Every supervisor who works for me earns the position. If this is the way you handle responsibility, then forget even thinking about being in charge. Now get to the area Mrs Barnum gave you and get working - AND you will be doing the gents urinals. Understood. Avril, this is a formal warning."

Emphasising her point, she added, "I shall be back shortly and will come to find you on your area. I am extremely disappointed in you."

With hands on hips Christine watched Avril flounce off, her large earring hoops swinging defiantly. Christine rather hoped she would storm out but, no, she headed back to her area. Christine marched in her wake, with a parting, "I will see you in an hour, Avril." She turned towards the escalators and stopped in her tracks.

Did she hear "Fuck you?" DID SHE? This was not the time to have a major show down, but Ros was right, this woman was trouble, double trouble and certainly not supervisor material.

With that Christine hurried up to the second floor, worried that she would find a similar situation there. Instead, Mandy came to meet her. "We are winning but I am worried about the black ladies. They have a pace of their own. I just want to put a bullet up their backsides."

She smiled and added, "Mathilda and Evelina are so fat. Thank goodness we've tabards and not overalls. You should have seen me trying to do the poppers under their armpits. Even the X-X-L tabards wouldn't meet. Had to leave the top poppers undone. They just giggled 'Cor, don't tickle Mandy' as I dug into the ripples of fat. We'll have to invest in larger sizes or put in looped elastic extensions. Do they do XXXL? But you know, they are just lovely ladies. It was such a laugh!"

Christine nodded, "You are doing brilliantly, Mandy. I know what you mean about size though. They must be at least 20 stone. I have a feeling they are not going to be able to cope."

Interestingly though, it was Evelina, big black, motherly Evelina who a short time later, with a concerned look on her face, touched Christine's arm and, pulling at Christine's skirt lightly, pointed to a large brown blood stain on the back of her dress. "You alright, missus? I thought you'd like to know. Like."

"Oh God" Christine thought. She had started her period, and how! To Evelina she flashed a smile. "Thank you so much for telling me. I'll be fine. I'd better go and deal with it."

Christine rushed to the ladies and quickly took off her dress, rinsing the back in cold water. She squeezed it out and was conscious for the rest of the afternoon that she had a suspicious light brown damp patch. One thing, it should dry quickly if she rushed around. She reached for a green tabard and hoped this would cover most of the stain.

Evelina's sensitive words remained with Christine – she wondered vaguely if it was this which made her more tolerant to the ambling speed of operation every black employee seemed to adopt. It would be understandable in the heat of

Africa or Jamaica but here in Ipswich, it was irritating when other employees seemed twice as efficient. Still in today's climate of equal rights, she couldn't afford to have a dismissive, racist attitude to anyone remotely coloured, let alone as black as night, like Evelina. Little did she know at that time what an important role this lady and her friends would play when the company faced orchestrated bigotry and they quietly proved just how non-racist Monthind really was. Evelina would soon become a key supervisor and Christine would be singing the praises of her reliable West Indian ladies. Oh yes, she had a lot to learn.

At the break, Christine, carefully placing her damp patch to the wall, thanked everyone and said how proud she was to be working on this contract, how important everyone of them was to the organisation, how each of them had a vital contribution to make to the running of their successful company and how honoured they were to be cleaning such a prestigious building.

She shot a hard look at Avril who gave a toss of her head. "Together we are going to change the image of cleaning and make it a job to be proud of and make it rewarding and fun for you all." There were a few interested expressions, a few sceptical raised eyebrows and a few vacant faces – completely lost. Time would tell. So …… "Thank you ladies and gentlemen, and now back to work."

They worked on and on. Christine felt like death but determinedly kept smiling and encouraging.

The following week there were whispers on the cleaners' grapevine that Mrs C had miscarried in Willis. It even reached Maria at Halls. Hadn't anyone considered that with all the stress of this contract, she might just have started a heavy period, early?

By the end of the weekend, the building had responded. The toilets gleamed, cleaning cupboards were organised, and the men, in general, had proudly mastered their brand new scrubber dryers. A supervisor was appointed for each floor although Christine had serious misgivings about Joyce, the rather timid lady, who was asked to take charge of Avril's floor. She knew in her heart she wasn't strong enough to stand up to Avril and that this wasn't going to work.

Most importantly of all, the ladies were able to pinpoint their areas, although one or two still had vacant looks on their faces. At lunch time on Sunday, one, rather overweight Suffolk lady, Edna, declared she couldn't cope, "I'm fazed. I'm real fazed. I can't find nothing. This building gives me the willies." And one of the black ladies, Maxime, refused point blank to go up the escalators, even wedged between Evelina and Mathilda…. Ros had Christine in fits describing the three large black elephants trying to mount the escalator … Maxime shrieking, her eyes rolling, sandwiched between the other two. Four attempts they made before Security moved in and mildly suggested they took the lift. …. but "Maxime weren't none too 'appy with them lifts, neither."

Ros had eventually taken both reluctant ladies on one side and suggested that they might like to go and work for Mandy at BComm. There was so much scope now to juggle staff and find the right slot in the jigsaw for each person. Edna was very happy to transfer and they solved Maxime's escalator terror by putting her on the ground floor.

Ros was always prepared to listen to each complaint and each worry with admirable patience. She and Christine complemented each other – Ros listened, came up with possible solutions and Christine made the decision and delivered it.

Time and time again, Christine would say, "There's an answer to every problem" with Ros thinking: "Fine. As long as you're happy!" But somehow they complemented each other – good cop, bad cop?

CHAPTER 31 - STEADYING THE SHIP

Christine was relieved. Hanna arrived, raring to go for their Monday morning meeting. Her daughter's wedding over, bride and groom despatched on honeymoon, Hanna had telephoned on Sunday evening to ask how the clean had gone and here she was joining Christine at Willis to face the music on Monday.

There were issues, as they expected, like sacks of rubbish left in the lift and the odd feather duster sticking out of a bucket, but Mr Trenchard and Ted Ryan knew the problems. They were prepared to be lenient, at this stage.

Back again in the evening Christine felt good introducing Hanna, or rather Mrs Hammond, to the cleaners, as the Contract Manager and together they walked the floors, getting the feel of the building and their assorted collection of employees. Bob Walker already had his guys understanding their routines but adjustments were needed.

Hanna had spotted Filo in the middle of reception, rotating his polishing machine, his hips gyrating gently. The office staff descending the escalator had a perfect view of him performing below them. They each made a careful detour around him and his machine, some fearful he might scythe their legs from under them, others just plain annoyed that he was blocking their direct exit from escalator to front door. His mind was certainly not on cleaning the floor. He had a faraway look, clearly on another planet.

Hanna pounced, "Vhy you clean here? Are you stupid? People come down to go home and you right in zer vay? You must do zis area last, you stupid man."

She summoned Bob and said "I don't think zis man should be in ze most important place in the building. Vot is the matter viz him?"

Bob grinned, "Yeah, Filo is a bit thick but I think he'll get there. He could be on drugs" - Christine's eyes widened - "but he's very willing and can certainly handle a machine. You're quite right, I need to put one of the other guys here. It's just that I wanted to keep an eye on him and this seemed the best place for that."

Hanna was nodding her head. "Yes, ve must vatch him. Maybe you should put Dick with him and zey double up. "

Bob agreed although he did think this could exacerbate the situation. Sure enough the next evening, there was extrovert Dick, a wonderful mimic, also on a floor machine doing a perfect impersonation of Filo. He had a captive audience of office staff descending the escalators and even the security men on the reception desk were laughing. Filo quickly cottoned on and his movements became even more fluid, soon the two were swaying in unison, all that was lacking was the reggae music. At least they weren't impeding anyone's exit and the floor gleamed.

Christine, walking through with Bob to inspect a problem in the boiler room, took one look at this display and chuckled. "What's this supposed to be? Synchronised cleaning. Filo looks as though he's transported."

Bob smiled, "Yes, I think he's having a religious experience! Have you heard what he's singing?" Christine had to admit that Zion Train by Bob Marley was not a Negro spiritual she was familiar with, but she could see that Filo was well into it, in a 'spiritual' way. Bob explained "Mrs Hammond suggested putting Dick here to keep an eye on him and you have been stressing the importance of making work FUN. Don't worry, honestly."

"Fine, Bob, but we are not here to provide evening entertainment for the office staff. If Filo needs to chill out perhaps you should put him in the Chiller Plant room!"

"Nice one," laughed Bob. Wow, Mrs C had cracked a joke.

The following week Christine and Hanna found Filo cleaning the stairs from the bottom up. "Filo, vot you think you are doing?" asked Hanna.

"Cleaning the stairs, what else Miss?" he replied with a broad white smile.

"You have to start at the top and brush the dirt down, can't you see that?" This from Christine. Was he thick or was he thick?

"OK Miss." He picked up his broom and dustpan and brush and happily started up the stairs. "Filo, you only need the broom at the top – you won't need the dustpan and brush until you get to the bottom. Leave them here."

"Cool, Missus. Cool." He swung himself up the six flights of stairs with the agility of an ape, his long left arm hauling himself up. After three flights he turned and gave them an enormous grin, white teeth gleaming and a cheeky wave of the broom. Hanna and Christine watched mesmerised.

Christine sighed. Her patience would not cope with this for long. She wondered if this was time to tackle the red and orange crocheted hat. But decided that could be an instruction too far for Filo. She didn't want to "rock the boat", not realising that this expression was from another of Bob Marley's hits! Thank goodness Hanna was going to be in charge of the team here. She would certainly have her work cut out to mould them into shape.

At the moment though, it was more important to tackle the problems on the first floor. Avril was stirring things. Christine had a gut feeling that Avril and Hanna were going to clash spectacularly. She felt Hanna was made of stronger stuff but having seen Ros cowed, she wasn't prepared to take any chances. There was no way that nasty piece of work was going to come out on top this time. Christine would make sure of that.

Avril had again reorganised things and cut her own area down to little more than 15 desks. When Christine and Hanna challenged her, she said she was just trying to make, "The floor fair."

"Fair for whom? I see nothing fair in your having 15 desks while everyone else has three times that number," snapped Christine.

Two staff, including Joyce who had reluctantly taken on the position of supervisor, had already asked for a transfer from this floor, nervous to say why but everything screamed at Christine: "Avril, big bully Avril". To Hanna Christine had said, "I didn't realise you could have bullies outside school. We need to nip this in the bud."

Avril seemed to be able to intimidate anyone and everyone, and her language was to the point and colourful. She talked to office staff working late, sowing seeds of doubt about Monthind …. "This new company don't know what the heck they're doing. They've mucked up all the bleeding systems and think they know better."

Things came to a head when one Friday evening Christine and Hanna were alerted to trouble on the first floor by Doug, one of the security men. They arrived to find Avril, backed by at least four of her cronies, screaming abuse at Doreen, a woman aged about 35 with loose red hair and a fake orange tan which was getting redder by the minute.

"You bitch. Don't you speak to me like THAT! I'm supervisor 'ere and I'll get you." Avril's voice was at fever pitch. A small crowd was gathering.

"I'll call you what I like." This from Doreen, "You haven't changed, you selfish whore. Why should the rest of us work our arses off so that you can swan around like a la di dah bloody madam? You're plain evil, you are. Evil Avril. Yeah, that's what they call you, you lazy cow."

With that she launched herself at Avril, clawing for her eyes and grabbing a handful of hair. As quick as a flash Hanna moved in to pull her back but Avril's mettle was up "Come on girls, get her." Avril attempted to attack Doreen who, no match for 6' 2" Hanna, was being pulled backwards, arms flailing.

Christine quickly put herself between them, arms out and her eyes flashing. She bellowed, "That's enough!" Avril and her cronies stopped in their tracks.

"I can't believe what I am hearing. You are behaving like fishwives. I won't tolerate this behaviour. I am sacking the lot of you. You will leave the building instantly, every one of you! As for you Avril, you are just a no good, trouble maker and I want you out now."

"You can't bloody do that." This from Avril who moved forward threateningly, eyeing Christine.

"Oh yes, I can. I most definitely can," retorted Christine. "You just watch me. You've been nothing but trouble since we started."

"I'll report you!" retorted Avril. "You can't bloody sack me. It's unfair dismissal. I'll 'ave you."

"I hardly think that will come in to it, Avril. In fact, I can have you charged with causing an affray and assault. You were fighting. You were supposed to be in charge on this floor. You will leave the building this minute."

"I aren't bloody leaving. She started it," pointing at Doreen. Hanna had released her grip on Doreen but still kept a restraining hand on her shoulder.

"Do I call Security and have you escorted out or will you leave of your own accord?" Christine was ice cold. "You have conducted yourselves appallingly, all of you, but I hold you, Avril, in particular, responsible for this. Everyone here is to collect their belongings. EVERYONE."

"Mrs Hammond, escort them to the cupboard to get their things. I will be waiting in reception. The office will contact you with your P45 and payment due."

Everyone seemed to freeze. "Did you hear what I said? You are FIRED. Now. Out now." reiterated Christine, her voice still quivering with anger.

"Mrs Hammond, see that they talk to no one. I am reporting this to the Senior Security Guard. I will see you all in reception in two minutes to collect your passes."

Various office staff disturbed by the commotion had left their desks to watch. Some nodded, some made the odd remark to a colleague and one picked up the telephone.

313

Christine marched to the escalators, back straight and head high. Reacting to the telephone call, Ron Hurrell, Head of Security rose to his feet and came to meet her. "Is everything OK?"

"Far from it. I am afraid I have sacked most of the cleaners on the first floor, including Avril."

"Well done. We were surprised that you had kept her on. She is a nasty piece of work. Do you need any help?"

"I would be most grateful if you would witness my handling of this. It's not going to be pretty. I have a feeling Avril may be difficult. Mrs Hammond and I have already prevented what could have been a brawl."

They could hear the remnants of the row as the women descended the escalator. "You cow, you bloody cow. I'll get my husband on you."

Mrs Hammond's voice could be heard. "Stop. Zis is disgraceful, ladies."

Christine walked towards the escalators followed by Ron with another security man behind him.

"Avril," this from Mr Hurrell, "I suggest you quieten down or I shall take this further. We have had numerous documented complaints about you. You have been formally warned by me in the past, but this is the final straw. I understand you have been fired. You are out. Finish."

"It's 'er fault. Bloody Doreen. She started it."

Christine took this up, "Well, Doreen is leaving too. You all have probationary contracts and I don't want any of you working for me. If you wish to dispute anything, put it in writing. Hand your passes in, please. Avril, wait. I want to have a private word with you."

"Not bloody likely. Wait till my husband hears about this. He'll get you. You and your fancy ways. You don't know nothing about running a cleaning company. We'll be back … just you wait and see."

Ron Hurrell stepped forward, "I doubt that, Avril,   As Head of Security here, I will make sure you never have access to this building again and I suggest you watch what you say. Just go home without any more trouble. I don't want to have to call the police."

Avril gave him a vicious look before she headed for the exit, slinging her pass on the floor.

Ron was shaking his head. "We're glad to see the back of her. She has been nothing but trouble, always telling tales, always setting off one cleaner against another. Take my advice and keep well clear of her and her cronies. If you have any further trouble, come and have a word."

One by one, seven ladies handed in their passes. They filed out heads down, several looking shame-faced.

The last, Doreen, looked as though she was going to say something, "Mrs Chapman …" she began, but Christine just shook her head and pointed to the exit.

Hanna was quick to collect herself, looking at her watch. "Ve have just three ladies and 20 minutes left to clean ze whole floor. I'd better go find zem. Zay vill be very vorried. I vonder if ve could come in tomorrow, Saturday, and sort things out."

Christine turned to Mr Hurrell. "Do you think that would be possible, Ron?"

"Leave it to me. Just let me know who and when they are coming in tomorrow and give me the names of any new staff you appoint on Monday."

Christine turned to him and said with a grateful smile, "Thank you Ron, sincerely, for your support."

"My pleasure. That's what we are here for." He beamed.

Christine and Hanna headed up the escalators to the first floor. After reassuring the few staff who remained and generally tidying up, they made arrangements to come in on Saturday and they finally left for home.

By the time she had put the car in the garage and opened the front door, Christine was shaking. What had she done? Sacked goodness knows how many staff and left the contract very short handed. She was appalled at herself and poured out the whole story to Pete, ending with, "I can't handle this, I really can't. And what happens if Avril comes back with all her friends?"

Peter was looking at her wide eyed. "You are going to be just fine. Well done. I am so proud of you. That took guts, tremendous guts. That was absolutely the right thing to do. From now on people will know you are the boss and not to be messed with."

"But I didn't think. I just lost it. I was so angry. I knew I had to do something radical. Heaven knows what the repercussions will be."

CHAPTER 32 - REPUTATIONS AND RELATIONSHIPS

News of the multiple sacking spread quickly. This was a side of the "nice" Mrs Chapman no one had seen before. "She sacked the whole floor. – all twenty cleaners." "You should have seen her. Snorting anger, she were. Sorted Avril out some. And that Mrs Hammond, she tackled Doreen. Had her in a half Nelson. Don't get on the wrong side of her. She'll break yer neck. " "Yeah. She's German. D'you reckon she's a Nazi? They say some of them got away."

Poor Hanna. This fed back to her. She took it to heart badly and she came to Christine on the brink of tears. "Zey hate me. Zey are saying I am a Nazi, zat I wear jack boots and have a whip. It's not true."

Christine looked at her in amazement. Here was an incredibly capable woman – tall, elegant with tremendous presence. The first time they met Christine knew Hanna was special and since then her respect for her had grown. She lacked confidence; she even tried to walk in the road when they were together. 5' 6" Christine had been furious – "Get on the pavement. Use your height. It is a tremendous asset. You can look down on everyone. I wish I were as tall as you. Never ever walk in the gutter again." Indeed every time she saw Hanna stooping she held up an upright finger in her direction, raised her eyebrows and grinned.

"Hanna, I employed you BECAUSE you are German. You are hard working, you are diligent, you are honest and you have an authority about you which none of these other ladies have. Hold your head high and ignore them. I want to know where you heard this."

"Zank you, but it is easy for you. You aren't German."

317

"Hanna, stop right there. One or two of the cleaners are ignorant. They don't like being pulled up, they are jealous of your position and your authority and they are going to stoop to the lowest level. Deep down they know you are right and they know you are fair."

Christine continued: "I get it too, you know. There are rumours flying around that the only reason we got the Willis contract is that I am having an affair with Robert Black. You just have to rise above these things and treat them with the disdain they deserve."

Christine resolved to keep an eye on the cleaners' grapevine.

Generally cleaners seemed to be responding. Everyone had to clean some part of the toilets. After Avril's refusal to clean a toilet in any shape or form, Christine was determined that no one was looked down upon as the loo cleaner. Indeed, Janet and Bob who serviced the toilets during the lunch period were a credit to the company. Bob became master at unblocking the toilets, something he often wanted to share with Christine. She took it in her stride, open-eyed as he regaled the culprits which might be anything from padded bras to a bucket of cement, from condoms to MacDonald's' polystyrene packaging.

Slowly areas were modified and the atmosphere improved. Was it because Evil Avril, the queen of bullies had gone? They would never know. One thing Christine did know was that Hanna was a great asset. Her integrity and her strength ensured that when there were problems she would deal with them fairly and firmly.

Hanna had an unlikely ally in Pauline Masters who worked on the ground floor, Pauline was obviously revelling in the drama. Sidling up to Christine after the despatch of Avril, she crowed, "Cor. Well done, Mrs Chapman. You and Mrs Hammond showed her straight. She were a bully at school. Once a bully always a bully. But you watch your back – she won't forget this in a hurry. Good job, you've got Mrs Hammond. She won't stand no nonsense neither."

Christine, "Yes, Pauline, we need to stamp out any nonsense. Give Mrs Hammond every backing you can. Now come on, we have work to do."

Pauline could be guaranteed to fuel the cleaners' grapevine but she would also rally the troops. Ros had had doubts about her – her white stilettos and sexy tight skirts – but when Pauline entered the building she changed her shoes to flat black pumps. With the change of shoes came a change of personality – Pauline who loved her bingo and her nights out with the girls, became fiercely protective of her team.

She loved her job with a passion, knew everything about everybody but used this knowledge with compassion and concern – for the most part!

Pauline had taken on board totally, Mrs Chapman's claim – "We may do the cleaning, but we are proud of our work and will look like the professionals we are!" Indeed Pauline's appearance was always immaculate, a crisp white shirt beneath her green tabard, and even if the skirt did show quite a lot of leg, her tights were always perfect, totally ladder free. She had exquisite hair professionally cut and was never seen without perfect make-up.

Pauline blossomed – she took it upon herself to organise the social functions, coffee mornings, bingo and the highlight night out with the Chippendales whenever they came to the Regent.

She was also tremendous at taking under her ample wing the shy youngsters, desperate to earn some money. For many it was their very first job, the first time they had worked. They were so nervous and totally overwhelmed by the building and the scale of the work. She took mothering them to heart.

Pauline was also immensely practical and ruthlessly opposed waste. In fact she was put in charge of ordering cleaning materials – Peter was sure she must have Scottish ancestry, so thrifty was she. Under Pauline's management consumption of toilet rolls by the office staff went down by 12%. Christine never knew how. No cleaner would have dared to pinch anything and even secretaries thought twice about removing toilet paper to use instead of tissues.

Rumour had it that Pauline numbered the inside of the cardboard centres so she could trace any wayward toilet roll at source. "Do you Pauline?" Christine asked her once. "No of course not - it would take hours, but I tell the cleaners we do spot checks to keep track of 'em. No harm in that! Last thing I want is my loo rolls on a stall in Nacton car boot sale."

She had been known however to take the toilet rolls off the desks and put them back in the toilet roll dispensers. The office staff, knowing they were in the wrong, dare not complain.

Whenever cuts were needed, Pauline could be counted on to hit the target. Peter called her "My dragon of a quarter master or, should we say quarter mistress."

Avril's departure had repercussions but Ros was jubilant. "Avril was a nasty piece of work, a bully and a bigot. We are well shot of her, but wasn't it a tad excessive to sack the whole floor, Chris?"

"To be honest, it would have been impossible to sort out who was with her and who wasn't, who was at fault and who wasn't. They would have all blamed each other and to be honest it is simpler to start all over again," said Christine with a shrug. "Anyway, I'd done with pussyfooting around Avril."

Ros sighed, ready as ever to pick up the pieces. They were still several people short. "I'll get Hanna to help me. Perhaps she can do some recruitment."

Hanna had yet to learn the value of Monthind's recruitment methods or maybe she was desperate. She just phoned everyone on the list Ros gave her and asked … "Ven can you start?" Possibly she was having visions of cleaning the whole floor on her own.

One lady, Claire Browning, whom Hanna recruited in this way, reported for duty on that Monday and was instantly thrown into the deep end. Mrs Hammond put her working with Dawn, market trader Dawn, who in ten minutes flat had completed Claire's training, given her the low-down on the company and recruited her to help with a youth club disco the following Saturday.

Dawn was a laugh and a half. She talked non-stop at maximum volume to ensure she could be heard on the other side of the market, or in this case the other side of the first floor, and everyone was "dearie". "Want a hand, dearie," this to Claire struggling to change her vacuum cleaner bag. "Working late tonight, dearie" this is to a harassed office worker. Dawn reminded Christine of a feisty Yorkshire terrier. Her short hair bristled and she shot from one job to another, spotting a coffee mark on a table or a smear on the glass – out came her immaculate duster and with a quick purposeful rub the offending mark disappeared.

From her stall in the market Dawn knew everyone. This was to become a major asset for Dawn, born and bred in Ipswich, was on first name terms with every market trader and almost everyone who frequented the bustling market. She soon became the company's vetter in chief. No one was taken without their credentials being passed by Dawn.

Ros would ring Dawn "Hey Dawn what's the low down on Rosie Inchcape." "Wot 'er that lives with Tom Penny? She's a luv – a real good un. Where are you thinking of putting her? Just don't take her ole man – he's a lazy bugger." The next time, "Angie Archer – she lives on Gainsborough. You don't happen to know her do you?" "Oh yeah, Angie Arsehole they call her – you don't want to know. She's a real shit and she's on benefits big time."

Those she didn't know she delighted in working with "I'll train 'em up and let you know."

The atmosphere on the first floor changed overnight. They were still not up to full strength again but everyone lent a hand, including Christine and Hanna. Peels of laughter could frequently be heard and the camaraderie was tangible, with Claire and Dawn at the centre.

Hanna was thrilled. Claire was a gem, a natural leader. Within two weeks she was running the first floor and what a happy ship it became. Dawn in the meantime was quite content to slot in anywhere, except on Friday which she insisted on taking off to run her local youth club.

Christine later learnt that Claire's husband had had an accident working at British Fermentation on the docks in Felixstowe. He had hurt his back badly and Claire was now looking to boost their income - yet another of her ladies with a huge burden on her shoulders.

Hanna took over the morning meetings with Robert Black. Christine secretly blessed her for this as she had come to dread them. He picked up on everything – there was never a pat on the back and it was hard to keep morale up with the cleaners when she had to constantly report back on his trivial complaints and niggles. She had tried to rectify the minor issues without telling the cleaners but with Hanna, Mrs Hammond, now taking over this liaison, it was going to be harder to keep everyone happy. Hanna, true to her Germanic roots, was direct and at times, far from diplomatic, but she was fair and effective.

Christine tried not to resent Mr Black, after all he was only doing his job. How many times over the next twenty years would she remind herself, "Robert Black's unremitting campaign for perfection made Monthind's service second to none."

At Willis Faber the specification was constantly stretched. With each new demand, they achieved new knowledge – how to clean ducting, steam cleaning of carpets, deep cleans of kitchens, sterile cleaning of clean rooms. Gradually as the years flew by, there was nothing they couldn't tackle; indeed they became experts in every aspect.

At this stage, however, it was hard to view the constant niggles in a positive light. The latest nit-picking complaint had been "There's too much laughter on the floor. Staff working late can't think!" Bang goes fun when you are working – mind you Dawn could be heard a mile off. She was even a match for the vacuum cleaner. Hanna could sympathise with the office staff desperately trying to work late, their train of thought constantly penetrated by Dawn's piercing market trader voice "Must tell you this one, dearie…." or "Caulis is up 20p this week … criminal it is!"

Training had to be the answer. Train the supervisors. Christine took the initial session on appearance, courtesy, manner and fun. "You are the ambassadors of our company. We are the envy of our competitors because our staff look smart, are polite and work hard. We are proud to be cleaners and we are respected by our customers. Train your girls to be considerate. If for example someone is working late and you need to empty his bin always ask, "Excuse me. I don't mean to disturb you but could I empty your bin? Will it be a nuisance if I vacuum a little later?" Never vacuum around people who are working etc. etc. Never shout across the office. Have consideration for others."

She then handed over to Mandy, trainer in chief, who explained the use of the cleaning materials and the correct cleaning systems. Will took over for machine training and Bob for Health & Safety. The team was growing.

Gradually each supervisor was given the task of training her new staff. This seemed to be working very well until one evening several months later Christine overheard a training session which perhaps lacked her finesse and delivery. Lilian (Tweedle Dee), newly appointed as Ground Floor Supervisor for the Ladies, was giving her first training session to new staff:

… "Yer tabard must be clean and pressed. Wash yer dusters – can't clean with a filfy cloff. Make sure you use deodorant – we don't want no complaints that you're stinking the office out." All good direct advice but unfortunately it culminated with …. "And Mrs Chapman says we'll have no fucking swearing on this contract. Okay?"

Christine groaned … this wasn't quite how she would have put it but maybe it was the way to get the point across. She still remembered the first time she cleaned and the lady who trained her, Joan, tucking her rubbish bags in her waist band, her trusty toothbrush and her wonderful banter … blue for loos. That had to be the ideal way to learn, on the job one to one. Training was so much more than a quick ten minute blast of a briefing.

Each day, there seemed to be a new story of hardship and of courage. The more Christine heard the more she realised that Monthind mattered, that it was going to play a crucial role in the lives of the people they employed.

People came to work for all sorts of reasons. Bob had started because he had a suspiciously big tax debt, Mandy and Will to pay for Josie's ambitious wedding, Dick, she suspected, came merely to get away from his whingeing wife. According to Bob, Dick's wife, Jealous Josephine hung about outside the building every night, waiting for Dick to finish. She wouldn't come in and turned her nose up at cleaners. She was a social worker! God help her clients, thought Christine.

And then there was Dear Darryl, so quiet, so willing, bullied at home, bullied at school but with the ladies at Monthind he flourished. They mothered him, they treasured him. Pauline brought in a special treatment for his acne and tactfully slipped it into his jacket pocket. Her fussy daughter said it smelt yucky and made her skin itch so she would have thrown it out.

Slowly Darryl's confidence grew. He was reliable in the extreme and gradually he began to use his initiative. He now worked every weekend to earn overtime, money which he paid to his mother. He was still painfully shy to talk to but Christine knew that Pauline, outspoken Pauline, would look out for him. She smiled and wondered how long it would be before Pauline found Darryl a girlfriend.

Each and every one mattered. She felt they were all part of the family, her family. But could she cope? Was she being stupidly altruistic? Was it achievable or was this just her ridiculous dream?

Christine was worried – the business since the start of Willis Faber was eating her up totally. She knew she was neglecting the family. Friends were quietly helping out. Mrs Larson, whose children were the same age as James and Anya, regularly took the girls to ballet and the boys to Cubs. Another friend took them swimming every Saturday morning at 8.00 a.m. which gave her a chance to do the weekly shop. It was such a relief to go to Sainsbury's with her list and whip through filling a trolley to the brim. When she got back Peter's morning drugs were beginning to kick in and he was ready to eat a little breakfast over the Saturday paper.

He hadn't been well. The last visit to the Marsden had been worrying. The consultant, Mr Davidson, wanted to start chemo again. They knew each time the prognosis was worse. Peter's hair began to fall out which hit Peter hard. He had always had lovely thick auburn hair and now it was falling out in ominous clumps. Every morning there were tufts of it on the pillow and nothing Christine could say could hide the fact that the bald patches were appearing. For days after each session he felt sick.

The chemotherapy nurse at the hospital had talked about getting a wig and she had given them the address of the nearest wig supplier in Ipswich. Anya had asked Peter "Daddy why is your hair falling out. I don't like it." James compounded it, "Yes, Daddy I can see your white head. Are you going to be bald all over?" Christine hastily made an appointment.

They went along armed with photos of Peter at his best. The wig was matched to Peter's normal auburn hair and looked good.

He muttered as they drove home … "The real test will be the children. Let's see if they notice." If only Christine could speak to them first… Anya would be fine but heaven knows what James would come out with.

Friends, she knew, would be diplomatic. Although there would always be one – and one there was! A neighbour. He himself was almost bald, younger than Pete and when he saw the wig, he bluntly said, "Looks ridiculous man. I don't know why you just don't go bald gracefully like the rest of us." Christine could have killed him.

What he didn't realise was that baldness with chemotherapy didn't look normal. Bald patches appeared and odd hairs stuck out. The effect was odd and untidy, and signalled the tell-tale message that you are going through chemotherapy. Peter was still not prepared to admit to anyone that he had cancer. He was so certain he would get better. He hated the thought of people knowing and the pity. He also felt, probably correctly, there was such a tremendous stigma attached to cancer that it would mean the end of his career.

Christine collected the children from the Convent and on the way home stopped in Crouch Street to buy them a bar of chocolate each. Sitting in the car, James with his Milky Bar and Anya with her Maltezers, Christine quietly told them about Daddy's wig. "Please can you tell Daddy, he looks better today and that his hair is lovely."

Anya nodded but James immediately asked "Why?" Christine tried to explain, "Daddy's very unhappy about his hair but it looks much better – the hospital have found the answer."

As things would have it, when they arrived home the children burst in, James did not even notice – he was far too busy telling Peter about Stephen's new bike. Anya just went up and gave her Daddy a big hug.

Christmas was coming and the children were excited. The Convent was doing a nativity play. Anya was Mary. James was in the choir. Fortunately Christine wasn't required to do any costumes – just to turn up.

In the rush to get organised, she hadn't been able to do a proper meal, just a sandwich. They arrived with not a minute to spare. Anya rushed ahead – she had to change. Christine helped Peter from the car and as they entered the church Sister Aidan, James's teacher, came up to them beaming. In her lilting Irish brogue she said, "Loverly to see you Mr Chapman. How are you now? I've saved you a place at the front. And James, what about you? In good voice, I trust?"

As quick as a flash James pipes up, "I'm very, very, hungry, Sister."

"Are you now, young man?" Sister Aidan, nodded, head on one side.

Christine felt guilty. Before she could say a word, Sister Aidan looked at James and said with her lovely sing-songy inflection, "Well, you'd better come with me now. I think I might be able to find the odd mince pie."

James was seen five minutes later taking his place in the front row of the choir with icing sugar all round his mouth and a smug look on his face. He proceeded to lick his lips and smile cheekily at his mother all through the opening carol, "Away in a Manger".

James to the rescue again. Christine was feeling so emotional but somehow her naughty son helped her keep things in perspective. Somehow each time she came to church she was finding it more and more difficult not to eye the crucified Christ with a resentful "Why aren't you helping us?" but then she looked at James - James cheerful as ever, accepting everything as normal. How easy it was to be four!

Peter gave Christine a gentle nudge – there was a special light in his face as the carol soared, the audience joining in while Anya, playing the part of the Virgin Mary, lifted baby Jesus from the manger with exquisite tenderness and gently pulled the tea towel away from his face to show him to Joseph, her tall gangly friend, Verity Moore. Peter was visibly moved. Christine put her arm through his, wondering if this would be their last Christmas. She blinked back her tears. She had to keep strong and to try to believe there was hope.

It was strange but here in church at Christmas she could respond with a cosy inner glow of goodness but she had no faith in the power of prayer, the way her mother-in-law did. In fact, if she were honest, the church had become an added pressure.

Anne, Peter's sister, had at last told her mother and father that Peter had cancer and that the prognosis was not good. They were devastated. Trying to focus her mother on the hope of a recovery, together Anne and the family succumbed to the full Catholic thing. They arranged regular masses to be said at their local catholic churches, held vigils and then had contacted the priest at St James the Less, Peter's church in Colchester. Peter was not pleased – the last thing he wanted was for people locally to know he needed praying for.

Father Seamus O'Leary, the local priest, began to visit. At least this seemed to help Peter come to terms with his doubts. Christine welcomed him tentatively, if only because it meant someone else, someone far better placed than her, could answer Pete's fears. For Peter, Father Seamus O'Leary was a kindred spirit. Their backgrounds, their training, their beliefs were allied. The priest's years of intensive theology had made him an intellectual but he was a man of the world and they could talk, and pray together.

For Christine he was an anathema – no, that was far too strong. Could he be her conscience, perhaps? It wasn't his fault that the Catholic Church was so all consuming. She just longed to challenge more strongly all the dogma, all alien to her simple C of E faith but she knew it probably just boiled down to resentment on her part. All the masses, all the prayers being said – honestly, would they do any good?

As she shut the door after him she snorted, "I can't believe he spends his life, on his knees praying. There are so many practical ways to help people. What a waste of time. What a waste of good manhood. At least Peter got away."

"No," she thought, "that's unkind. Christmas is coming - Peace on earth and love and joy and all that." Their message was sincere and she must make a big effort to "open her heart".

CHAPTER 33 – CHRISTMAS PARTIES

But it was also Christmas for the company. This was their first Christmas at Willis. Each department held a Beer and Bangers party and the weekend team had spent every Sunday through December cleaning up after them. The parties seemed to get wilder, some departments were more restrained than others, but free beer all night and greasy bangers and chips, were a lethal mixture. Aviation and Marine Departments vied with each other to drink their opposite numbers under the table.

Christine was called in at nine o'clock one Sunday morning by a despairing Bob, "Mrs Chapman, I am so sorry to call you on a Sunday morning but you have to come and see the state of things. Dribbles of vomit down the escalator glass. Tomato ketchup and mayonnaise sachets squirted all over the place. Honest, I am not exaggerating. I've spoken to Security and they think you should know."   It was so unlike Bob to ring her on a Sunday – it must be serious.

"Not a problem, Bob. I will be right there." She drove the car to Ipswich well in excess of the speed limit. She wondered how much tomato ketchup had hit its human target. "Lots" she hoped maliciously.

Bob hadn't exaggerated. The trajectories of tomato sauce, like exaggerated trails from snails after a wet night, stood out like fat red caterpillars as they climbed the bright yellow walls and snaked across the green carpet. The crimson tomato stains and the purple wine spillages on the carpet would involve painstaking hours to remove through spraying and blotting, spraying and blotting. Gill and Dawn sat back on their haunches in despair … piles of soggy paper, stained pink from their careful blotting surrounded them. "It makes you want to scrub but we know what that will do to this carpet. The trouble is the carpet pile is so thick and the wine has soaked in real deep. We will be blotting for ever."

Christine nodded. They were absolutely right. "Thank you so much. Your technique is spot on. Just do the best you can. We will have to carpet clean the whole floor but I will recommend that we do that at the end of January when all these wretched parties are over. Have a quick break now – I'll talk to the guys too. I need to record all this and I want your input."

Bob and Dick were tackling the dried up vomit. "If we'd known, we'd have come in late last night. It would have been so much easier when it was fresh. And the beer spillages – looks like whole glasses have been spilt and just left."

Christine knelt down and inspected a large brown patch in the carpet. Sure enough, the beer had penetrated right through to the depths of the tufts. It was a substantial spillage and no attempt had been made to mop it up.

Dealing with the deposits of vomit in the toilets was bad enough but in the large pots holding the ornamental palms at the top of the escalators, it was a dedicated task. The coloured pebbles had to be removed and sterilised. The plants were then watered with a mild organic pine solution to absorb the smell of sick and flush it through.

Christine was furious. This was entirely unnecessary – why did people behave like this? – Office workers, people who should know better.

Her despondent crew came over to the central coffee station. She thanked them all and acknowledging her sympathy, apologised, "I am so sorry. You have all worked your socks off. You must be sickened."

"You could say that!" said Bob with a wry smile. "And totally pissed too boot."

Christine continued, "We'll get you help and I promise you'll get double normal weekend rates. You deserve it and it will, I think, go some way towards sweetening the pill."

They all brightened visibly, especially when she told them to take as long as they needed. They needed reinforcements. She had telephoned Francesco and Maria and they were on their way. They would lap this up and fresh pairs of hands always helped. With luck by lunchtime they would all be singing, not perhaps opera - more likely, "I'm dreaming of a white Christmas."

She asked Bob to telephone her with a full report when they finished, and suggested they all stopped off for fish and chips if they worked after 5.00. Christine extracted £40 from her purse and handed it to Bob. They all returned to the task with renewed vigour. Even Doug on security thanked her for coming in.

As she drove home, she became more and more incensed. Her indignation grew. She slammed the front door. Peter and the children looked anxious. The angrier she got, the more determined she became. Willis were going to pay – not only would the cleaners get a bonus, but they were going to have a Christmas party too, funded by the profit!

She heard from Bob. It had taken over three times as long as normal to clear up. The fish and chip shops were all closed on a Sunday evening so they had gone to the pub and had a drink and several packets of crisps instead. Bob had paid out £28, a lot cheaper than fish and chips, as he was at pains to point out!

Christine thumped out a two page report illustrating in explicit detail the extent of the problem. She did not mince her words. She would deliver it to Mr Trenchard in the morning with an invoice – four times the normal charge for cleaning up after a Beer and Bangers Party. Her report made it clear that their service was not to be abused and as she ended with the time and date, she felt better.

On Monday morning Mr Trenchard was expecting her. He had already had a graphic report from Security. He studied her epistle, looked at the invoice and nodded. "I am sorry. I totally agree with you and will take this further. Have you had problems with these parties in the past?"

"Yes," said Christine. "But we have always taken them in our stride. There have been the odd nasties to deal with, like the weekend before last when there was vomit in the toilets and outside the building, but I have just paid a bonus to the guys who cleaned it up. This time it is totally out of order. Were there no senior management there?" Mr Trenchard raised a quizzical eyebrow. Senior management had obviously been there.

Three days later she had a formal letter of apology from the director of the department concerned, accepting the invoice and paying an additional sweetener for the cleaners.

Ros was gleeful and set about organising the Monthind Christmas Party. Surprise, surprise! - She had no trouble getting permission to hold it on the restaurant floor at Willis. All the Monthind staff – now over one hundred, were invited. Maria and Francesco (Frankie as he was now affectionately known by one and all), Mandy and Will with their teams of cleaners, as well as Peter and the office staff.

Ros thought of everything. Everyone received a Christmas card personally signed by all the office staff and a large box of Quality Street chocolates (another company tradition in the making). Key staff were given Christmas bonuses and there were special acknowledgements for those that had been outstanding.

Janet Jolly – not to be confused with Butch Janet – worked at Willis over the lunch period specifically to service the toilets. She tidied up, topped up the Janitorials and generally ensured they were immaculate. In the evenings she again checked the toilet roll dispensers were full, while the other ladies cleaned. Never, ever anywhere in the building had the toilet paper run out since Janet had been appointed. Lunchtime and evening she was always there. The Willis staff loved her. Nothing was too much trouble. She was charming and discreet, whether comforting a sobbing young lady whose boyfriend had dumped her or proffering a handful of her own scented Kleenex tissues to someone streaming with cold. (She kept several boxes, bought from Boots, on her trolley.) "Tissues are much softer than loo rolls," she would say, but also acutely aware that she would cop it from Pauline if she dispensed toilet paper.

Janet was always there, unobtrusive, gentle and always immaculately turned out. She wore her tabard with pride and loved her job in her own words – as "Loo Lady".

So on the night of their very first Christmas party when Christine read out her name, "I am proud to present the Attendance Award to … Janet Jolly", everyone beamed and applauded with gusto. As Christine presented her with a huge bouquet of flowers, Janet burst into tears. Christine put her arm round her and gently asked why the tears. She replied "I've never had flowers before and …. To get a bootiful booquet like this, in cellophane, you don't know …."

335

A big sob. "How I'll get them home I dun know? I can't go on the bus with them." Another sob, "What will my husband say? He won't like it one bit!"

"Don't worry Janet. I can take you home – it's on my way- you live off London Road, don't you."

"Oh! Would you? He wouldn't shout at you."   And the tears streamed down her face, until one of the ladies at the front handed her a long string of loo paper – that made her look up and smile, especially when a voice yelled out, "Pauline, did you see that!"

The presentations continued:

Francesco received a large bottle of Asti Spumante to acknowledge the fact that he had been part of every initial clean and proudly claimed to know every contract. Maria got a cheque to go some way towards the cost of ingredients for Panettone which caused another cheer! (Two months later she gave it back to Christine asking if she could exchange it for real money because none of them had a bank account.)

There were several more presentations to those who had regularly covered staff shortages and lots of hugging as friends approved.

Finally Christine thanked everyone and wished them all a Happy Christmas.

Staff sat around the large tables in their comfortable groups, laughing and joking. The wine and lemonade, often mixed together to sweeten it, flowed. Ros felt they should buy a sweeter wine like Blue Nun or Liebfraumilch another year but when they discussed it in the office Jen stated slightly sourly that it wasn't a bad idea if it was watered down with lemonade, muttering under her breath that it would keep the level of sobriety up as well as keeping the cost down.

The nibbles, including cakes from Maria, sausage rolls from Pauline, bridge rolls which the girls in the office had done, and mince pies from Gill and her mother were hungrily devoured.

At the end of the evening, Christine couldn't help noticing that Pauline was scooping up the paper plates and carefully putting all the left-overs into white plastic bags. Peanuts, crisps, sausage rolls, half full bottles of lemonade. Nothing was dumped.

She discreetly handed two cardboard boxes to Lilian and Phil to take home to their family, five children ranging in age from 13 to 3.

Noticing that Christine had seen this, Pauline came over and whispered in her ear that Phil had lost his job and they were "real strapped fer cash. "You know Mrs Chapman, Lil's dead worried about Christmas and the kids will love all this party food. Don't you worry though, we always tell Security," she added hastily. Christine looked slightly shocked. She knew so little about her people, their worries and their hardships. She just hoped the children hadn't been left on their own, although the eldest was probably almost old enough to officially babysit. She handed Pauline a couple of full bottles of wine before Ros could put them in a box to take back to the office, "Pop these in too."

Ros collected up about six unopened bottles of wine. It was always handy to have spares in the office, not to drink, of course, but as thank-you presents for the men. "What shall we do with the bottles that are half full?"

337

"I think you'd better empty them down the sink." Christine frowned. "I don't want our staff rolling down the street drinking from bottles."

"As if any of us would!" retorted Dawn. "Don't worry Mrs C. We'll just cork 'em up, put 'em in a bag and take 'em home for our hubbies. We don't want no wastage now, do we now? And my ole man loves his Liebfraumilk."

"Dawn, I think it's a French wine …"

"Oh well, he won't worry about that."

Christine shrugged and shook her head. "Do what you like but just don't upset security." She looked around for Janet, aware they should be going.

Hanna had warned Christine before that Janet's husband and son were slobs who did nothing around the house and expected her to wait on them hand and foot.

Christine could see that she was hovering anxiously in the background with her flowers so, beckoning her over, she collected her handbag and hastened Janet away, guiltily leaving Ros and the others to clean up.

Janet carried her bouquet self-consciously as they left the building and blushed deeply as Doug on Security called, "Well deserved, Janet. Happy Christmas".

As they walked up the garden path to Janet's house, the door was flung open. The horrid little man in his vest and shiny jogging bottoms stood astride in the doorway. "Where the hell have you been?" Suddenly, he espied Christine, who had taken the bouquet from Janet.

"Happy Christmas, Mr Jolly. I'm Mrs Chapman. I gave Janet a lift home because I wanted to meet you and tell you how fantastic she has been. She achieved perfect attendance but you know no one can do that without backing. I just wanted to thank you for the support you give her. A supportive family is terrific. Thank you so much. Can I come in for a moment?"

That shut him up. What a pig. What was it about these working class men who bullied their wives? Who often even abused their wives? No wonder so many of her ladies loved their jobs. The only place they felt valued. She handed the bouquet to Janet, "The flowers are a thank you from us all. I hope they will last over Christmas."

Janet smiled nervously … and started to move to the kitchen. "Will you have a cup of tea, Mrs Chapman?"

"No, No Janet thank you." She wouldn't stop. She needed to get back to her family. She held out her hand, "Mr Jolly have a lovely Christmas – I hope you will come with Janet to the party we are having in February. We like to say thank you to everyone who supports our staff and I think you'll enjoy the beer!"

Driving home, she wondered what sort of Christmas Janet would have, waiting hand and foot, no doubt, on that evil little man, as he sat doggedly watching his choice of programme on the telly.

CHAPTER 34 - LOURDES

Peter's mother, Ma, as he called her, had gone to the top. She had contacted the Catholic bishop at the Arundel and Brighton Dioceses - determined Peter should go on a pilgrimage to Lourdes. Lourdes? Christine was horrified. What was she playing at? Did she really believe in miracles, did she really?

Christine panicked. Peter couldn't go alone. He needed so much help, just to get dressed, and it would be very difficult for her to get away now with the children, the Willis contract and the business pressures. She also knew he couldn't go with his parents. Not that they had suggested that.

She spoke to Ros. Ros too was a devout Christian. She was adamant that if Peter wanted to go, they should go. She assured Christine the business would be fine.

But the children? Who would look after them? – Christine's mother? Perhaps she could come for the week and friends would help.

Christine reluctantly spoke to her mother. Christine's father had died just three years previously and to date she had kept Peter's illness a secret. Granny Pip lived in Devon so it had not been difficult to keep her in the dark. As Peter's appearance got more and more gaunt, it was obvious that as soon as they met at Christmas she would have to be told. She agreed to come and look after the children – it would be a break for her but she expressed her scepticism in no uncertain terms, "Lourdes, Christine – do you honestly think that will help? Do you have to pay for it? Personally, I think you'd do far better have a week away pampering yourselves in a decent hotel in Devon."

Christine tried to explain … but it fell on deaf ears.

On the next visit to the Royal Marsden, Peter spoke to the consultant, gentle Mr Davidson, who, to Christine's horror, told Peter he should go. "There is nothing more I can do, I am afraid." The latest scan had shown the tumour on the liver had grown. Peter asked about a donor liver but the surgeon just shook his head grimly, "The liver is like a compost. If we gave you a transplant, the cancer would grow again infecting the donor organ." They were devastated.

Lourdes. Christine started to read about Saint Bernadette and the sacred grotto. The pictures of the crutches hanging up, discarded by healed pilgrims. What absolute twaddle. She thought the whole thing a hideous hoax.

She dreaded the very idea of travelling with scores of sick people, albeit there would be helpers and nurses. But a week? How would the children cope? Perhaps a nanny, if her mother couldn't come. It was a long way off. The pilgrimage went in July.

Two charmingly understanding ladies from the Arundel & Brighton pilgrimage office, told her not to worry. All she had to do was to get to Portsmouth dock, the ferry port, where they would be waiting and where everything would be taken out of her hands. They would be allocated a handmaiden who would be Peter's carer and a "brancardier", a young man who would push his chair everywhere.

Peter would be given a wheel chair and would sleep in the patient's car in the Wagons Lit train. She would be able to spend time with him but would have her own sleeping bunk a few carriages away for the long train journey across France. There would be qualified doctors and nurses on board throughout. Priests would also be there on call. They assured her that the hotel accommodation in Lourdes was five-star and that the whole experience would be wonderfully uplifting.

Christine thought it sounded exhausting. She talked to Pete at length. He was going through a crisis, blaming himself for leaving the church for being a bad Catholic, for spending months abroad, for being a bad father etc. He was desperate about leaving her to bring up the children alone and kept repeating "I so wanted to see Anya married. I never will now."

Christine fighting not to cry, gently asked him if he thought he could manage the trip. His quiet answer was "I have to. You heard what Mr Davidson said, I am in God's hands now."

Meantime his mother had called them to say that Lady Sarah Fitzallan Howard, "You know the Duke of Norfolk's daughter," was organising the pilgrimage and the Bishop of Arundel & Brighton, Cormac Murphy O'Connor was leading it, as though this made them privileged to be included. Somehow though it did make Christine feel better – 250 sick people were going – well over 1000 people in total, so perhaps it wouldn't just be a large group of devout Irish Catholics, sick sad widows, ancient nuns telling their rosaries and gaga invalids hobbling around on crutches. Regardless, they had to go.

They arrived at the dock in Portsmouth. She drove to the Port reception where they were met by the Pilgrimage organisers. Immediately Peter was allocated a wheelchair. He was not happy but a kindly doctor patted him on the shoulder and said, "Take it, son. If you don't need it, your wife and I can take it in turns to have a sit. Believe me Lourdes is hilly and a test even for the fit and strong!"

The Channel crossing was smooth and without incident but the train journey worried her. How could she relax? Peter was five lurching carriages away, in the patients' car. She was sharing with three ladies she had never met before. She hated this. She had to keep up appearances to keep Peter happy. She made her way to him as often as she could but the aisle between bunks was a thoroughfare for doctors, handmaids and the catering staff. Peter hadn't slept either but he was quick to praise the doctors and to make light of his ailments in comparison with others far worse off than he. Miserable and feeling helpless, Christine bit her tongue and made her way back to her carriage.

The train's stately arrival into Lourdes was spectacular – the basilica in the early morning light dominated the beautiful valley. Faint strains of the Ave Maria gradually grew louder, ensuring a hallowed hush as everyone stood at the train windows to marvel at the beauty of the scenery and the spectacle of the basilica silhouetted against the sky. There was an air of expectancy and wonder.

Then came the unloading of the train, the bustle, the noise. Patients on stretchers were taken off first. Christine shuddered – it reminded her of a scene from a WW2 war film. She and Peter waited, absorbing the organisation and the sense of expectation but at the same time anxious to get to their hotel room. Neither of them had slept well.

Eventually Peter, hunched in his wheelchair, was allocated a handmaid, a pretty teenager called Annette, and a brancardier, Jerry. Then came the walk to the hotel. Christine felt for Peter. The wheelchair bumped and jolted on the cobbles and they weaved through hundreds of hideous tourists in T shirts and trainers, cameras slung round their necks. Jerry did his best to manoeuvre through the crowds and tilted the wheelchair carefully as he mounted the pavements.

The garish shops with flashing Madonnas, statues of Saint Bernadette, plastic bottles of Holy Water and chilled cans of Coca Cola all mixed up together. The endless slow moving queues of pilgrims, many in wheel chairs or peculiar carriages with hoods. What had they come to? Christine could feel her anger mounting. She was really going to struggle with this.

The masses – two a day. The candle lit procession – the Ave Marias echoing in the valley, so hauntingly beautiful. The young people so upbeat and wanting to please but she found everything slightly false and unnerving.

The priests, she secretly watched them – they seemed to glory in their status, like actors on a stage in their glorious costumes. Humility? There they were in their magnificent, rich robes, laughing and chatting together as though this was one big holiday – an old boys outing.

She observed the suffering around her – how many of those poor people were really going to be healed? Old ladies bent double, men with sticks, youngsters hobbling bravely on crutches and the ashen faced stretcher bound. She wondered what the purpose of the whole trip was. They didn't all believe surely that they would be cured or was it, as it was for Peter, a final desperate hope?

Certainly for the young people who were giving up two weeks of their summer holidays, to dedicate themselves to caring for others, they would go home "well satisfied", feeling good about themselves, having made lovely friends and coming away for the better.

Some of the patients were enjoying the affection, the caring and the company of cheerful young carers. For them it was an escape from a dreadful care home – a genuine holiday. Perhaps some of them really believed that they would return blessed, even healed and certainly with hope for the future.

Christine felt none of this – she was just assessing the harm this might have done. Peter seemed tired and drawn. A pilgrimage to Lourdes is no doddle even for the fit and certainly not the holiday she would have chosen for the seriously ill. The train journey is long. Every road is steep, there are steep steps everywhere. The waiting either in the beating sunshine or the cold wind and even the rain seems endless and the weather is never the same from one day to the next.

On one occasion in a huge underground cathedral, she was separated from Pete so that he could receive the special anointing of the sick and a blessing along with hundreds of other poor suffering people. She sat rows up, high above the priests and the sick, like a distant voyeur in the inexpensive seats at a football match. She looked down at his hunched figure in a wheel chair, recognising his wig and his smart blazer.

Suddenly, the desperation of the whole charade hit her and she began to sob, silently to begin with, then with the sobs wracking her whole body. The people on either side eyed her anxiously. She knew no one. Someone passed her a tissue. But it was sodden immediately. More tissues arrived. The pretty young girl on her left put her arm around her. "Are you alright?" Christine nodded – what could you say? That's my husband down there and he's dying. She felt totally alone, totally bereft and totally abandoned. This pilgrimage was supposed to help?

People stood around her. Several thousand voices swelled, the sound reaching a crescendo. "Bind us together, Lord, bind us together with cords that cannot be bro – o-ken. Bind us together, Lord, bind us together, Lord, Bind us together in love." The refrain mesmerised her and she wanted to reach out to Peter. The pile of sodden tissues grew.

But eventually she pulled herself together, as she must. She was angry with herself, red-eyed and puffy faced. This wasn't about her. She was here for Peter. He was going to get better. Whatever she might feel, this was about Catholic faith and Peter had plenty of that.

Perhaps this was what she needed, alone with strangers, and to look from afar at the situation. She had to try to embrace it.

At least she could lose herself in the music, the incredible sound of thousands of voices all raised in wonderful harmony. The hymns new to her, Bind us together Lord, Lord of the Dance, haunting Ave Maria's, even the canned versions over the loud speakers, constantly reminded her why they were here and somehow soothed her. She had even learnt to say the Hail Mary in French … as well as Latin and English. Sigh. She was still not totally comfortable.

And then there were the baths – the whole thought of this repulsed her. Being dipped half naked, or was it totally naked, into the holy water, wrapped in a cold, wet sheet. How many other pilgrims had been dunked in the same water, wrapped in the same grey sheet? No, she really did not fancy that.

But horror of horrors – they weren't subjecting Peter to that? The thought of his emaciated pale frame being man handled into one of the grim stone baths horrified her. He surely wouldn't agree to it. She had to make sure it didn't happen.

No, she mustn't say anything. Perhaps it was in the baths where the miracles happened. Sighing heavily, she realised she was here, she must give everything credence – just in case. Oh God, to be home, back to normality and where she felt she had some control. This was awful, just awful.

But the evening before they were due to make the tortuous journey home, she suddenly found an extraordinary sense of peace.

One of the Nuns had asked them if they wanted to go to the Grotto late at night. Christine was dubious – they had been several times before as part of the huge crowd, but Peter nodded. He acquiesced to everything.

Jerry happily agreed to collect them. They quietly crossed the deserted street from the hotel and made their way silently to the Grotto. Clouds flitted across the clear moonlit sky, and brilliant groups of stars shone above them. With the moon reflecting in the puddles they stood silently in front of the Virgin Mary's statue with just a handful of other worshippers. The white figure of Our Lady set high up in its alcove in the natural rock, looked ethereal, making Christine reflect that this is how Bernadette must have seen her in her visions.

Jerry had silently handed the locked wheelchair to Christine, whispering – "Just wave to me when you are ready to leave."

The sensitivity of this eighteen year old student was, for Christine, one of the wonders of Lourdes. He had been at their side constantly. He checked the daily schedule, anxiously enquiring if Peter wanted to be involved. He took infinite care not to jolt the wheelchair having picked up that Peter winced with pain at every jarring manoeuvre. And here he was, waiting silently in the shadows, instead of downing pints of beer in the bar, as so many of his mates must be doing.

Peter sat wrapped in the blue and gold Arundel and Brighton blankets, his eyes fixed on the ghostly white statue. Strangely Christine didn't feel the cold, strangely she didn't feel tired or impatient. She just felt the need to say thank you …. For what, she wasn't sure. She was just glad she had come. She moved to Peter's side. He looked up and said quietly, "It's going to be OK." She smiled and bent down, taking his hand in hers. Oddly comforted, she nodded and said after a while, "Are you ready to go?" Peter lent back, his eyes closed and Christine turned to beckon Jerry who, as they made their way silently through the now deserted streets, said in a hushed voice, "I'll be waiting for you after breakfast in the morning to take you to the train. I've asked if I can stay with you till we get back home."

This was music to Christine's ears. Jerry who had become adept at smoothing the way and interpreting Peter's every need, talked to them about his Mum who had MS and about his dream to become a doctor. Here was a lad who would go far and Christine hoped that her comments about him on the questionnaire she had been asked to complete, might somehow find their way onto his CV.

The long journey home was completely different. People had made friends and were at ease with each other. The prayers over the train's loudspeaker system were personal and she recognised the deep warm voice of the Bishop and the dulcet Irish lilt of the priest who had stayed in their hotel. The prayers were punctuated by jokes about the young carers and the hymns by songs like "We'll Meet Again" and "The White Cliffs of Dover".

For some it had been a holiday, for others a chance to make lasting friendships. For two young helpers it had been an opportunity to find romance with like-minded youngsters who at school would be mocked for their faith. For others it was a time of contemplation and quiet acceptance of their fate. Sadly for some, it marked the end of a brief respite from their tedious, daily existence. Tomorrow they would be back in their dreary care homes, back at home alone with the memory, and perhaps with a ray of hope that someone they had met would remember them, would even visit. Everyone seemed at peace, even uplifted and although there were tears as people said their goodbyes and their thanks on the dockside, many of them were genuine about keeping in touch.

As they disembarked numerous people they had met came over to wish them well, doctors, nurses, priests and friends from their hotel.

Jerry insisted on escorting Christine to the car in the car park, putting the cases into the boot and helping settle Peter into the passenger seat. Then he solemnly shook hands with Peter, saying, "You're going to get through this, mate." "Yes," replied Peter, "and you're going to make a brilliant doctor." Both spoke with total conviction. Christine had been holding back her emotions, but as she hugged Jerry, humbled that this strong young man cared and that he had paid (as had all these young carers) to spend his holiday looking after them, she felt the tears welling up. She thanked him yet again and she was amazed to hear herself saying, "Please keep in touch."

They drove home from Portsmouth, exhausted but somehow she felt better equipped to face the future. Perhaps that was the message of Lourdes.

CHAPTER 35 – EXPANSION

Granny Pip and the children welcomed them back delighted, each having had enough of each other to last a very long time. Christine's mother was anxious to get home but not before she had made a few snide remarks, "No miracle then?" Christine found herself retorting sharply, "Mum, that wasn't what it was about!"

"No? Well why on earth did you go then?"

"It was about preparing for the future – in Pete's case, for death." Christine shocked herself. She had never considered that he might not recover. Even in Lourdes where two sick people on their Pilgrimage had died, she never once imagined that Peter would die. Appalled, she couldn't believe she had said that, but she realised with a jolt that it was the truth.

What's more, it silenced her mother. What's more she now had hope. Despite what the consultant had said, "There is no cure. This melanoma is terminal," Peter seemed so much better.

Granny Pip left in the morning, her attitude quite different. She and Christine hugged and her mother said simply, "If you need me, just ring."

Ros reported on Monthind, proudly telling her that everything had been fine. Whether it really had been or not Christine would never know.

Working from the kitchen table had become impossible. Peter was finding the constant activity, the phone calls, and the deliveries of cleaning materials, disruptive. There was never any peace. Ros desperately needed help with the wages and the admin. Finding staff to come and work for them was not a problem. There were numerous ladies who wanted part-time work to fit around their families. The problem was where could they work? They had to find an office.

Anya's very best friend was Natalie and James's best friend was Stephen and now they all attended the Convent together. Their mother, Simone Abbott, was an enormous help to Christine by constantly ferrying the children to and from their evening activities. Their father, Jonathan, was a commercial estate agent and as soon as Christine mentioned to him the need to find an office with stores, he was on the case and within a week had come up with what sounded like the ideal solution.

They could take on a small amount of the available space on offer at the moment but there was plenty of room for expansion later. He arranged to show Christine the building, where the best thing was the low rent. It was well within their range and that was more than essential at the moment – if something can be more than essential!

The offices were on the opposite side of town for Christine, the East side. She wondered whether it was always true that the most salubrious houses were always built on the west side of town, the West End. Wasn't it due to prevailing wind blowing all the nasty odours from west to east? Certainly that applied to the East End of London years ago, but here and now? Perhaps that was more than she needed to worry about at this precise moment!

On arrival at their potential new offices they looked at the rooms on offer – four in total. The house had been the old Rectory and was a beautifully balanced building, but surprise, surprise; despite its age there were plenty of power points.

She immediately fell in love with the high ceilings and the proportions. Upstairs was occupied by a naval architect and seemed to be full of drawing boards but very few people.

Jonathan took her and introduced her to the landlord, a Mr Les Champion.

Mr Champion was anything but Christine's idea of a Champion. He was small with a hump back, his hair looked greasy and he had large flakes of dandruff on his collar. When he leered at her as he took her hand and bent over it, Christine thought he was going to kiss it and promptly stepped back bumping into Jonathan. She pulled herself upright, pleased that in her heels she towered over this seedy little man. His smile was fixed, showing his huge rabbit teeth, yellow and desperately in need of flossing, and little globules of spittle in each corner of his loose, half open mouth.

She suppressed a shudder because everything about this odd-ball of a man was creepy. He was the landlord, the boss though, so she must not let her personal susceptibilities get in the way. There were things which needed sorting and now was the time to sort them if they were going to exist amicably side by side. She could imagine him rubbing his hands in glee at the thought of having this naïve, woman who had never rented before as his tenant, she glanced at Jonathan.

She really liked the offices and most of all the low cost rent, which unbelievably included electricity and water, at almost half the cost of what she would pay in the west of town. The worries about prevailing winds palled into insignificance and she forced herself to focus!

The leering, spooky little landlord, with his fixed toothy smile still in place, said, "I gather you've looked around. Everything's been newly painted. You won't have any problems here. Now come into my office and we can have a cosy chat." Christine supressed a shudder and nodded coldly, saying in an attempt to tone down the strength of the word cosy! "Yes, there are one or two things we need to sort out."

Mr Champion clicked his fingers at the lady working at a Dickensian desk laden with bills, some on large metal spikes and others held together with enormous black bulldog clips. "Jean, we need coffee."

"No thank you," said Christine sharply. "I prefer to talk without distractions." They moved through into a large meeting room. Mr Champion sat down and indicated Christine to the chair to his right. She moved to the other side of the table and Jonathan joined her facing their adversary.

"Firstly, Mr Champion, the toilets. We cannot countenance sharing lavatories with other tenants or your staff." Christine came straight to the point. "Secondly, we need four guaranteed parking spaces."

"Well, now the square footage you are renting only warrants two …"

"Mr Champion, two parking spaces are not enough for me. It has to be four or …" Shaking her head, she started to pick up her notebook but before she could rise, Mr Champion put his hands up defensively. The fixed smile still in place but he was beginning to realise that Christine was no push-over.

"Maybe, um maybe we can juggle things around. I suppose a couple of the lads can park over the road."

"And the toilets....?"

"It's only Mr Jones from upstairs and the lady in the shop that use them," he wheedled.

Christine shook her head. "That's not acceptable, Mr Champion. We can't countenance sharing with anyone else. We must have them for our sole use, we will clean them, maintain them and we don't want any complications. I should tell you now we are expanding fast and I shall certainly need more space before the end of the year. These offices have been empty for over six months and, I am sorry, but my references are exemplary.

There are other options we are considering. In fact there are numerous offices we have to look at so I would prefer not to waste my time or, indeed, your time." Again she started to rise.

Mr Champion was pulling at his chubby fingers. He opened his mouth to talk. The spittle, now in foam form had spread beyond the corners of his mouth and he looked appealingly at Jonathan, who shrugged his shoulders and smiled. "Sorry, Les. I think you've just met a lady who knows her mind, and she has a point, there's plenty of empty office space around. One thing I can vouch for is that you won't have any trouble from Mrs Chapman and that counts for a lot these days!"

There was a silence. Mr Champion was looking at her hard. Christine met the look and raised her eyebrows questioningly. Mr Champion nodded slowly, "Ok, but we will need to review things at the end of the year."

Christine standing now ... "May I leave it to you gentlemen to organise the paper-work with the extra parking and the toilet issue fully addressed. Also, there are to be no increases of any kind for a year unless we require more space when we can, of course, review the situation."

Christine reluctantly extended her hand, allowing the tips of her fingers to briefly make contact. Why did she find this man so repulsive?

Outside, Jonathan put his hand on her arm. "Wow, you are one tough cookie. I thought I was going to have to fight your corner but you don't need me. Les quite fancies himself as a property developer and owns property all over town. He's loaded, is as tight as a tick and fleeces everyone but you handled him perfectly AND I reckon you will have him eating out of your hand." This was not a vision Christine relished.

"Don't, Jonathan, he gives me the creeps, he's so obsequious and seedy. But it is funny, you know, because it feels good to be on the other side of the coin for once. I am always having to make concessions and to persuade people to employ us and to grovel when our service isn't up to scratch. I rather like the role reversal being the buyer not the seller. Mmm the boot's well and truly on the other foot today and I've got what I wanted." Horrified suddenly at her attitude, she added, "But I wasn't nasty was I?"

"Noo oh. Not nasty but you knew what you wanted, and no one was going to mess with you. I can see now why you've got quite a reputation and I think Les Champion has met his match! But watch him in the future!" Jonathan was laughing.. "Shall we go somewhere and have a cup of coffee now to celebrate?"

Shaking her head, Christine said, "I don't think that's a good idea and I have so much to do."

Jonathan was clearly disappointed at this abrupt rebuttal but the last thing Christine wanted was for someone to see her with Jonathan and then tell his wife that they had been in some café together.

Two days later Jonathan rang to ask if he could pop in as he just needed her signature - everything had been sorted and she could even move in before the end of the month with no extra payment.

"Oh Jonathan, you are a star!"

"No Chris, you're the one that pulled it off superbly. You've really got an amazing deal you know and I had to laugh because that has to be a first with Champion.

He told me he sat outside your house watching you take in a delivery – the delivery man doffed his cap and called you Mam while you checked everything off on the delivery note, getting the poor guy to unload and stack a full pallet of cleaning fluid for you in the garage. Les was highly impressed - 'I could do with her running things for me. What do you reckon, mate, think I could make her an offer?'"

Jonathan was laughing. "I told him I would think twice about it as you'd probably eat him for breakfast."

Christine was slightly unnerved at the thought of her future landlord watching her house but Jonathan clearly thought it was amusing.

With a proper office they would now be able to take on the admin staff they so desperately needed. Ros was thrilled as they urgently needed a book-keeper, for a start. A friend of Christine's had come in occasionally to help out but she suddenly thought better of it saying "I value our friendship

and worry that if we work together we might well fall out."
Ros nodded, for the friend had surely hit the nail on the head when she had said "Christine likes her own way."

Nonetheless, very soon afterwards she had recommended a friend of her own, Jen, another single Mum who needed the flexibility of taking time off in the school holidays.

When she heard that it was their "company policy" to keep non-essential administrative work to a minimum during school holidays and that their policy was that VAT returns, year-end accounts and the like were all completed during term time, making the company perfect for everyone with children, she jumped at the job. She soon learnt, however, that nothing must interfere with the payroll, which had to be done on time. Living as they did from hand to mouth, cleaners had to have their wage packets in their hands on the same day at the same time every week, come hell or high water.

Despite this, there was a sympathetic attitude to taking time off for child sickness, dental appointments, breast screening or whatever and on many an occasion a child with a runny nose was found tucked away in a corner drawing or colouring quietly. After all, they were all in the same boat – juggling children and work with not a man between them.

As a result of this flexibility in the office there was also an unwritten rule that whenever a cleaning crisis arose or a new contract started, the office staff were there pulling their weight. Everyone was expected to lend a hand cleaning and whenever there was an initial clean, the office staff were there in force, Christine at the fore.

All this meant expenditure. Christine was determined not to draw a salary until her debts were settled but she struggled to cover the mortgage, school fees and food. She had no qualms about the company paying for the car or even for Rebecca, after all she was cleaning the "office", at least up until when they moved, of course.

Christine had reluctantly borrowed £6000 to finance the capital equipment needed for the Willis Faber contract promising to pay it back within six months. She really baulked at paying interest to the bank. Even the thought of borrowing the money hurt. She had made an arrangement to see Mr Clough, the Midland Bank Manager and prepared for the meeting carefully with Peter rehearsing every word with her beforehand. She up-dated the Business Plan taking great satisfaction in their achievements since the days of Halls and AUEW.

The fact that the Bank Manager lived just four doors away from them in Elm Drive may have had a bearing on the ease with which she secured an overdraft. Ever since, however, he had insisted on a three monthly meeting with management accounts plus annual accounts being presented to him for a formal review. Christine resented this, not so much because it was an infringement of their affairs but more because she was terrified he would pick up that she didn't really understand how to read the accounts.

Christine may have looked at the accounts with some dismay but she was a true a disciple of Mrs Thatcher's grocers' economy, and certainly harkened back to Mr Macawber's sound financial advice as to the secret of business success "Annual income twenty pounds, annual expenditure nineteen pounds nineteen and six, result happiness. Annual income twenty pounds, annual expenditure twenty pounds ought and six, result misery."

CHAPTER 36 – CHAMPION LOSES

What Christine did know was precisely what it cost to run each contract and exactly how much they made every four weeks. She was always looking for ways to up the value of the contract, to increase the rate of pay to the cleaners and, of course, the profit margin. With her finger on the pulse in this way she had absolute confidence that the overall figures had to add up.

She suddenly realised with horror that the new office would need furnishing. There was no way she was going to ask Mr Champion for help but they did need at least four desks and chairs and they certainly couldn't afford anything new, although she dreamt about a huge desk for herself, the sort she frequently had to sit opposite at BComm and Willis.

It would also be useful to have a large table to use for meetings. Well, that was no problem because they could have the dining room table. Peter reminded her that the furniture he had had in his office had been stored and would be perfect. Christine hadn't even been aware of this – with horror she realised that when Peter was working she really hadn't got involved or been interested in the day-to-day stuff. How things had changed!

The move wouldn't be a problem. Will would borrow a van from the Co-op dairy and come over with Francesco at the weekend and sort out the furniture. Will was itching to see the office and he and Mandy had become good friends with F and M. Maria insisted on coming too so she could clean up after them. How blessed Christine was! The only trouble was it all cost money!

Ros would run down the supplies in the garage but all future orders would be delivered to the new premises.

Christine had to concede that Les Champion was co-operation in the extreme, handing over the key personally and offering his lads to carry things in for them.

Peter's old desks looked unkempt and dusty. Maria washed them down and then, as a true Italian, asked Christine for olive oil "for feeda da wood". Not happy at the thought of using her expensive culinary olive oil on these dirty old desks, Christine had triumphantly come back with a bottle of rather dark linseed oil which Peter had for years used on his cricket bats, saying, "I think this might be just as good!" She had paused as she took the bottle from the shelf, reflecting sadly that Peter would have no further need of it now, before handing the bottle to Maria who removed the screw top with difficulty and sniffed suspiciously. Unimpressed she muttered, "Eez smell … old." Christine tried to reassure her telling her, "But Maria it is very good for wood. The English cricket team use it for their bats! You try …"

Totally mystified about this odd smelling oil and its English use, Maria, obliging as always, took a duster and proceeded to polish. The result was astonishing and even Maria was smiling. She used the entire bottle and held up her hands now stained dark brown, "Eez OK but, you know, Olio olivio smell better," but she stood back with a smile of satisfaction on her face as she admired her work.

The desks had come with an assortment of typists' chairs and three rather battered filing cabinets which were far from ideal but they would have to do.

As for the toilets, subjected to Monthind's vigorous regime, they were transformed in no time. Maria was over the moon and … out came the panettone as they all sat down for a coffee. Christine could tell Will was itching to get back to Ipswich and she knew that by nightfall the cleaners'

361

grapevine would be circulating a vivid description with every detail of their new HEAD OFFICE.

They were becoming increasingly behind with paperwork, and with the need to man the telephone in the evenings, Christine knew she had to cut Ros's hours during the day so that she could handle problems which arose during the evening cleaning period. On top of this she herself was getting more and more stressed about Peter. Now they had an office they could recruit more help to take away the mundane admin work as well as the payroll and the accounts which Jen was now looking after. A trained secretary would be far too expensive and anyway what woman with any qualifications would want to work for a cleaning company? Christine was well aware that the stigma really existed.

Convinced the way forward was to recruit and train someone young, they advertised for an office junior. Ros was delighted at the response and set about interviewing several young girls. She finally convinced Christine that Bev, straight from school, would be the perfect choice despite the fact that throughout her interview Bev hadn't once smiled.

There was no eye contact and she clearly was very, very nervous. Young Bev was tall, almost six foot, and gangly, but her school report was superb - the words 'hard working', 'conscientious', 'diligent' and 'a sound team player' clinched it. She had also taken a course in audio typing and when Ros had asked her about this, she had reluctantly admitted she had been top of the class.

Bev's first week was agony for all concerned. She was desperately shy and obviously terrified of Christine but dear, maternal, Ros, patient as ever, showed her how to make the tea and lay out a letter. Once she had mastered this she proved remarkably fast at typing, the

362

golf ball typewriter hummed under her nimble fingers. To begin with she took every letter she typed for Christine to Ros for proof reading and several attempts later with Ros's approval she would put them in the "for signature folder" at the end of the day. Christine quickly realised the need to spell every name, and even tricky words like practice and practise, as she dictated into the machine. Slowly Bev plucked up confidence and began to ask the difference and Christine soon found she could put funny comments on the machine and even have a little joke with her budding secretary.

Taking on more office staff meant that they needed more room still. Christine dreaded the day she would have to tackle Mr Champion. She had learnt early on to avoid him. On the couple of occasions when she had bumped into him coming out of the shop, he had immediately tried to engage her in conversation, putting his hand on her arm to restrain her flight and leering at her through his foggy glasses. She was beginning to wonder if she was really getting obsessional about cleaning when she felt the urge to clean Mr Champion's glasses. She wished she could ask Peter but his sense of humour had totally left him – pain control was all that mattered now.

She asked Bev to make an appointment for her to see Mr Champion. She extracted the rent document from the filing cabinet and spent an hour with Jen calculating how much extra space they needed and what it ought to cost them based on their previous canny deal.

As luck would have it they had learnt that the naval architect was planning to move – there were far too many rooms upstairs for just one man. There was also space at the back of the courtyard, next to Mr Champion's offices. Christine's skin crept at the thought. She was going to have to spell out what she wanted.

She walked into Mr Champion's office. "Take a seat, my dear." Christine suppressed a shudder – he so reminded her of Fagin, the Ron Moody version, sucking his teeth and rubbing his hands together. "Jean is just going to bring us a coffee." She could tell he was getting cosy. "Mr Champion, as I expected we are going to need more space very shortly. I have heard that the naval architect is moving out ..."

His mouth was working fast, like a rabbit nibbling lettuce, showing his evil, yellow teeth. "Well, that's not for sure, my dear. And ..we ..err .. have other plans." He sniffed.

Christine raised an eyebrow. Why was it when she didn't like someone, she became coldly calculating and a formidable opponent? "Mr Champion, let's not beat about the bush. We need more space. It will be in your interest and in mine if you can release additional office space upstairs for me fairly quickly. I am sure you don't want vacant offices or the trouble of finding new tenants, and I would prefer not to have to move, incurring heaven knows what extra costs for new stationery, telephones etc."

"But, my dear, it would be better if you could move in here next to me, until we sort things out with Mr Miller. He isn't sure exactly when he wants to leave. That will give us time to work out what's best." Mr Champion smiled his ingratiating smile.

Christine could see a drip forming in his left nostril. It was beginning to change shape. Concentrate .....

She coughed. The drip was growing, Mr Champion reached for his handkerchief. "But that will mean we have to move twice. Have you spoken to Mr Miller? Perhaps if you offered him the space over here rent free, he might be very happy. After all you would be receiving rent from me for the whole building. At some stage too we are going to need more room for stores – then perhaps we could look at the stores over here." Christine pushed it hard, confident that she knew more about Mr Miller than Mr Champion did.

After all, she had talked it over carefully with Ros. Ros, who was everyone's agony aunt, had had several conversations with Alistair Miller about his estranged wife, his children and his worries about his business. He used to employ two people in these offices but there just wasn't enough work to support them, so he had decided to move to West Mersea, the island hub of sailing in the area. He had earmarked offices above a ships' chandlers very close to the flat he had found. That way he would be close to the yachting fraternity and to his children, and wouldn't have to worry about the tides morning and evening. Residents of Mersea Island had to contend with high tides regularly cutting them off from mainland Essex.

With this information from Ros, Christine knew she had the best solution for everyone, although perhaps Mr Champion would need a little persuading. The yellowish handkerchief had caught the drip. She swallowed half of her black coffee and then stood up, smiled and said, "Thank you so much for the coffee, Mr Champion. Please give it some thought. I would appreciate if you could come back to me by the end of the week – I just know we will be able to work this out together." She gave him her most persuasive smile and held out her hand.

Needless to say, two weeks later things were settled and Mr Champion's lads were in at the weekend, giving upstairs a lick of paint before once again helping with the move. Christine now had a huge office to herself, with a "boardroom" table for meetings. Actually it was Simone and Jonathan's old dining room table and chairs, but it looked good! Christine had asked Jonathan to check the new tenancy agreement with Mr Champion. He had refused to charge so she had insisted on paying him over the odds for the table. Bev, to her credit, planned the whole move. She and Ros had the main office which also served as reception, Jen and newly recruited Nicola formed the accounts department in the quiet back room, and stores would be downstairs.

Gradually, over the months, Bev had blossomed and they were able to laugh about her early habit of hiding in the huge walk-in stationery cupboard rather than answering the telephone. It had taken several weeks before she plucked up courage to take calls especially when there was no one else there to ask what to do.

Jen, who had taken over the payroll and the accounts was already beginning to struggle as they took on more cleaners and the weekly wages process became more and more demanding.

A suggestion from Christine to put everyone on a monthly salary was met with horror by the cleaners. Very few had a bank account and even more wanted their money cash in hand, because it was theirs, not their husband's, and they counted on it to pay for food, school meals and to save a bit for Christmas. Eventually they risked a compromise – wages would still be paid in cash but once a fortnight.

Encouraged by their success with school leaver Bev, they then recruited Nicky, whose school report highlighted her instinctive aptitude for figures. Barely five feet tall, she tottered about in her very high heels and her very mini 'mini skirts'. She was a perfect contrast to Bev – short, outgoing and feisty but surprisingly they became the best of friends and made a striking pair when they went out together.

Nicky, aged just seventeen, lived with a gormless guy who was out of work and spent most of his time fishing off Walton pier. She had had no home support and both Ros and Jen extended their parental roles to include Nicky. They pushed her to study, arranging for her day release to attend college. They pushed her to take her accounting exams and regularly counselled her when she and boyfriend, Leroy, had a row. More and more frequently Nicky would be found sobbing over the wages "He doesn't want me to go to evening classes at college. He wants me home every night with dinner on the table. He's going to kick me out and then where'll I go?"

Bev who had wonderful support from home and who had never had a boyfriend looked on in horror.

Not totally sure whether Nicky was attention seeking, or genuinely afraid of Leroy, Jen and Ros eventually persuaded her to leave Leroy and go and live with her Gran. What a transformation!

CHAPTER 37 – THE CLEANERS' BALL

The girls in the office, Jen and Ros included, were excited as arrangements for the Cleaners Ball got well under way. This was the first time Monthind had done a Christmas Party for the whole company which they now calculated numbered over 400 staff so if only half of them came and some brought their partners, the number attending could be as many as 300.

Jen had organised a savings scheme, £1 per week. Some of the cleaners had been saving for months, some even putting away £3 per pay-day towards a new dress for the event.

It was agreed that a bus would be provided from the centre of town, with drop off points on the way home in all the big council estates.

The original plan was to have a sit-down meal, just simple roast chicken followed by apple pie, but as the numbers increased Jen became more and more concerned about the cost of everything. They had never imagined the turnout would be so high. Drinks were not to be free – it was even agreed that they would not subsidise prices at the bar either. Christine was adamant about that and if Christine was adamant then that was how it would be.

There would be a disco for dancing and in Christine's mind she was also adamant that she would not be dancing to it!

After much discussion amongst the office girls, they decided they could do a more-than-adequate buffet that would reduce the cost to well under £8 per head, half the cost the hotel had quoted for a sit down meal. Bev's mother, Sandra, who had been in catering, then took over organising it, saying she'd love to help. Christine was amazed, particularly as she was adamant she didn't want paying for her time, just for the food she bought.

Wherever Christine went people were talking about it. What colour frock they would be wearing? The girls at Willis were in a frenzy. Mathilda wasn't going to buy an new outfit. "I'm wearing me anniversary Sunday best." Pauline reported that "Anne's wearing a floaty jobby and she says it's a bit see-frough. I said to her go on girl you'll knock em for six in that."

"What are you going to wear, Mrs Chapman?"

Who was on the top table? Who was sitting with who? 'Who was sitting with WHOM?' was certainly not how their staff would say it!

It was an eye-opener for Christine as she realised that this was going to be the social night of the year, or their lives, for many of her ladies. For some, this was their one night out, and, boy, were they going to have a party. Come to think about it, this would be HER one night out for a year and, boy, she was dreading it.

"Well, Chris, what are you going to wear?" The girls in the office wanted to know.

"I think a suit of some sort."

"You can't do that – you've really got to be glamorous. Everyone's saying you'll be in a really fab dress. You're so elegant. Everyone's saving up. It's going to be great." "And," added young Bev "NO BLACK. You'd look stunning in red."

Humph! Eighteen year old secretary tells boss how to dress! Elegant, my eye! Christine smiled – what a long way young

Bev had come in a year. She knew too that the office staff were after something. This sort of flattery always had a price!

Christine was in despair – she had plenty of smart business suits but nothing for evenings – since Peter's illness she hadn't been out in the evenings at all and she had lost so much weight. But the last thing she wanted was an evening dress, let alone a red dress.

Eventually she decided to go to the ladies boutique, Angela's, in up-market Long Melford and ask for help. She normally went once a year and bought three or four expensive business suits.

This time she arrived and there was Marissa, Marissa who had such a good eye and could be depended upon to say "NO, that doesn't work."

"What sort of suit are you after this time, Mrs Chapman?"

"No suit this time Marissa. I need something really glamorous, I've been told, for our Cleaners' Ball, which is rapidly turning in to the society event of the year for my staff," said Christine with a resigned groan.

Marissa looked at her, "Oh, how lovely." Marissa was the sole of discretion. Anyone else would have said "Whose ball?" and sniggered. "Do you want long or would something calf length be better?"

"Well, I'm really not sure. You see, I want something sophisticated but something I can wear afterwards … but unfortunately no black on my secretary's orders, would you believe."

"Let's find a few things for you to try on. How about cocktail length and perhaps a green? You always look lovely in green."

Marissa was good – she selected a green dress and a short, beautifully cut black jacket, plus a pair of black evening trousers to go with the jacket, making another outfit. After all - green was the company colour. No bare shoulders or plunging necklines.

Thank goodness, she had got that sorted. She was also relieved to hear from Ros that Hanna had formed a committee at Willis to co-ordinate the numbers, the buses (they were now going to need three) and the evening's entertainment. Dick had sourced a DJ to do the disco and Bob had been appointed MC. They had decided not to have set tables, people could sort themselves out when they arrived.

Unbeknown to Christine, everyone in the office had played their part – Ros and Jen had cooked 200 sausage rolls each, Ros's kind hearted neighbour, Claire, had for the last two days been cooking and cutting up quiches and pizzas.

The day before the big event, Bev's Mum, Sandra, organised as a true caterer must be, had cooked two dozen eggs and mashed them with mayonnaise for the sandwiches, beaten up tuna with sweetcorn for the rolls and sliced four cucumbers, endless tomatoes and prepared the lettuce, all of which were carefully stored in plastic containers.

Nicky had stayed with them overnight and she and Bev had joined Sandra in the kitchen early on Saturday morning to butter the sliced bread, both brown and white (with Flora for speed and to make it go further), before making endless rounds of sandwiches and carefully packing them into large plastic ice cream boxes. Bev's Dad was despatched to Tescos to get the long list of crisps, Mexican chips, baguettes and peanuts.

Sandra, with more pizzas in the oven, was hoping to have time at the end of the day to make lots and lots of garlic bread, wrapped in foil to keep it warm.

Everything was designed to fill people up and absorb the drink!

Rumour had it that there was going to be a cabaret. Dick and Bob were in charge and rehearsals had apparently been going on for weeks. Christine wondered vaguely how Peter would cope with a "cleaners' cabaret" but perhaps they could slip away beforehand.

The evening duly arrived. Christine drove, wanting to minimise the length of the evening and the strain for Peter. She managed to park by the door as the buses from the various pick-up points disgorged their loads of laughing ladies into the car park behind. Where were the men? Eventually, she picked out one or two, hanging back and looking slightly out of place.

Christine, feeling good in her green dress and Peter, his suit hanging loose on his emaciated frame, made their way into the hall, to find all the office staff had been there for most of the afternoon getting things ready. Nicky and Bev had been changing in the toilets for the past hour … "glamming themselves up" as Ros put it.

Peter found himself a seat at the bar and then proceeded to buy drinks – his tab growing by the minute. As he said, it was so difficult not to. All these gorgeous ladies kept coming up to him and saying "Good evening Mr Chapman. How are you?"

The only one he recognised was Hanna because of her height - and anyway she always looked elegant. With the others, until they introduced themselves, he hadn't got a clue. Waving frantically at Christine he said "Don't' leave me alone – I haven't a clue who these women are."

"Nor have I" replied Christine laughing "I honestly haven't – don't they look just wonderful. It's so difficult when they are not on their contract and all looking so glam and with make-up. The funny thing too is when they introduce their husbands, THEY just don't seem right either. "

"Well, I'm just buying everyone a drink and hoping for the best. Guess you'll have to pick up the bill."

My God was that butch Janet? – Christine recognised her from her walk. Huge purposeful strides. She looked stunning in black trousers, white shirt and velvet jacket. Heading straight for Mandy who looked lovely in her pale blue outfit with yes, what else, a peacock blue jacket, her mother-of-the-bride outfit, and Will in his suit, already red in the face and pulling uncomfortably at his tie and collar. Will, grinning at Janet, said "Alright mate. Can I get you a drink?"

"A pint would be fine."

Christine couldn't believe it – the last time she had spoken to Janet she was going to have Will's guts for garters. Indeed, her very words were "When I next see him I'll tell the stupid bugger in no uncertain terms to keep his purvey pecker in his pocket."

Here they were now talking amiably like the closest of friends. Christine moved over to Janet who, pint in hand, was reminiscing about the wedding, "Mandy, you looked lovely. That outfit's smashing. You know, Josie's wedding did us a favour – we've all got the perfect outfit for tonight." "Yes," replied Mandy "Will's wearing a suit – second time running, and it's not for a funeral! YET!" she said with a look that spoke volumes. Smiling again, she continued, "Josie and Jim are coming a bit later – Mrs Chapman said they could cos they're all part of the Monthind family. And it's funny. We ARE, like, a family, you know."

This registered. Christine smiled, touched at Mandy's words.

She was relieved to see the bar was now lined with at least six men but there was no getting away from the fact that they were heavily outnumbered by women, women of every shape and size. This was definitely going to be a ladies night with a difference.

Peter was still sitting on his bar stool and out of the corner of her eye, Christine noticed Pauline tottering up to him in the tightest white satin dress imaginable, her white 6" heels wobbling precariously – "'ello, Mr Chapman. You all on yer own, so I thought I'd come and say 'ello. I'm Pauline from Willis. We've spoke a lot but I've never had the pleasure to meet you. .. Sorry," as she attempted to pull down her dress "Just squeezed meself in, no room for undies!" she giggled. Peter's face was a picture.

"Just wanted to say, Mr Chapman, while it's on me mind …. toilet rolls is up. An' if you want to know the reason .. Well, 'alf the office staff 'ave colds. Can you bear that in mind when I put me next order in. I wouldn't want you to fink, I've lost me grip." She gave Peter a sickly sweet look.

Peter, looking slightly surprised, quickly recovered and said "Of course Pauline. I'm so glad you've told me otherwise I might have thought …. they'd all got the squits! Now what'll you have to drink."

"Oh … the squits! Oh …You are a one, Mr Chapman. I'd never have said that. No, they just got the snots," she put her hand over her mouth to contain her laughter at her own joke. "Oh and since you ask, could I be a devil and have a double vodka and tonic? I don't usually have a double but since it's Christmas and you're paying, why not?"

She giggled some more and then went all coy as she sidled closer, making Peter even more uncomfortable – in a comfortable kind of way! "You know, Mr Chapman, I try ever so hard with them loo rolls but sometimes I just tear my hair out. I just don't know where they go. And when Will came over last week and took 6 dozen off me cos his order hadn't come in. Well, I told him, just this once and he'd better get his act together and I want them back by next Friday, and I'd be checking with you. He said that's all right because you said Pauline's got a big stock and it's good everyone supports each other. Trouble is you've got to keep track of the light-fingered buggers and you want to watch our Will, he's one of the worst. He's all mouth and trousers. But don't you worry none, Mr Chapman. You got other things on your mind. You can count on me to keep him straight. I just wanted you to know like."

Barely drawing breath, she continued, "What with him and Bob, it's a good job security won't let no one but me have the key. Them men, they'd be helping themselves right, left and centre and the stores would really be right f.ff… mucked up, if you know what I mean."

375

The realisation that she might have almost muttered the forbidden word, made her pause. She put her hand to her mouth and giggled. "oops .. nearly!" Peter quickly jumped in "You are doing a great job, Pauline. Keep it up. I rely on you totally, you know. Here's your double vodka … Now I wonder if you could possibly find my wife?"

Pauline beamed and, grasping her double vodka, gave a little bob – "Thank you ever so Mr Chapman. I'll tell you everyfing wot I hear. You won't have no problem from me. Just you watch those men! Mrs Chapman don't trust 'em neither but me, I keep tabs on them. I'll go find her fer you." She looked around before carefully teetering across the dance floor, double vodka held high, with Peter staring after her and trying to assess if the 'no underwear' statement was true!

Christine, instructed by Pauline, hastened to the bar to join Pete.

Ros, all red in the face and worried, came over to them. "Bob's about to announce the food. You'd better get in first or you'll get caught in the stampede. Some of them have their plates at the ready already!"

Bev's Mum had produced a wonderful spread covering four trestle tables – a huge buffet of substantial soak-up food - pizzas, sausage rolls, sandwiches, quiches, finger rolls filled with tuna, hot garlic bread and even hamburgers cut into four. In between there were cocktail sticks with pineapple and cheese squares and small bowls of olives but somehow they looked twee and slightly pretentious.

Sure enough the queue was building up, "Can you carry two plates? I'm half starved. Cor, look at them sausage rolls – home made, I reckon. I could eat the flippin' plate." "Well, leave some fer us," this from someone six in line down the queue.

Bev's Mum was standing behind the tables looking a little anxious. "I really hope there will be enough. I have got extras boxes under the table, but not enough for gannets who take two plates each ..."

"Don't worry about us – we'll grab something later and I am sure a lot of people will have eaten already," Christine reassured her. Unconvinced, Ros braved the queue and retrieved a plate of sandwiches which she brought to the bar. "I am just worried that we won't stand a chance. I reserved a table for us over there. Come on because Bob's now about to let them loose on the food."

Bob, proudly sporting a smart black bowler hat, was already relishing his role as Master of Ceremonies. He was carrying a shiny metal mop bucket. "What on earth is he doing with a Kentucky mop bucket," Christine muttered to Ros.

At that moment, he grabbed a spoon off the serving table and proceeded to bang resoundingly on his bucket ... "Grub's up, you lot! Queue to left, no pushing and don't be greedy. We want to make sure there's enough for everyone."

Peter looked at Christine, laughing – "I like his style – I wonder what the professional Toast Masters at the Connaught Rooms would make of your Bob!" Christine smiled remembering the last dinner dance they had attended together – maybe three years ago.

The noise gradually abated as everyone, with plates piled high, tucked in. Bev's Mum was still smiling. Ros, fussing as ever had gone up to her at least three times asking, "Is there going to be enough?" "I think we are going to be OK," Sandra replied, heaving a sigh of relief, "They can still come back for seconds."

An hour later with everyone having eaten their fill, Bob appeared again, this time on the small stage normally reserved for the dance band, and once more banging on his bucket he announced, "Ladies and Gentleman, as your MC for the evening, I am pleased to announce that this evening's unmissable entertainment, performed by our very own staff will start in ten minutes. You've just got time to replenish your glasses or … do the other, before they start. Just don't mess up the toilets – management's here in strength tonight and we don't want no complaints." He winked and pointed at the office table.

Nearly twenty minutes later, the queue for the ladies having finally diminished, Bob, now looking very dapper in his bowler hat and natty black suit, was again banging on his bucket.

"Right folks, here we go …. Monthind presents the show of the year!"

To the accompaniment of Bob's bucket drum roll, Dick emerged from back stage, large orange scarf round his balding head, with pink sponge rollers protruding from underneath, attached to heaven knows what. Bob called for a warm welcome for "Our Doreen." Acknowledging the applause, Dick removed the fag from his generously lipsticked, red mouth, and called out loudly "Evenin' all." To which everyone responded "Evenin' Dick." "Doreen, d'you mind!" He promptly lifted his skirt to reveal hairy legs with Doreen Batty stockings round his ankles and large brown slippers with a pompom on the front, before performing a wobbly curtsey.

CHAPTER 38 – SHOW TIME

Bob, hushed everyone, announcing that tonight was going to be all about 'Them and Us'. "He ain't Dick, he's the competition, he's Doreen, one of them from B.O.G.S., the competition, and I, I'm Mrs Chapman's right hand man, here from Monthind to show you how it should be done."

Dick had by now collected a mop and bucket from the side of the stage and was proceeding, fag in mouth, to mop the dance floor, periodically stopping for a drag, dropping his ash on the floor, and giving one of the guys sitting at the nearest table, a coy look. He dipped his mop in the bucket and then flicked water in that general direction. Shrieks and protests followed.

He then winked at Mandy who, knowing what was coming, ducked into her husband's lap, yelling. "Not me, Dick. Get her," pointing at Dawn.

Bob then announced – "Now this is how you should mop a floor. Our very own Francesco will demonstrate." The music started and on came Francesco in the tightest, green T-shirt, moving sexily like a Flamenco dancer to the strains of Ravel's Bolero and mopping in perfect figures of eight round the unfortunate Doreen who was still flapping his mop about in the middle.

Bob, now equipped with blue and white cleaning cloths, a yellow duster and a spray bottle of GLEAM, proceeded to professionally clean the tables nearest the stage. He carefully polished the empty beer glasses and occasionally downed the dregs of an almost empty glass to be greeted by a howl of, "Get awf, that's my beer."

Whereupon he took his Gleam spray and aimed a fierce squirt of water at the unfortunate complainant.

Dick now flopped in a chair at the side of the stage, legs wide apart, his scarf and rollers awry, announcing, "I'm all in. Ain't half hard this cleaning lark. Think I've had a drop too much, mate!"

Bob replied, "Don't worry me ole tea me ole china, I've got just the thing to sober you up. Open yer gob!" Dick obliging as ever, opened his mouth. Bob takes the Gleam spray, "Don't you worry. I've got just the ticket. Monthind's miracle spray – sorts out anything!"

Everyone screaming, "Oh No! God, you'll poison him!" Big wink from Bob "D'ya think I'd kill me best mate off. What d'ya think I've got in here?"

Giving Dick another squirt, they link arms and, joined by Francesco, sing together to the tune of Rock of Ages:

Gin and tonic
That's the best
Sink a bottle
Take a rest
Mrs C does all the time
And in the office it's a crime
To be sober when doing pay
That's why it's wrong – or so they say.

"Doreen" had pulled his headscarf from his head, dropping a couple pink rollers in the process. Francesco with a big wink at the audience, picked them up and attempted to fasten them once more to Dick's shiny head. Dick who by now was mopping his sweaty brow with Doreen's head scarf, flicked it at Francesco who ducked, before like Wimbledon champions they flung rollers and headscarf to their screaming female fans. Finally, bowing, they exited the stage to whistles, hearty applause and shrieks of "More, more."

Bob held up his hand for quiet - the audience participation beat the local panto hands down.

"Calm down. Can I have a bit of hush? Ladies and gentlemen, please welcome our next act, our very own dancers – the Monthind Moppets."

Can-can music blared forth and the ladies emerged, led by Josie. The applause was thunderous. Josie was followed by Kathy, Pauline, and Jill. Then, after a weeny pause, out came Cissie, Jill's Mum, and Edna, neither in the flush of youth. Mandy had flatly refused to be part of the show, saying she was too shy and too old to do the Can Can. But 63 year old Cissie when she heard they were two short, had volunteered. Cissie had then persuaded her friend Edna, another game old bird, mentally alert and incredibly fit for her age to join them. Edna had turned 70 two weeks ago declaring "You are only as old as you feel". With the two mature ladies on either end – Cissie with her white cauliflower curls and Edna with her World War II roll kept in place by a stack of hair pins - Jill and Pauline next to them, and the glammy youngsters in the middle, they filled the stage.

The dance routine had been organised by Josie – she had always been good at dancing and Irish Kathy was there too – she said she'd love to try "cos dancing was me passion until "Oi got kicked out of River Dance," her Irish dancing class, "fer using me arms." With her arms wrapped carefully around Josie and Pauline, she was in her element and her kicks were spectacular and greeted by appreciative cat calls.

Sadly the kicks tailored off down the line to a sort of creaky knee bend produced by Cissie and Edna, two bars behind. Nonetheless the encouragement they received helped them raise the bar a notch or two. "Come on Ciss, get 'em up!"

As they lined up all Peter could think was "Hell. Pauline - she said she'd got no knickers on!" Peter was obviously not alone with this knowledge. Bob and Dick, still in his slippers, had positioned themselves on the end of the front row. Pauline seemed to have aroused the curiosity of a number of her male colleagues (Alf and Darryl included) as they vacated their spots at the bar and headed towards the stage.

Little did they know that Mandy, who had done the costumes, had bought cheap French knickers from the Co-op with her staff discount and had then trimmed each leg with yards of frilly lace. "We don't want to get a reputation," she said primly. "Spoil sport," retorted Pauline with a laugh.

Gasping, whether by design or necessity, Cissie and Edna, each let go at either end of the line, Edna bending over double to try and get her breath back. Cissie began clapping and then encouraged the audience to do the same. Uninhibited now by the ladies on the end, the kicking got higher with the girls managing to turn a complete circle in the middle of the stage before finally all taking a bow to wolf whistles and shouts for Encore.

Bob leading the applause thanked the girls before inviting Francesco, now changed into his usual dazzling white shirt, and Maria to sing "O Sole Mio". Bev and Nicky were busily handing out sheets with the words of the songs and explaining that everyone had to join in the chorus. The audience were still discussing the merits of the Can Can so Bob picked up his bucket and bashed it loudly, "Can we have a bit of hush for our final number from Frankie and Maria. This is guaranteed to bring tears to yer eyes. O Sole Mio …and you all know it from the tellie. You've all got the words on the sheet but don't come in until I give you the nod."

Onto the stage walked Maria's sexy young nephews, Julio and Aiberto, each with a guitar. The audience erupted. Frankie and Maria joined them and waited. The lads struck up the chord and quietly picked out the tune. The audience hushed as Francesco began to sing… O Sole Mio. The music had everyone swaying and as Maria joined in, more than one eye was dabbed. The Italian couple sang the opera version beautifully, perfectly in tune with each other. The audience, of course, knew the tune well from "It's now or never", Elvis's version. Bob pointed at the song sheets and invited the audience to join in. The mood changed immediately as the words were registered:

It's now or never
So Mrs C
We love to work for
Your company
We love the rates you pay
And that is what we
were told to say

We're office cleaners
We scrub away
Make all things spotless
for little pay
We love it
What can we say
Three cheers for us then.
Hip hip hooray

Everyone was watching Mrs Chapman, some of them a little anxiously, to see what her reaction would be but she was roaring with laughter and wagging her finger at Bob who was vainly attempting to get them all to join in the last verse.

His lively audience weren't having that. "Encore Frankie. Encore Maria" and the stamping began. "Encore, Encore."
Francesco led Maria to the centre of the stage and put his arm around her …. "It's now or never" They sang in broken English to wild cheers from everyone, the sentimental words from Elvis' song, bringing tears to many an eye.

Pauline, still in Can Can costume, was faintly overheard whispering to Mandy.
"Don't Maria look just like one of them opera singers? You know, what's her name, Callas? No maybe not, the fat one more like. Joan Thunderland, Sunderland or something. My husband loves her singing Jerusalem all wrapped up in the Union Jack. But, she ain't no prima donna, our Maria. Salt of the earth. Big bust, big heart, I always say. And as for her ole man, ole Frankie, he looks a real dish, just like Rosanio Brazzio, you know 'im out of South Pacific." She had a dreamy look in her eyes and continued gazing wistfully at Francesco whose voice had finally lapsed back into the original Italian, giving up the struggle to master the English Elvis Presley words.

"Cor,that Frankie, he aren't half sexy! Never fancied them foreign Ities none but I go weak at the knees when he sings. Shame they're out on that builders contract – we could use a bit of singing at Willis! And them two young lads with them – Maria's nephews. Cor …. They'd do us very nicely. "

Bob was banging determinedly on his bucket. "Right
you lot. Just one more "It's now or never" and sing the
words proper. I don't want none of your common as
muck Just one Cornetto – we're a class bunch!"
He raised his arms, "One, two …" Everyone joined in

It's now or never.
Come hold me tight.
Kiss me my darling
Be mine tonight.
Tomorrow will be too late
It's now or never
My love won't wait.

Needless, to say there yet another encore and huge
applause from the floor as Bob announced that this was
the end of the show and called on "Mrs Chapman to say
a few words".

Christine's was still shaking with a mixture of emotion and
laughter as she stood up and joined Bob on stage. She
wanted to keep her thanks brief but she was determined to
show how much she appreciated the tremendous contribution
from everyone. "Bob, if you really wanted a pay rise,
singing's not the best way to ask! You are all stars and you
deserve it. Thank you so much for tonight and for every night
you all work to make this company such a success. There
are one or two people who have worked especially hard to
make tonight such a success."

Ros was standing by with a very large basket of flowers – for
Sandra who had done the wonderful food. There were
smaller bouquets too for Mandy and all the Can Can ladies,
and for 'our very own opera soprano, Maria', bottles for the
men, including the guitarists, and Christine finally dedicated a

special thank-you to "dear Doreen" who managed a wobbly curtsey and muttered "Well, dun I get no flowers then," as she unceremoniously grabbed her bottle, and "our compere Bob for great entertainment. It's been a wonderful evening. Thank you all. And now on with the dancing!"

The DJ winked at her, patently itching to turn up the volume. He was obviously a Roy Orbison fan with his heavy dark glasses and black sideburns – there the resemblance stopped. On closer scrutiny Christine could see he was beginning to go bald on top, despite the long black comb-over. Flashes of hairy beer belly peeped between the buttons which were gamely straining to hold his pink shirt together. He was related to Dick's ex and generally played at the Labour club on a Saturday night, but he'd agreed to do this one for a laugh, plus £50, beer and grub, and also because he wanted to see Dick in drag!

Sure enough, he called out loudly "Ladies and Gentleman, the next number is especially dedicated to our Doreen" and as he moved the keys "Pretty Woman", burst forth. The ladies erupted. Dick, by now relieved of his skirt but still with trousers rolled up above his knees to show stockings and slippers, took to the floor, bowing and loving every minute of the limelight.

Not for long. There was an immediate surge, a female surge, towards the dance floor. Christine started to laugh, this was fun. The can can girls had changed out of their costumes. There was stick-thin Dawn in black trousers and lace top, dancing with Gill in her white blouse and green full skirt which flared out in a perfect circle, and her Mum, Cissie, now back in her red Crimplene suit and black patent shoes. Then there were the young girls, Bev and Nicky from the office, and Pauline looking sooo sexy and trying to entice every man in turn onto the dance floor, Alberto and Julio foremost of course. Lou and Becky and their team from Eastern Water had come on the second bus and Mandy's ladies including the girls who had joined from POCS were up there in force, twisting and jiving. Favourite upon favourite followed - Mamma Mia, Crocodile Rock. The DJ was brilliant varying the pace. He asked for requests - Bev and Nicky immediately asked for the Birdie Song and were soon showing off their perfectly synchronised actions, joined by Bev's Mum, Sandra, who was now completely relaxed. There had been plenty of food.

Darryl, in his black suit and winkle picker shoes, hair smarmed back propped up the bar looking wistfully at the girls. Suddenly Pauline espied him and dragged him protesting onto the floor where he was immediately enveloped by Tracey and Shelley. Wow, what a mover – couldn't quite match Francesco but …. Oh, our Darryl, he was a dark horse.

The odd couple were smooching. Who was that with Will? Oh, phew, Mandy had taken her jacket off to reveal a beautiful low cut dress. Christine breathed again. There were several groups of three or four giggling ladies, their arms around each other – perhaps for support – doing a sort of bouncy rugby scrum. Several sexy girls with legs up to their armpits and very short skirts were gyrating independently, keen to attract … but who …the male scope was limited, but no one seemed to worry. They exuded energy, fun and enjoyment, occasionally bursting into song. "Waterloo … oooo!"

Phyllis lurched onto the floor with her video camera in her hand. She peered into the lens, pointing it happily in all directions until her daughter Shelley came up "God, Mum,

you are sooo embarrassing, you've still got the cap on!"
She whisked it off and handed the camera back to her
mother.

Peter was a star as he danced with lady after lady.
When he courteously asked Claire to dance, she looked
terrified and tried to refuse, "Oh Mr Chapman, I honestly
can't dance." But he took her arm and smiled,
reassuring her. Pete was such a competent dancer he
waltzed her round the floor with ease and her face at the
end was a picture.

"I thought you said you couldn't dance!" He smiled.

Pauline went all giggly on him, Mandy just blushed and was
clearly proud to be asked. When Peter asked Ros to dance,
she thanked him for asking her but told him straight to sit
down. "Don't you think you have done enough?" She was
right because finally when he got up with Christine for the last
waltz, he looked all in. Christine was concerned that he had
overdone things but she hugged him to her, her emotions all
mixed up. She was so proud and so happy. It had been a
triumph.

As she drove him home, she said "Thank you darling for
coming. I don't know how you did it."

On the Monday morning the office was abuzz with the sole
topic of conversation being the Ball:

"You couldn't measure the value – just looking at everyone's
faces. And the Thank-you's – cleaners don't normally say
thank you but here they were queuing up to say good night
and thank you." "Best night of my life, Mrs Chapman. I'd
like to help next time." "I hope we can see the pictures."
And so on and so on.

Jen's partner James had been snapping away. "Used up two films. Everyone's asking for copies – I hope they are good enough," he said worriedly.

Everyone was automatically assuming that it would become an annual event. Christine resolved to do more – not only was it good socially but as a team building exercise this was the tops.

Discussing it later with Jen and Ros they agreed that this must do more for staff morale than anything. "Oh yes," said Ros, "The girls are already talking about what they can do for next year. In all their collective years of cleaning no other company has ever done anything like this."

"There's so much talent out there too. You can really spot those who have charisma." "That lady who helped with the raffle – who is she? I gather she's only been with us a couple of months." Christine had already earmarked her as supervisory material.

"And nobody got drunk!" Ros sighed, "Pity some of the office workers can't take a leaf out of our book." "Well, I'm not sure about that," said Jen. "Darryl had had a few and was looking pretty green. I saw Pauline propelling him to the gents and yelling at Alf to help. Hope he wasn't sick on the bus. What is great though is that everyone looks out for everyone else."

Yes, how true that was.

CHAPTER 39 – THE END

From the day of the ball Peter's health deteriorated rapidly. It was so sudden. He didn't feel like eating, his skin turned yellow. Christine was beside herself. The local GP referred her yet again to the Royal Marsden but when she spoke to the consultant, his voice deepened, "I am so sorry there is nothing more I can do."

Christine immediately rang the GP again asking why the Marsden wouldn't see them. Dr Bernie just said quietly, "Christine, it is not fair to put Peter through the journey. He needs peace and quiet and all the love you can give him just now."

The pain had become very much worse. Peter now asked for painkillers and when she went to the pharmacy, diamorphine prescription in hand, she was amazed when the head pharmacist said "I'll make up that one myself." The drug caused all sorts of other problems, most frightening of all were the sudden hallucinations. Convinced he was on a business trip to Norway, Peter shouted at her to pack his case and get him to the airport. He struggled desperately to get out of bed before finally collapsing back into a coma again.

She still couldn't accept that there was no hope. The surgery arranged for a MacMillan nurse to come. Finally, she listened to Jane, the nurse. With heavy heart Christine telephoned Anne, and said "I think maybe you should speak to Ma and suggest that they come. Peter is getting worse." But still the full implication didn't register.

Ma and Pa and Anne and Michael came and stayed nearby in a local hotel. Christine found it hard when they all encamped in the bedroom, sitting grim faced at the foot of the bed with Ma and Anne taking it in turns to hold Peter's hand. He drifted in and out of consciousness, sometimes muttering incoherently, sometimes recognising them.

Three days ticked by with Michael having to go back home to look after the boys and to go to work. Anne stayed on knowing her mother was near to breaking point. Ma, with her rosary beads in her hands, kept repeating "No one should lose their only son. My boy, my boy." Then quietly praying the rosary once more, the low repetitive words seemed to soothe her.

Christine's mother was staying in the spare room, looking after Anya and James, trying to keep some sort of normality in their lives.

Christine tried to juggle everything, taking the children to school, washing and caring for Peter and making the odd telephone call to Ros. She felt guilty when she deserted her post at Peter's bedside but Ma clearly wanted this and seemed relieved when Christine left. Christine fully understood that she and Pa needed time alone with their son but she began to resent their presence.

Once the children came home from school, Ma and Pa left. Christine brought the children in to see Pete, to hold his hand. They were full of school news - James had got all his sums right. Anya had helped her teacher at break making special labels for everyone. Downstairs they both were so normal, both wanting to watch something different on television.

Upstairs with Daddy, James, at the age of four was completely oblivious to Peter's deterioration and chattered away about wanting fish fingers for supper, while Anya, always the sensitive one, would ask anxiously, "Daddy, are you better today? Can I stay up here with you?" A little later, when, called by Granny Pip to have supper, Anya, reluctant to go, looked questioningly at Christine who nodded and said, "Daddy needs to sleep now". Later that evening Peter looked at Christine, "I shall never see Anya married, will I? It's my biggest regret."

Christine's eyes filled with tears as she tried to say, "None of that … you've got to keep trying Pete. We can manage … all that matters is that you keep fighting."

The following evening, the children were at ballet with Simone but due back any moment for their supper. Jane was preparing Peter for the night and Christine had just put on her coat to go to the Convent for a parent's evening. Suddenly, Jane called her, "Christine come quickly." Christine sensed the concern and urgency in her voice…. Car keys in hand she went to the side of the bed. Jane had been taking Peter's pulse but she stepped back. Suddenly Peter raised his hand reaching upwards, reaching up to what? Christine took his hand and then suddenly she knew, she knew that he was reaching up to somewhere only he could see. She knew that this was the moment... this was the moment he was leaving her.

Jane stepped forward, reaching over from the other side of the bed, and placed her fingers on Peter's neck, feeling for his pulse. After a few moments, she shook her head slowly, before whispering. "I'm sorry."

Christine gazed in complete disbelief. She sat down on the chair feeling slightly sick. This couldn't be.

Jane took over – "Stay here quietly. I'll tell your mother and 'phone Anne. Mrs Chapman will want to be here."

All Christine could think about was the children – what would she tell them?

She looked with horror at Peter, his face sunken, his eyes open. Jane's eyes followed hers and quietly she leant over Peter.

The next hour was a blur. The door bell rang. Simone stood on the doorstep smiling, with Anya on one side and James on the other.

Christine stood in the doorway. "Simone, Peter has just died." It sounded so blunt. The children seemed to freeze. Anya certainly understood but James just gripped Simone's hand, tugging at it. She looked down at him and said, "Just a moment James, I'm going to pop you back in the car with Stephen. I think it would be a good idea if you and Anya came and spent the night with Natalie and Stephen."

"No, Simone, could you just telephone the convent. I am supposed to be there for parents' evening. I think the children need to come and see Pete. We'll be OK."

OK they certainly weren't. Christine went around in a complete daze. People seemed to come and go, everyone wanted to help. Jane took over with incredible efficiency.

The funeral was arranged by Peter's sister. Christine was in a dilemma about the children – should they come or not. She spoke to Sister Francis at the Convent. James would not understand what was happening and would fidget through the service. Anya could well be traumatised by the event.

After a long talk with the caring sisters, Christine decided to ask the Convent to give the children the option. There would be something nice happening at school or they could go with Mummy to the special church service for Daddy.

Both decided to stay at school, but the senior class, Sister Francis and many of the nuns from the convent attended the service.

Christine had decided she must have a new black outfit, Peter would have liked that. She carefully chose a smart black suit and a pill box hat with a perky feather to give her confidence.

For Christine the whole day was like a dream, a bad dream. She felt like a pawn. She felt hollow inside.

She was helped into the funeral car by Michael, Anne's husband – he had been a rock. They arrived at the church and walked down the aisle towards the coffin - Peter's coffin. Three small arrangements of white flowers sat on the top, just family flowers. She still couldn't believe it had come to this.

The centre of the church was packed and as she stood alone to lead the family to the front pews she vaguely noted people. There at the back was Ros, and beside her, filling the whole row were Francesco and Maria, Mandy and Will, Bob, Hanna and Pauline. What were they doing here? There were other faces too – were they from the cleaning company too? Had they taken time off work to come?

On the other side of the aisle in the very back seat she noticed Joan and Freda. She was fighting now to keep back the tears - they had come for her.

Moving down the church she noticed Guy and Alison and lots of other people she faintly recognised and those she didn't, possibly from VE, Peter's old company. Lady Sarah Fitzallan Howard and Leila and Thomas from Arundel and Brighton and the pilgrimage to Lourdes. She glanced at the sea of heads all turned to her and focused her gaze on the coffin. The funeral director motioned her to allow Peter's parents and Anne and Michael into the pew to her right.

The long catholic mass was endless, the journey to the cemetery harrowing and then the final lowering of the coffin into the freezing ground. Everything was bleak and cold and so very sad.

Back at the house Rebecca had prepared hot food but it soon ran out. They had just not expected so many people.

The drink flowed, people were talking quietly, sharing memories of Peter, but Christine just wanted everyone to go so that she could try to piece things together. She knew too that she had to collect the children from school – that was going to be the first test.

Later that evening, alone with Granny Pip and the children, she shivered – what was she going to do?

She hadn't even considered this … Peter was always going to be there. He was always going to pay the bills, to make the decisions. He hadn't told her what to do if he wasn't there. She had no idea where to start. The night was endless, she went over and over again the whole ghastly sequence of events.

All sorts of things went through her mind. Why hadn't the hospital picked up the cancer when Peter had that mole removed four years ago? If they had recognised it for what it was and treated it then, he might still be here.

She felt angry, she wanted to sue them. But then what was the point. Nothing would bring Peter back now.

She had no idea about money. Did they have insurance? Presumably the house would be hers? Who would know about this? She must look at the mortgage documents. Where did she start? Her brother in law had helped her register the death but little had been done beyond that. Fortunately she had her own bank account but the funeral costs had to be paid.

Sleep escaped her and at 6.32 a.m. precisely James bounced into her bedroom, breezy as ever. "Can I have Coco pops for breakfast? Sister Aidan says I don't have to come to school today if I don't want to."

Bleary eyed Anya followed. "Can we stay at home today, Mum?" Christine looked at them – yes, it would be lovely just to stay at home and sit on the floor with her arms around them both and cry. She shook herself, "No of course, not. It is a school day and you have to go. We might go in a little late but just this once. Granny Pip is going home in a bit so we need to give her a big hug and a wave."

She had to start getting into a routine again. There were endless phone calls to make, beginning with the bank, the solicitor and their insurance broker.

"We'll all have a special breakfast with Granny Pip and then I'll take you to school when we are ready."

Soon after mid-day, she quietly put the children into the car and drove to the Convent. Everyone was at lunch but as soon as she rang the door bell one of the young nuns gently told the children to go to the dining room and took Christine straight to Sister Francis's office.

She was ushered in and offered a cup of coffee. "Now, my dear, we are here to help. You need have no worries about the children, they are in our hearts and in our prayers. You are all part of our family."

Christine dissolved – this was the first time she had cried. She sobbed uncontrollably feeling total despair.

"That's right. You let it out. You have been strong for so long but you know God is here for you. Everything in life happens for a purpose. Peter was a man of God and he will find peace and comfort in heaven."

Slowly, Christine got her sobs under control, the sodden pile of convent tissues growing before her on the desk.

Cup of coffee in hand, she gave a lop-sided grin and said, "Sorry – first and last time!"

Over the next few days she learnt that the house was mortgaged up to the hilt, and that there were debts from the business Peter had tried to set up. Her financial situation was not good – the biggest outgoings were the mortgage and the school fees. She weighed up her options – she still had her part time job with the Study Centre and she had been told she would qualify for a widow's pension. She would sell Peter's car and she could manage with her little VW Beetle. And then there was the cleaning business - but without Peter's business brain behind it, that was never going to work. Anyway she couldn't bomb off to Ipswich every night now that he wasn't there with the children. They couldn't be left on their own.

If she worked part-time and claimed benefits she could probably manage. She would have to sell the house and find something smaller with half the mortgage. She would take

James out of the Convent straightaway and send him to the local County primary school, after all he would benefit from male company. That would reduce school fees by half. Anya would have to stay until she took the 11 plus. If she managed to pass she would go to the girls' grammar school. There was no need now even to think about fees for a Catholic boarding school.

One thing for sure was that she wanted the children here with her. She had never liked the idea of boarding school. That brought her to the subject of religion, she had always been determined to keep her C of E status, happy that the children grew up as Catholics under Peter's guidance but now she wondered. After Lourdes she felt a little more comfortable with Mass even if she still struggled with the peculiar catholic concepts of confession and the Immaculate Conception. She owed it to Pete. Yes, she needed to talk to the priest and Sister Francis.

When she went to collect the children, other mothers were standing in huddles talking. Immediately, Simone came over to her. "How can I help, Chris? How can everyone help? Just say the word and we are all standing by. You know you must ask. Please." The trouble was Christine didn't know how anyone could help. She didn't know what she was going to do about anything.

For example, what was she to do with the cleaning company? She really didn't fancy driving to Ipswich every night in the rain and the snow and it was becoming such a responsibility - all those people to pay and worry about. Anyway, she really was out of her depth. It was fine when she could just do the cleaning and be with her ladies but now it was a whole new ball game. No, she would have to find a way of wriggling out of that. She had better phone Ros and tell her.

CHAPTER 40 – SO WHAT NOW?

Christine spent the weekend deliberately giving the children a great time. They went to the cinema to see "Bambi". James loved Thumper but Anya started to sob when Bambi's mother died. Christine sighed – she was going to have to be so careful.

She was awake at crack of dawn on Sunday … she just couldn't face Mass knowing that all eyes would be on them. Prayers would be said for Peter, for widows, for the bereaved – THEM. No …

She couldn't face that.

Instead, they played cards - Snap and Strip Jack Naked. Wicked!

Together they cooked roast chicken, making the potatoes into funny shapes, "Look Mum, this one looks just like your nose!" "Thanks, James it's just a horrid big, blob!" "And it's got a gaggog!" Gaggog was their private family name for bogey. "Ugh I'm not eating that one. James you are bedusting!" This from Anya. James never used disgusting.. bedusting was his word, and it was even more disgusting than disgusting. How she was going to miss these fun word games they used to have, so often started by Pete.

No. Why should they miss such things? She had to keep these things going. Concentrate … scrummy apple crumble and custard for pud. This was a real Sunday lunch.

In the middle of the afternoon she plucked up courage and phoned Ros. Ros's reaction was typical "Oh thank God, thank God. I am so relieved to hear from you. We've all been so worried."

"I am sorry Ros. I have left you with everything. How are things?"

"Just fine, Chris, just fine. But everyone will be so pleased when you are back at the helm. Hanna has been wanting to phone. I've told her to leave it and leave it. Is there any chance that you could drive over to Ipswich tomorrow evening and just have a chat with one or two people? I'll come up and look after the children."

"Yes, I suppose so," said Christine reiuctantly "but I honestly don't know what I'm going to say. I just don't know where I'm going, Ros. You know, I can't manage this without Pete."

Ros just said, "It doesn't matter. Just go over and see everyone before you decide anything. I'll come to yours about five and bring Kerrie. She will love spending time with Anya and James and she can help me put them to bed and read stories. My friend, Claire will come in and look after my boys until I get back. "

Feeling she had no choice, Chris agreed and soon after 5 the next day she found herself driving up the A12. She fumbled for a tape – When I survey the wondrous cross, Lead me Oh thou great redeemer … all her favourite uplifting hymns … helped her on her way and by the time she walked through the door at Willis she was feeling quite composed.

Ron, Head of Security, left his seat and walked toward her. "How wonderful to see you," he beamed. "Everyone's been so worried. It's truly great to have you back." Christine nodded, secretly amazed that anyone from Security should care and she murmured a quiet "Thank you Ron" in reply. She could see Hanna coming down the escalator "Oh Chris, zis is so good, so good. Ros said you were coming so I've got everyone vaiting for you in the restaurant." She had brought staff together from all the different contracts.

Christine frowned. She hadn't expected this. She had planned to quietly go round to see Hanna and Mandy, Maria and Francesco but here they all were, hundreds of them, all grim faced, all quietly waiting.

She stood there in front of everyone, totally unsure of what to say – she had no idea where she was going. Should she try to get her job back at The Study Centre, should she sell the house and move to Ipswich, should she try to keep the cleaning company going?

Hanna started to talk, "Mrs Chapman, ve are so very happy you are here ..." Christine could see she was welling up.

Before she could say anything, Bob Walker stepped forward. "Mrs Chapman, I know I speak for everyone when I say we are all so sorry about your husband. He was a super bloke. We know you've had a really tough time. We wanted to help but we didn't know how to. So …. so, we've just made sure that there hasn't been a single complaint.

Christine looked at the faces before her, some of the women were dabbing their eyes. They were all silent, looking at her waiting. She ….she had to say something.

She took a deep breath and stepped forward not having any idea of what she was going to say. All she could think was: 'Not a single complaint … not one…?' Not a single complaint? – No, there hadn't been. Suddenly, like a flash from heaven she knew what she had to say.

"Thank you. Thank you all from the bottom of my heart. I have come here this evening to thank you for your support and to tell you that together we are going to build the biggest and the best cleaning company in East Anglia – one which cares for its cleaners as well as for its clients. We are going to support each other, as you have supported me, and we are going to show everyone that cleaning matters. I am going to dedicate myself to achieving this because the past few months have shown me that I have the best team in the business."

There was an audible gasp and then a pause ….

Hanna and Bob hugged each other and several of the staff punched the air "Yeah, We're gon'na be the best and the biggest!" Bob started to clap and everyone joined in, their faces gradually breaking into a smile. To her amazement Christine too joined in, clapping with everyone else.

"Vonderfoll, that eez vonderful," chorused Hanna. There was a buzz, it grew louder. The relief was palpable. At last Hanna raised her voice above the noise, "Now off to work you lot, we can't rest on our hunches" … once again muddling her metaphors.

Christine smiled and repeated to herself, "Yes, that's what we are going to do – together. Build the biggest and the best cleaning company." They really are a great crowd.

Maria and Francesco came up to her. "I 'ave a panettone in my bag for you and ze children. I bring one every week for you. Mr Oliver, he very worried about you. You want more bizness, he help."

Hanna looked at her "You see, Chris, everybody loves you. They want to help. And you know, their jobs matter. For many of them, zey pay for ze food on ze

402

table. Zay ave been very vorried. Everybody is so 'appy. "

"Yes, Hanna. I have to say I hadn't realised fully. Thank you. I just hope I can live up to this. I must get back now. Ros is looking after the children. I've got a lot to think about."

She got back to the car and drove home in silence. Before she could put the key in the door, it flung open, Ros and the children were there to hug her. "So we are going to build the biggest and the best cleaning company in the country!" Ros looked at her and grinned. That wasn't quite what she had said but Hanna had telephoned and the cleaners' grapevine was responding! The children were bouncing up and down in excitement. They didn't understand but Ros's relief and delight had rubbed off!

She lay in bed for the first time thinking constructively about the future. Peter had known she would need something. He had understood their precarious finances, the mortgage, the school fees. He had recognised the potential of the cleaning venture. He had paved the way. How naïve she had been. Now, here she was floundering. She had to pull herself together, after all she had to think about all those people working for her -- there hadn't been a single complaint. She owed them something – but what had she pledged?

Just what had she pledged?

Oh God!!